INTERNATIONAL SERIES OF MONOGRAPHS IN
PURE AND APPLIED MATHEMATICS
GENERAL EDITORS: I. N. SNEDDON, M. STARK, K. A. H. GRAVETT
and S. ULAM

VOLUME 76

HANDBOOK FOR
COMPUTING ELEMENTARY FUNCTIONS

Handbook for

COMPUTING ELEMENTARY FUNCTIONS

BY

L. A. LYUSTERNIK · O. A. CHERVONENKIS
A. R. YANPOL'SKII

Translated from the Russian by
G. J. TEE
University of Lancaster

Translation edited by
K. L. STEWART
English Electric Co. Ltd.

PERGAMON PRESS

OXFORD · LONDON · EDINBURGH · NEW YORK
PARIS · FRANKFURT

Pergamon Press Ltd., Headington Hill Hall, Oxford
4 & 5 Fitzroy Square, London W.1
Pergamon Press (Scotland) Ltd., 2 & 3 Teviot Place, Edinburgh 1
Pergamon Press Inc., 122 East 55th St., New York 22, N.Y.
Pergamon Press GmbH, Kaiserstrasse 75, Frankfurt-am-Main

First edition 1965

Library of Congress Catalog Card No. 64–22370

This is a translation with corrections of the original Russian *Математи-ческий анализ — Вычисление элементарных функций* (*Matematicheskii analiz — Vychisleniye elementarnykh funktsii*), published in 1963 by Fizmatgiz, Moscow

PRINTED IN POLAND (D.R.P.)

CONTENTS

APPENDICES

I. Special Polynomials and Other Functions

PREFACE

THE solution of many mathematical problems requires the computation of values of elementary functions for various values of their arguments. Even in antiquity and in medieval times, tables were prepared of the values of trigonometric functions and formulae for the approximate computation of certain functions, for instance Heron's iterative formula for the extraction of square roots (cf. Ch. I, § 3.6, 1°). Subsequently, the computation of values of elementary functions, and the construction of tables of them, was a most important factor in stimulating the development of mathematical analysis. Indeed, power series were invented for this very purpose—by Mercator for logarithms; by Newton for trigonometric and inverse trigonometric functions, and also for power functions; by Euler for the exponential function, etc. Iterative processes (e.g. Newton's method) were also applied for solving equations.

Mathematicians of the eighteenth century (Lambert, Euler, Lagrange, etc.) used continued fractions to represent elementary functions. In recent years, the technique of expansions in orthogonal polynomials has been widely applied for computing functions. The Chebyshev polynomials, which give good convergence, have proved to be particularly useful for this purpose.

Since the advent of program-controlled high-speed electronic computers, which make it possible to evaluate elementary functions on a large scale, various algorithms have appeared for computing values of these functions to a specified accuracy. The choice of algorithms depends upon the peculiarities of the machine, e.g. the accuracy required for the computation, the availability of fixed-point or floating-point arithmetic, the amount of "memory" which is available, etc. Usually an algorithm which is selected is used as a basis for constructing a "standard program" (or sub-routine) which is stored in the machine, to be entered whenever values of the function are to be computed. These algorithms are frequently based on orthogonal polynomial expansions, or on iterative methods, etc.

In recent years a large number of works have appeared, which are devoted to the computation of various functions by

ix

a variety of approximate formulae. The new formulae appearing
in the literature have been from time to time combined with
previously-known formulae, systematized and presented in the
form of tables, handbooks, etc. As an example, we cite the widely-
known and extremely detailed *Tables of Integrals, Sums, Series
and Products* by I. S. Gradshtein and I. M. Ryzhik. But for the
elementary functions, the only book which has appeared is the
recent handbook by Hastings, Hayward and Wong [49], containing polynomial and rational approximations. Material from
their book is used in this present handbook. But there has not
appeared so far any comprehensive collection of computational
formulae for the elementary functions.

In this handbook we describe methods for computing polynomials, elementary rational functions, exponential and logarithmic functions, trigonometric and inverse trigonometric
functions, hyperbolic and inverse hyperbolic functions, and
in addition a number of formulae relating to them are given.
These methods and formulae play an important role, since much
of the labour involved in the numerical solution of problems
consists of computing values of the elementary functions, and
of various combinations of them. This handbook gives many
distinct representations of the elementary functions, in the form
of power series, series of polynomials (orthogonal and otherwise),
continued fractions, limits of iterative processes, etc.; and it
gives a large number of approximate formulae for computing
the elementary functions to various degrees of accuracy. The
main part of this handbook is concluded by a description of
algorithms which are used for computing the elementary functions
on the computers "Strela", BESM, M-2, M-3 and "Ural".

In the appendices we give some brief details of certain functions
which are connected with the elementary functions, and which
are encountered in the handbook: the hypergeometric function,
the Gudermannian, harmonic polynomials, and certain special
polynomials. The polynomials of Legendre, Chebyshev, Laguerre
and Hermite are treated separately, and numerical tables are
given of some systems of numbers and of special functions, which
are used in representing elementary functions.

The material in this handbook is arranged in the following
manner. Each section is devoted to a particular function or group
of functions. Some general information is given about the function,
followed by material concerning the computational methods,
which is arranged in the following order: power series expansions,
infinite products, expansions in polynomials (orthogonal and
otherwise), series of polynomials for approximations to any

degree, specific approximating polynomials, continued fraction expansions and other series of rational approximations, specific rational approximations, and finally iterative processes.

Since all of the elementary functions are analytic, it is permissible to expand them as power series, continued fractions, etc., in some part of the complex plane. We have in mind principally functions of real variables, but in a number of cases we observe that an expansion is valid in some part of the complex plane.

For many of the formulae, we include tables of the coefficients entering in the formula.

In some cases, we give an algorithm for computing the value of a function "digit by digit", i.e. an algorithm for computing successively the digits α_0, α_1, α_2, ..., of the binary representation of a number y.† In this representation

$$y = \alpha_0 \cdot \alpha_1 \alpha_2 \ldots \alpha_n \ldots,$$

(where the α_i are either 0 or 1) denotes that

$$y = \alpha_0 + \frac{\alpha_1}{2} + \frac{\alpha_2}{2^2} + \ldots + \frac{\alpha_n}{2^n} + \ldots$$

In this handbook we use the following uniform notation. If a specific approximate expression $Q(x)$ is given for a function $F(x)$, then the error is denoted by $r(x)$:

$$r(x) = F(x) - Q(x).$$

The upper bound for $|r(x)|$ over the region being considered is denoted by r. The relative error $r(x)/F(x)$ is denoted by $\varepsilon(x)$, and the upper bound for $|\varepsilon(x)|$ over the region under consideration is denoted by ε.

If a function $F(x)$ is given by an infinite series

$$F(x) = \sum_{k=0}^{\infty} a_k(x),$$

then the remainder term of the series is denoted by $r_n(x)$:

$$r_n(x) = F(x) - \sum_{k=0}^{n} a_k(x). \tag{0.1}$$

We shall use the compact notation for continued fractions, i.e.

$$F = a_0 + \frac{a_1}{d_1} + \frac{a_2}{d_2} + \ldots + \frac{a_n}{d_n} + \ldots$$

---

† A general treatment of "digit-by-digit" methods is given by J. H. Wensley (1959), in "A class of non-analytic iterative processes", *The Computer Journal*, **1**, 163–167. (G.J.T.)

instead of

$$F = a_0 + \cfrac{a_1}{d_1 + \cfrac{a_2}{d_2 + \cdots + \cfrac{a_n}{d_n + \cdots}}}.$$

We denote by $\dfrac{A_n}{D_n}$ the nth convergent of the continued fraction:

$$a_0 + \frac{a_1}{d_1} + \frac{a_2}{d_2} + \cdots + \frac{a_n}{d_n}.$$

If F, a_i and d_i are functions of x, then

$$A_n = A_n(x), \qquad D_n = D_n(x).$$

Sometimes the expressions for

$$\frac{A_n}{D_n} = \frac{A_n(x)}{D_n(x)}$$

are written underneath corresponding "links" of the continued fraction:

$$a_0 + \frac{a_1}{d_1} + \frac{a_2}{d_2} + \cdots + \frac{a_n}{d_n}$$

$$\frac{a_0}{1} \quad \frac{A_1}{D_1} \quad \frac{A_2}{D_2} \qquad \frac{A_n}{D_n}.$$

Chapter V of reference [1] should be consulted for the recurrence relations between the A_n and the D_n.

The difference

$$r_n(x) = F(x) - \frac{A_n(x)}{D_n(x)} \tag{0.1'}$$

is denoted by $r_n(x)$.

Similarly, if $y = F(x)$ is regarded as the limit of an iteration sequence $\{y_n\}$ $(n = 0, 1, 2, \ldots)$, then

$$r_n(x) = F(x) - y_n(x), \text{ etc.}$$

In all of these cases, if the function is given over some interval, then r_n denotes an upper bound for $|r_n(x)|$ over that interval:

$$|r_n(x)| \leqslant r_n.$$

The following notation is used for the relative error:

$$\varepsilon_n(x) = \frac{r_n(x)}{F(x)}, \qquad (0.2)$$

and ε_n denotes the upper bound for $|\varepsilon_n(x)|$ over the corresponding interval.

The following points should be borne in mind, in connection with the references given to the literature. The first number printed to the right of a formula or table indicates the source from which the formula or table is taken: the number is that of the reference within the bibliography at the end of this book. The second number, enclosed within round brackets, indicates the page number in the source.

In conclusion, we wish to express our deep gratitude to V. Ya. Pan for sending the manuscript of his work on optimal methods for computing polynomials, to V. S. Linskii and A. N. Khovanskii for their assistance in selecting the material, to V. I. Vazhenin and M. N. Obuvalin for providing some formulae concerning the approximation of functions by polynomials, and to I. Ya. Akushskii, Ye. A. Zhogolev and G. S. Roslyakov for sending material concerning the algorithms employed for computing the elementary functions on several computers.

INTRODUCTION

ONE of the most commonly occurring of all mathematical operations is that of computing values of elementary functions: rational, power, trigonometric, inverse trigonometric, exponential and logarithmic, hyperbolic and inverse hyperbolic.

For hand calculations, the evaluation of elementary functions reduces to using tables, with some interpolation if necessary.

At the present time there exists a very wide choice of tables of the elementary functions, with varying accuracies and notations (cf. the *Handbook of Mathematical Tables*, [4], [16]).

In recent years, there has been a marked increase in the amount of computation, in connection with the advent of computers. With these machines, it is inconvenient to read in bulky information about functions (e.g. extensive tables); instead numerical algorithms are used for computing functions. These algorithms reduce to performing a certain number of elementary operations, and only a small amount of information needs to be read into the machine (e.g. the coefficients of formulae).

In these machines the elementary operations include: arithmetic operations; operations such as taking the modulus of a number, or its integral or fractional part (cf. the reduction formulae in Ch. III, § 1.1, 6°, which are described in terms of these operations); and certain logical operations controlling the computational process (e.g. if different algorithms are applied in separate parts of the range of the argument, then for any given value of the argument the logical operations will direct the computation to the appropriate algorithm).

As a consequence of the demands of machine computation, an extensive literature has arisen which is devoted to representations of the elementary functions, and algorithms for approximate computation of them. Handbooks of this general type (e.g. Gradshtein and Ryzhik [26]) contain material on the representation of functions by power series; other books (e.g. Khovanskii [34]) represent functions by continued fractions; and a number of papers in the journal *Mathematical Tables and Other Aids to Computation* (now called *Mathematics of Computation*) represent functions by expanding them in series of orthogonal functions. The well-known handbook [49] contains much material on best-approximating polynomials and rational approximations to the elementary functions. The manuals for various computers describe algorithms for computing elementary functions, which form the basis of the "standard programs" employed for computing these functions on the machine: the algorithms used on a number of computers are collected together in Chapter IV.

The choice of an algorithm is determined by the characteristics of the computer, e.g. the accuracy with which computations are performed, the system of arithmetic (in the binary system the computation of exponential and logarithmic functions reduces to evaluating 2^x in the interval $(0, 1)$, and $\log_2 x$ in the interval $(1, 2)$ or $(\frac{1}{2}, 1)$: iterative procedures for computing "digit by digit" may be restricted to the binary system, etc.); the nature of the given number (in machines with floating or fixed point); the choice of elementary operations (on machines without automatic division, in a number of elementary operations it is convenient to use algorithms not requiring division: e.g. instead of using Heron's formula for computing $\sqrt{x}$, we may use an iterative process together with a special algorithm for computing $1/x$; cf. p. 29).

Approximate methods for computing a function $f(x)$ on an interval (a, b) reduce to computing some function $\varphi(x)$ which is "close" to it. The "error of the method" is the difference

$$r(x) = f(x) - \varphi(x). \qquad (0.3)$$

In order to estimate the accuracy of such an approximation, it is necessary to introduce certain numerical characteristics of the error $r(x)$ over the range (a, b), which are called "norms" of the function $r(x)$. The most important norms are the following (which were in fact, used already by P. L. Chebyshev):

(1) The *"uniform norm"* of the error $r(x)$, i.e. the maximum value of $r(x)$ in the interval (a, b):

$$\|r\|_c = \max_{x \subset (a, b)} |r(x)| = \max_{x \subset (a, b)} |f(x) - \varphi(x)|. \qquad (0.4)$$

(In fact, $\|r\|_c$ is the same as r, as defined above.)

(2) The *"quadratic norm"* of the error $r(x)$ (or mean-square norm) over the interval (a, b) is defined as:

$$\|r(x)\|_2 = \sqrt{\int_a^b [r(x)]^2 dx} = \sqrt{\int_a^b [f - \varphi]^2 dx}, \qquad (0.5)$$

or, more generally, if ϱ is some function of x which is positive over the range (a, b), $(\varrho(x) > 0)$, then the quadratic norm with weight $\varrho(x)$ is defined as:

$$\|r(x)\|_{2,\varrho} = \sqrt{\int_a^b r^2 \varrho \, dx}. \qquad (0.5')$$

Polynomial approximations are the most useful form of approximation function since they can be computed in a simple manner, and rational functions likewise are very useful. Let $f(x)$ be a function which is continuous over the interval (a, b). We shall denote the set of nth-degree polynomials by $\{P_n(x)\}$. For any specified norm of the form (0.4), (0.5) or (0.5'), and for any specified interval (a, b), there exists a polynomial from this set for which the norm of the difference

$$r(x) = f(x) - P_n(x)$$

is minimized, and moreover this polynomial is unique. This polynomial is called the *nth-degree polynomial of best approximation to $f(x)$ on (a, b)* (in the sense of the given norm). If we speak simply of a "polynomial of best approximation", then this is to be understood in the sense of the uniform norm.

We shall now make some comments on several ways of representing functions.

1. Power series. The elementary functions can be represented as power series in a number of ways. We shall consider the Taylor–Maclaurin series for a given function $f(x)$:

$$f(x) = \sum_{k=0}^{\infty} \frac{f^{(k)}(0)}{k!} x^k. \qquad (0.6)$$

Truncating this at the nth term, we get an nth-degree polynomial $S_n(x)$ (a finite Taylor series):

$$S_n(x) = \sum_{k=0}^{n} \frac{f^{(k)}(0)}{k!} x^k. \qquad (0.7)$$

The polynomial $S_n(x)$ has the following properties:

(1) $$f(x) = S_n(x) + o(x^n); \qquad (0.8)$$

where $S_n(x)$ is the unique nth-degree polynomial of best approximation $P_n(x)$, for which $f(x) - P_n(x) = o(x^n)$.

(2) Consider the system of nth-degree polynomials of best approximations to $f(x)$ over the interval $(0, h)$, either in the sense of the uniform norm or of the quadratic norm, with any weight $\varrho(x) > 0$. *As $h \to 0$, these polynomials tend to $S_n(x)$.* Hence we can say that *the polynomial $S_n(x)$ gives the best approximation to the function $f(x)$ in the vicinity of zero.*

The power series expansions of some of the elementary functions are particular cases of hypergeometric series (cf. Appendix § 3). The coefficients of the powers in the series for certain other elementary functions can be expressed in terms of Bernoulli numbers or Euler numbers.[†]

If a function $F(x, p)$ of two variables (x, p) is decomposed into a power series in p with coefficients $a_n(x)$, which are functions of x;

$$F(x, p) = \sum_{n=0}^{\infty} \frac{a_n(x)}{n!} p^n, \qquad (0.9)$$

then $F(x, p)$ is called the *generator* of the system of functions $\{a_n(x)\}$. Fixing a value of $p = p_0$ in (0.9), we get an expansion of the function $F_0(x) = F(x, p_0)$ in terms of the functions $a_k(x)$ (cf. for example, Ch. I, § 3.2, 1°). Fixing the value of x at $x = x_0$, we get the expansion $\Phi_0(p) = F(x_0, p)$ as a power series in p (cf., for example, Ch. II, § 1.2, 5°).

2. Series of orthogonal polynomials. A system of polynomials $\{P_n(x)\}$ ($n = 0, 1, 2, \ldots$) is said to be *orthogonal on* (a, b) *with weight* $\varrho(x)$ (where $\varrho(x) > 0$) if

$$\int_a^b P_n(x) P_m(x) \varrho(x) \, dx = 0$$

when $n \neq m$.

An extremely important role in the approximate computation of a function $f(x)$ is played by its expansion in a series of the polynomials $P_n(x)$ (cf. [I], Ch. IV):

$$f(x) = \sum_{n=0}^{\infty} c_n P_n(x). \qquad (0.10)$$

The computation of the first n coefficients c_n reduces to $(n+1)$ successive integrations of the function $f(x)\varrho(x)$ (cf. [I], p. 224). Truncating the series (0.10), we get a finite sum for the function $f(x)$:

$$Q_n(x) = \sum_{k=0}^{n} c_k P_k(x). \qquad (0.11)$$

[†] Cf. Vol. 69 of the I.S.M. in Pure and Applied Mathematics, Pergamon, 1965.

THEOREM. *The polynomial $Q_n(x)$ is the nth-degree polynomial of best quadratic approximation to the function $f(x)$, with weight $\varrho(x)$ over the interval (a, b).*

It is important to note that the polynomials $Q_n(x)$ give, in a number of cases, good approximations to $f(x)$ in the sense of the uniform norm. This holds particularly for expansions in Chebyshev polynomials, which are the set of orthogonal polynomials with weight function $(1-x^2)^{-\frac{1}{2}}$ on the interval $(-1, 1)$. They are an important source of polynomial approximations, particularly for the elementary functions. Sums of Legendre polynomials give rather good uniform approximations.

In this handbook, we give a number of expansions of the elementary functions in terms of the polynomials of Chebyshev, Legendre and others. Explicit expressions for some of these polynomials are given in Appendix I, § 4.5, and tables of values of these polynomials are given in Appendix II, Tables 7, 8 and 9.

3. Continued fractions (cf. [I], Ch. V). The principal source of rational approximations to a function $f(x)$ is its expansion as a continued fraction, of the form

$$\frac{b_0}{1} + \frac{b_1}{a_1} + \frac{b_2}{a_2} + \dots, \tag{0.12}$$

where the b_i and the a_i are polynomials in x. Then the convergents $\dfrac{P_n(x)}{Q_n(x)}$ for (0.12) give rational approximations to the function $f(x)$, which has been decomposed.

An important role is played by continued fractions of the form:

$$c_0 + \frac{c_1 x}{1} + \frac{c_2 x}{2} + \dots \tag{0.12'}$$

Let us be given a power series

$$a_0 + a_1 x + a_2 x^2 + \dots \tag{0.13}$$

The fraction (0.12') and the series (0.13) are said to be *conjugate* to one another, if the series expansion of the nth convergent of the continued fraction (0.12') differs from the series (0.13) only in the coefficients of powers of x higher than the nth. On page 282 of reference [1] there is given an algorithm for constructing a continued fraction of the form (0.12') which is conjugate to a given power series. We note that the continued fraction (0.12′) frequently converges to the corresponding function $f(x)$ over a larger region than does the conjugate Taylor series expansion.

Tilley's formula for the expansion of a function as a continued fraction is given on p. 303 of reference [1]. In the theory of continued fractions, it is the analogue of Taylor's series. On pages 309–311 of that reference there is given Obreshkov's formula, which is a generalization of Taylor's formula, by means of which series of rational approximations can be obtained for some of the elementary functions.

Let a given function $f(x)$ be expanded in the vicinity of $x = 0$ in the form of the series (0.13). The system of rational functions

$$\frac{R_k(x)}{S_l(x)},$$

where $R_k(x)$ and $S_l(x)$ $(k, l = 0, 1, 2, \ldots)$ are polynomials of degrees k and l respectively, form a system of Padè approximations if the expansion of the fraction $R_k(x)/S_l(x)$ in powers of x differs from the series (0.13) only in terms for which the power of x is greater than $k + l + 1$. This is a generalization of the system of convergents of the conjugate fractions (0.12).

4. Interpolation. Interpolation formulae are one of the sources of approximating polynomials. From the point of view of approximation, interpolation formulae for the range $(-1, 1)$ give good results if their nodes coincide with the zeros of Chebyshev polynomials (cf. Appendix I, § 4.6, and also [1], p. 255).

5. Best approximations, by polynomials and otherwise. The theory of best approximation by polynomials (or otherwise), in the sense of the uniform norm, was founded by P. L. Chebyshev.

Let a polynomial $P_n(x)$ of best approximation (in the sense of the uniform norm) be constructed for a function $f(x)$ over the range $[a, b]$. Then the difference

$$r(x) = f(x) - P_n(x)$$

attains the values $\pm h$, where

$$h = \|r(x)\|_c = \max_{x \subset [a,b]} |r(x)|,$$

at $n + 1$ points ξ_i in the interval $[a, b]$,

$$a \leqslant \xi_1 < \xi_2 < \ldots < \xi_{n+1} \leqslant b,$$

and if $r(\xi_i) = h$, then $r(\xi_{i+1}) = -h$ according to Chebyshev's theorem. Iterative processes for constructing polynomials of best approximation are based on this property of the polynomials of best approximation $P_n(x)$. We note that an interpolation polynomial for $f(x)$ with nodes at the zeros of the nth degree Chebyshev polynomial may be used as a good initial approximation to $P_n(x)$, or finite expansions in Chebyshev polynomials may be used instead.

We shall consider a more general problem. Let us be given a class of "well-behaved" functions $\varphi(x, a_1, a_2, \ldots, a_n)$, depending upon the parameters $a_1, a_2, \ldots, a_n$. For each choice of the values of these parameters, the norm of the error

$$\| r(x) \|_c = \| f(x) - \varphi(x, a_1, \ldots, a_n) \|_c$$

over the given interval (a, b) is a function of these parameters. That function $\varphi_0(x) = \varphi(x, a_1^{(0)}, \ldots, a_n^{(0)})$ of this class for which the norm of the error is minimized is said to give the *best approximation to $f(x)$ on (a, b)*. For many important classes of function $\varphi(x, a_1, \ldots, a_n)$, the error

$$r(x) = f(x) - \varphi(x, a_1^{(0)}, \ldots, a_n^{(0)})$$

of the best approximation retains the properties indicated above for the errors of polynomials of best approximation; viz. $r(x)$ attains its extremal values $\pm h$ (where $h = \| r(x) \|_c$) at $n + 1$ points, with alternating signs at successive points. Hence those methods for constructing polynomials of best approximation, which are based on this property, can be extended directly to these more general approximations. As an example we may cite the powers of polynomials

$$\varphi(x, a_0, a_1, \ldots, a_n) = \left(\sum_{k=0}^{n} a_k x^k \right)^{\alpha},$$

rational functions, etc. (cf. [49]).

6. Iterative processes. These consist of the construction of an iterative sequence $\{y_n = y_n(x)\}$ converging to the function $y(x)$, where $y_0(x)$ is an initial approximation and $y_n = f(y_{n-1})$ if $n \geqslant 1$. The most important sources of such processes are iterative methods for solving the equation

$$F(x, y) = 0, \tag{0.14}$$

whose solution is the function $y = y(x)$; e.g. Newton's method:

$$y_{n+1} = y_n - \frac{F(x, y_n)}{F_y(x, y_n)}. \tag{0.15}$$

We denote the current error of the approximation by

$$r_n(x) = y(x) - y_n(x).$$

With Newton's method,

$$r_{n+1}(x) = 0(r_n^2(x)).$$

This explains the rapidity of the convergence in a number of instances for this method.

EXAMPLE 1. $y = \sqrt{x}$ satisfies equation (0.14), where $F = y^2 - x$, $F_y = 2y$: (Heron's formula, cf. Ch. I, § 3.6, 1°).

$$y_{n+1} = y_n - \frac{y_n^2 - x}{2y_n} = \frac{1}{2}\left(y_n + \frac{x}{y_n}\right).$$

EXAMPLE 2. The function $y = \dfrac{1}{\sqrt{x}}$ satisfies (0.13), with $F = x - y^{-2}$ and $F_y = 2y^{-3}$:

$$y_{n+1} = y_n - \frac{x - y_n^{-2}}{2y_n^{-3}} = \frac{1}{2}(3y_n - xy_n^3)$$

(cf. Ch. I, § 3.6, 2°).

One should endeavour to choose the initial approximation $y_0(x)$ in such a manner that it can be computed simply (e.g. in the form of a linear function, or a constant), and such also that an approximation with the required accuracy is produced by as small a number of iterations as possible.

Newton's method is used for improving an approximation $y_0(x)$ to a function $y(x)$ satisfying (0.14).

7. Differential equations. The elementary functions are solutions of simple differential equations. For example, $y = \sin x$ and $y = \cos x$ are solutions of the equations

$$(y')^2 + y^2 = 1$$

and

$$y'' + y = 0;$$

$y = \tan x$ is a solution of the equation

$$y' = 1 + y^2,$$

etc. (cf. Table A on pp. 280–281 of [II]).

In machines which can solve differential equations, an elementary function may be evaluated by solving a differential equation which it satisfies. In [I], Ch. V, § 3, there is given Lagrange's method for solving one class of differential equation, producing the solution as a continued fraction expansion, which is applied there for producing expansions of the functions $(1 + x)^v$, arctan x, ln x, tan x, tanh x, etc. In his book [17], Lanczos describes the τ-method which he devised for solving certain differential equations, giving a series of polynomial and rational approximations for the functions which are the solutions of these equations.

COMMENT. Sometimes, the interval over which a function $f(x)$ is given is divided into sub-intervals, in each of which $f(x)$ is to be computed by a particular algorithm to the required accuracy by the minimum number of operations. But if a fine subdivision of the interval is used, then the "logic" of the computation is complicated and, as a rule, the amount of initial information needed is increased.

The elementary functions satisfy functional equations which connect values of a function for various values of the argument. These relations, together with appropriate transformations of the variables, enable us to reduce the computation of these functions to computing them over some definite interval. The following transformations of variables are frequently used: the transformation

$$y = \frac{2x - (b + a)}{b - a}$$

which linearly transforms the interval (a, b) on the x-axis to the interval $(-1, 1)$ on the y-axis; as a particular instance of this we have

$$y = 2x - 3 \quad \left(x = \frac{3}{2} + \frac{y}{2} \right)$$

which transforms the interval $(1, 2)$ to the interval $(-1, 1)$, with its inverse. The formula $y = 1/x$ gives a transformation of the interval $(1, \infty)$ to the interval $(0, 1)$ and conversely; $y = \dfrac{x - 1}{x + 1}$ transforms the interval $(0, \infty)$ to the interval $(-1, 1)$ and conversely.

EXAMPLE 3. Formula 1° in Ch. II, § 1.3, with $a = \ln 2$ and with the interval $(-1, 1)$ transformed linearly to the interval $(0, 1)$, reduces to the formula 2°.

CHAPTER I

RATIONAL AND POWER FUNCTIONS

§ 1. Polynomials†

1.1. General information. In computational practice, it is often necessary to evaluate polynomials for specified values of the argument. It is not uncommon for the approximate computation of the value of some function to be reduced to the computation of approximating polynomials.

Polynomials are often evaluated by *Horner's rule*,‡ according to which an nth-degree polynomial

$$P_n(x) = a_0 x^n + a_1 x^{n-1} + \ldots + a_{n-1} x + a_n$$

is represented in the form

$$P_n(x) = (\ldots((a_0 x + a_1) x + a_2) x + \ldots + a_{n-1}) x + a_n, \quad (1.1)$$

and the computation of the value of $P_n(x)$ proceeds in the order indicated by the brackets.

The evaluation of a polynomial $P_n(x)$ by this scheme requires n multiplications and $n-k$ additions, where k is the number of zero coefficients a_i. If $a_0 = 1$, then $n-1$ multiplications are required. It can be shown that for polynomials of general form, it is impossible to construct a scheme which is more economical than Horner's scheme, in the number of arithmetic operations required.

However, if polynomials of a special form are being computed, the number of operations required may be less than for the universal Horner's scheme. For example the computation of the power x^n by Horner's scheme involves the multiplication of n

---

† The properties of polynomials are explained in the book *Higher Algebra* (in Russian) by A. P. Mishina and I. V. Proskuryakov, in the series "Library of Mathematical Handbooks".

‡ Also known as *nested multiplication* (G. J. T.).

factors $(x . x \ldots x)$, requiring $n-1$ multiplications. But in order to get, say x^8, we could form successively

$$x^2 = xx, \quad x^4 = x^2 x^2, \quad x^8 = x^4 x^4,$$

i.e. only three multiplications are needed instead of seven.

A polynomial $P_n(x)$ is sometimes evaluated by a computation scheme consisting of two stages: in the first stage, by means of operations *confined to the coefficients of the polynomial*, it is transformed to a special form; in the second stage the polynomial which has been reduced to the special form is evaluated for specified values of its argument. It can happen that the number of operations required by the second stage is less than that for Horner's scheme. This type of computation is convenient when a polynomial $P_n(x)$ is to be evaluated for many values of x (since the first stage of the computation need be done once only), as for example in the case of a polynomial which is used for approximate computation of an elementary function. Hereafter, when we speak of the number of operations required for computing a polynomial $P_n(x)$, we shall have in mind the number of operations needed for performing the second stage only of the computation.

In all of the examples given below, the computation of a polynomial $P_n(x)$ by such methods is reduced to the successive computation of certain auxiliary polynomials — the first stage of the computation of finding the coefficients of these auxiliary polynomials.

As an example, we cite the scheme of J. Todd [29] for computing an arbitrary sixth-degree polynomial $P_6(x)$:

$$P_6(x) = x^6 + Ax^5 + Bx^4 + Cx^3 + Dx^2 + Ex + F$$

by means of the auxiliary polynomials

$$p_1(x) = x(x + b_1), \quad p_2(x) = (p_1 + x + b_2)(p_1 + b_3),$$

$$p_3(x) = (p_2 + b_4)(p_1 + b_5) + b_6,$$

where the coefficients b_i are determined in such a manner that

$$p_3(x) \equiv P_6(x).$$

By equating the coefficients of powers of x on both sides of this latter identity, we get a system of equations for determining the required coefficients b_i:

$$3b_1 + 1 = A,$$

$$3b_1^2 + 2b_1 + b_2 + b_3 + b_5 = B,$$

$$b_1^3 + b_1^2 + 2b_1 b_2 + 2b_1 b_3 + 2b_1 b_5 + b_3 + b_5 = C,$$

$$b_1^2 b_2 + b_1^2 b_3 + b_1^2 b_5 + b_1 b_3 + b_1 b_5 + b_2 b_3 + b_2 b_5 + b_3 b_5 + b_4 = D,$$

$$b_1 b_2 b_3 + b_1 b_2 b_5 + b_1 b_3 b_5 + b_1 b_4 + b_3 b_5 = E,$$

$$b_2 b_3 b_5 + b_4 b_5 + b_6 = F.$$

The system is readily solved by a method of substitution, leading to the solving of a quadratic equation: the coefficients b_i may be complex. If, however, the coefficients prove to be real, then the second stage of the computation requires only three multiplications and seven additions, instead of the five multiplications and six additions of Horner's scheme.

Similar transformations may be extended to polynomials of higher degree.

Yu. L. Ketkov [14] gave a general representation of an nth-degree polynomial for $n \geqslant 6$, which always leads to real expressions, and which requires $[\frac{1}{2}(n + 1)] + [\frac{1}{4}n]$ multiplications and $n + 1$ additions for evaluating an nth-degree polynomial.

Ketkov's scheme reduces, for instance when $n = 2k$, to successive evaluation of the polynomials:

$$N_2(x) = x(b_0 + x),$$
$$N_4(x) = (N_2 + b_1 + x)(N_2 + b_2) + b_3,$$
$$N_6(x) = N_2 N_4 + b_4 x + b_5,$$
$$\cdots\cdots\cdots\cdots\cdots\cdots\cdots\cdots$$
$$N_{2k}(x) = (N_2 + \bar{\delta}_k b_{2k-2}) N_{2k-2} + \delta_k b_{2k-2} x + b_{2k-1},$$

where $\delta_k = 0$, $\bar{\delta}_k = 1$ if k is even; and $\delta_k = \bar{1}$, $\bar{\delta}_k = 0$ if k is odd $(k \geqslant 3)$.

The condition that $P_n(x) = N_{2k}(x)$ leads to a system of equations for computing the b_i in terms of the coefficients of $P_n(x)$. In the paper [14], a computational method is given which always produces real coefficients b_i.

In the article [2], É. Belaga gives a strict proof of the impossibility of constructing a scheme for computing arbitrary nth-degree polynomials, in which the second stage requires less than $[\frac{1}{2}(n+1)] + 1$ multiplications and n additions.

We give below a scheme by V. Ya. Pan which, in the second stage of the computation of a polynomial $P_n(x)$, requires a number of operations which is very close to the number indicated in the work of É. Belaga.

1.2. V. Ya. Pan's method for computing polynomials.

1°. In order to compute a polynomial $P_n(z)$ in the complex plane, we construct the auxiliary polynomials $g(z)$ and $p_{2l}(z)$ $(l = 1, 2, \ldots, [\frac{1}{2}n])$, which are connected by the relations:

$$\left.\begin{array}{l} g(z) = z(z + \lambda_1), \quad p_2(z) = g(z) + z + \lambda_2, \\ p_{2l}(z) = p_{2l-2}(z)[g(z) + \lambda_{2l-1}] + \lambda_{2l} \quad (l = 2, 3, \ldots, k), \\ P_n(z) = \begin{cases} a_0 p_{2k}(z) & \text{if } n = 2k, \\ a_0 z p_{2k}(z) + \lambda_n & \text{if } n = 2k + 1. \end{cases} \end{array}\right\} \quad (1.2)$$

The first stage of the computation consists of the determination of the coefficients λ_i. The second stage, i.e. the successive evaluation of the polynomials $g(z)$, $p_2(z)$, etc., requires $n+1$ additions and $[\frac{1}{2}(n+1)]+1$ multiplications. Whatever the coefficients of $P_n(z)$ may be, if $n \geqslant 4$ there exist complex values of the parameters $\lambda_1, \lambda_2, \ldots, \lambda_n$, such that the formula (1.2) enables us to compute $P_n(z)$ for an arbitrary point z.

It is sufficient to consider the case of even n to explain the method for determining the coefficients λ_i. We write $p_{2l}(z)$ and $g(z) + \lambda_{2l-1}$ $(l = 2, 3, 4, \ldots, k)$ in the forms:

$$z^{2l} + \alpha_1^{(l)} z^{2l-1} + \ldots + \alpha_{2l}^{(l)} \text{ and } z^2 + \lambda_1 z + \lambda_{2l-1}.$$

respectively. It is easy to show that

$$\alpha_i^{(k)} = \frac{a_i}{a_0} \quad (i = 1, 2, \ldots, 2k), \qquad \lambda_1 = \frac{a_1 - a_0}{k a_0}.$$

We obtain

$$p_{2k}(z) = p_{2k-2}(z)[z^2 + \lambda_1 z + \lambda_{2k-1}] + \lambda_{2k}.$$

Removing the brackets and equating coefficients for each power of z on both sides of the equation, we get a system of algebraic equations for expressing the "parameters" λ_{2k-1}, λ_{2k} $\alpha_j^{(k-1)}$ $(j = 1, 2, \ldots, 2k-2)$ in terms of λ_1 and $\alpha_i^{(k)}$ $(i = 1, 2, \ldots, 2k)$, and accordingly, in terms of $a_0, a_1, \ldots, a_n$. Next, in a similar manner we find expressions for λ_{2k-3}, λ_{2k-2}, $\alpha_l^{(k-2)}$ $(l = 1, 2, \ldots, 2k-4)$ in terms of λ_1 and $\alpha_j^{(k-1)}$ $(j = 1, 2, \ldots, 2k-2)$, and so on until we get to λ_2. Thus we have obtained a set of values of $\lambda_1, \lambda_2, \ldots, \lambda_n$ as required. We note that the solution of each of the equations of the above system reduces to the solution of a single algebraic equation of degree l, where $l = 1, 2, \ldots, k-1$.

2°. There are several schemes for computing a polynomial $P_n(x)$ on the real axis (cf. [23]).

(a) *Scheme for evaluating quartic polynomials*:

$$P_4(x) = a_0 x^4 + a_1 x^3 + \ldots + a_4.$$

We represent $P_4(x)$ in the form

$$P_4(x) \equiv a_0 \{(g(x) + \lambda_2)(g(x) + x + \lambda_3) + \lambda_4\},$$
$$g(x) = x(x + \lambda_1),$$

where

$$\left. \begin{aligned} \lambda_1 &= \frac{a_1 - a_0}{2a_0}, \quad \lambda_2 = \frac{a_3}{a_0} - \lambda_1 \frac{a_2}{a_0} + (\lambda_1 + 1)\lambda_1^2, \\ \lambda_3 &= \frac{a_2}{a_0} - \lambda_1(\lambda_1 + 1) - \lambda_2, \quad \lambda_4 = \frac{a_4}{a_0} - \lambda_2 \lambda_3. \end{aligned} \right\} \quad (1.3)$$

For example,

$$\cos x \approx 1 - \frac{x^2}{2!} + \frac{x^4}{4!} - \frac{x^6}{6!} + \frac{x^8}{8!} = \frac{1}{8!} P_4(y), \quad \text{where} \quad y = x^2.$$

Then

$$P_4(y) = [g(y) + 5383 \cdot 125][g(y) + y - 4446 \cdot 875)]$$
$$+ 23978403 \cdot 984375,$$

where

$$g(y) = y(y - 28 \cdot 5).$$

(b) *Scheme for polynomials $P_n(x)$, where $6 \leqslant n \leqslant 12$.* We use the auxiliary polynomials

$$g(x) = x(x + \lambda_1), \quad h(x) = g(x) + x,$$
$$r_4(x) = [g(x) + \lambda_2][h(x) + x + \lambda_3] + \lambda_4,$$

and also (according to the value of n) the polynomials

$$\left. \begin{array}{l} p_6(x) = r_4(x)[h(x) + \lambda_5] + \lambda_6, \\ p_8(x) = p_6(x)[g(x) + \lambda_7] + \lambda_8, \\ p_9(x) = x p_8(x) + \lambda_9, \\ p_{11}(x) = p_9(x)[g(x) + \lambda_{10}] + \lambda_{11}. \end{array} \right\} \qquad (1.4)$$

Here,

$$P_n(x) = \begin{cases} a_0 p_n(x) & (n = 6, 8, 9, 11), \\ a_0 x p_{n-1}(x) + a_n & (n = 7, 10, 12). \end{cases}$$

The first stage consists of finding the coefficients λ_i, by a method similar to that described in the scheme (a).

With $n = 6$ and $n = 7$, the parameters can be expressed rationally in terms of $a_1, \ldots, a_n$.

We denote

$$p_6(x) = \sum_{k=0}^{6} \alpha_k x^{6-k}.$$

Provided only that

$$27\alpha_3 - 18\alpha_1\alpha_2 + 5\alpha_1^3 \neq 0,$$

there exist real values of the parameters $\lambda_1, \lambda_2, \ldots, \lambda_n$; and if these are substituted into the formula (1.4) the polynomial $P_n(x)$ may be evaluated for any real x.

For $n = 6$ and $n = 7$, this condition may be rewritten in the form

$$27 a_3 a_0^2 - 18 a_0 a_1 a_2 + 5 a_1^3 \neq 0.$$

(c) *Scheme for polynomial* $P_n(x)$ *for* $n \geqslant 5$. We construct the auxiliary polynomials $g(x)$, $h(x)$ and $p_s(x)$, where

$$\left.\begin{aligned}
g(x) &= x(x + \lambda_1), \quad h(x) = g(x) + x, \quad p_0(x) = x, \\
p_s(x) &= p_{s-1}(x)\{(g(x) + \lambda_{4s-2})(h(x) + \lambda_{4s-1}) + \lambda_{4s}\} \\
&\quad + \lambda_{4s+1} \quad (s = 1, 2, \ldots, k),
\end{aligned}\right\} \quad (1.5)$$

$$P_n(x) \equiv \begin{cases}
a_0 p_k(x) & \text{if} \quad n = 4k + 1, \\
a_0 x p_k(x) + \lambda_n & \text{if} \quad n = 4k + 2, \\
a_0[p_k(x)(g(x) + \lambda_{n-1}) + \lambda_n] & \text{if} \quad n = 4k + 3, \\
a_0 x[p_k(x)(g(x) + \lambda_{n-2}) + \lambda_{n-1}] + \lambda_n & \text{if} \quad n = 4k + 4.
\end{cases}$$

The second stage of this scheme requires $[\tfrac{1}{2}n] + 2$ multiplications and $n + 1$ additions.

There always exists a set of real values of the parameters $\lambda_1, \lambda_2, \ldots, \lambda_n$ satisfying the expressions (1.5), if $n \geqslant 5$ and if the coefficients $a_0, a_1, \ldots, a_n$ are real. In order to find these values, we may use the relations

$$p_s(x) = q_s(x) p_{s-1}(x) + \lambda_{4s+1},$$

where

$$q_s = (g(x) + \lambda_{4s-2})(h(x) + \lambda_{4s-1}) + \lambda_{4s} \quad (s = k, k-1, k-2, \ldots, 1),$$

and then apply the same method as above. The principal differences are the following: firstly, for all coefficients of $p_s(x)$ and for the three coefficients of $q_s(x)$, expressions are written in terms of the coefficients of $p_{s-1}(x)$ and λ_1; and then the parameters λ_{4s-2}, λ_{4s-1}, λ_{4s} are expressed in terms of the values found for the coefficients $q_s(x)$ and λ_1, by formulae which are analogous to the formulae (1.3) of the scheme (a).

If $6 \leqslant n \leqslant 12$ it is preferable to use the scheme (b) rather than (c), since the coefficients for this scheme (b) may be found, as a rule, more simply than for the scheme (c). Moreover, for $n = 6$ and $n = 8$ it requires fewer operations than does the scheme (c).

(d) In certain cases (e.g. on a machine with floating-point arithmetic), *when n is large and even* $(n \geqslant 10)$, the following scheme may be used for computing the polynomial $P_n(x)$:

$$\left.\begin{aligned}
g(x) &= x(x + \lambda_1), \quad h(x) = g(x) + x, \quad p_2(x) = h(x) + \lambda_2, \\
p_{2s+2}(x) &= p_{2s}(x)[q_s(x) + \lambda_{2s+1}] + \lambda_{2s+2} \\
&\quad\quad\quad\quad\quad (s = 1, 2, \ldots, k-1), \\
P_n(x) &= \begin{cases}
a_0[p_k(x) + 2^N x] & \text{if} \quad n = 2k, \\
a_0 x[p_k(x) + 2^N x] + a_n & \text{if} \quad n = 2k + 1,
\end{cases}
\end{aligned}\right\} \quad (1.6)$$

where N is a natural number.

Here,

$$q_{k-1}(x) = g(x), \quad q_s(x) = \begin{cases} h(x) & \text{for even } s, \\ g(x) & \text{for odd } s. \end{cases}$$

and $1 \leqslant s \leqslant k - 2$.

This scheme requires $n + 2$ additions, and $[\frac{1}{2}(n + 1)] + 1$ multiplications and, moreover, a shift of the decimal point corresponding to a multiplication by 2^N.

The following method is used to determine the values of $\lambda_1, \lambda_2, \ldots, \lambda_n$. First we fix the value of the natural number N and then, in the manner described above, we find the required real values of the parameters, corresponding to

$$\alpha_{2k-1}^{(k)} = \frac{a_{2k-1}}{a_0} - 2^N.$$

A drawback to this scheme is that the values found for $\lambda_2, \lambda_3, \lambda_4, \ldots, \lambda_n$ are real if and only if a sufficiently large value of N is chosen.†

§ 2. Elementary rational functions

2.1. Power series expansions.

$$1°. \ \frac{1}{a + x} = \frac{1}{a} \sum_{k=0}^{\infty} \left(-\frac{x}{a} \right)^k \quad |x| < |a|,$$

$$r_{n-1} \leqslant \frac{|p|^n}{1 - |p|}, \quad p = \frac{x}{a}.$$

For example,

$$\frac{1}{1 + x} = \begin{cases} \displaystyle\sum_{k=0}^{\infty} (-x)^k, & |x| < 1, \\ \displaystyle\frac{1}{x} \sum_{k=0}^{\infty} \left(-\frac{1}{x} \right)^k, & |x| > 1. \end{cases}$$

$$2°. \ \frac{1}{x} = \frac{2}{3} \sum_{k=0}^{\infty} \left(\frac{2}{3} x - 1 \right)^k, \quad 1 \leqslant x \leqslant 2, \quad r_{n-1} \leqslant \frac{1}{3^n}.$$

$$3°. \ \frac{1}{(1 + x)^m} = \frac{1}{(m - 1)!} \sum_{k=0}^{\infty} (k + 1)(k + 2) \ldots$$

$$\ldots (k + m - 1)(-x)^k, \quad |x| < 1;$$

---

† Similar economical techniques for evaluating polynomials are investigated by D. E. Knuth in "Evaluation of polynomials by computer", *Comm. Assoc. Comp. Mach.* **5**, No. 12, 595—599 (1962). (G. J. T.)

and in particular,

$$\frac{1}{(1+x)^2} = \sum_{k=0}^{\infty} (k+1)(-x)^k.$$

2.2. Expansions in polynomials, orthogonal and otherwise.[†]

$$1°. \ \frac{1}{a-bx} = \frac{1}{\sqrt{a^2-b^2}} \left(1 + 2 \sum_{k=1}^{\infty} p^k T_k(x)\right),$$

$$|b| < a, \quad |x| \leqslant 1,$$

$$p = \frac{a - \sqrt{a^2 - b^2}}{b}, \qquad r_{n-1} = \frac{2p^n}{\sqrt{a^2-b^2}(1-p)}.$$

$$2°. \ \frac{1}{a+x} = \frac{1 + 2 \sum_{k=1}^{\infty} (-1)^k q^k T_k(2x-1)}{(a^2+a)^{1/2}}, \qquad 0 < x \leqslant 1,$$

$$q = 2a + 1 - 2(a^2 + a)^{\frac{1}{2}}.$$

This formula is valid for complex a, provided that $|\arg a| \leqslant \frac{1}{2}\pi, a \neq 0$.

[†] A series of Chebyshev polynomials

$$f(x) = \sum_{r=0}^{n} {}' a_r T_r(x)$$

(where the $\sum'$ means that the first term of the series is to be taken as $\frac{1}{2}a_0$) is most conveniently evaluated by means of an algorithm analogous to nested multiplication. This algorithm, which was devised by C.W. Clenshaw ("A note on the summation of Chebyshev series", *MTAC* **9**, 118–120, 1955), consists of generating a sequence of numbers $b_{n+2}, b_{n+1}, \ldots, b_0$ by the recurrence relations:

$$b_{n+2} = 0, \quad b_{n+1} = 0,$$

$$b_r = 2xb_{r+1} - b_{r+2} + a_r \quad (r = n, n-1, \ldots, 0).$$

Then,

$$f(x) = \frac{1}{2}(b_0 - b_2).$$

Tables of the coefficients of Chebyshev series expansions (mostly to 20 decimal places) of a number of common mathematical functions are given in the recent publication: C. W. Clenshaw, "Chebyshev Series for Mathematical Functions", *NPL Mathematical Tables*, Vol. 5, H.M.S.O., London, 1962. (G. J. T.)

$3°.\ \dfrac{1}{a-bx} = \dfrac{2p}{b} \sum_{k=0}^{\infty} p^k U_k(x), \quad a > b, \quad |x| < 1,$

$$p = \dfrac{a - \sqrt{a^2 - b^2}}{b}, \qquad r_{n-1} = \dfrac{2p^{n+1}(n+1-np)}{b(1-p)^2}.$$

$4°.\ \dfrac{1}{x} = \dfrac{1}{\sqrt{2}} + \sqrt{2} \sum_{k=1}^{\infty} p^k T_k(3-2x), \quad 1 \leqslant x \leqslant 2,$

$$p = 3 - 2\sqrt{2} = 0{\cdot}1715728\ldots < \dfrac{\sqrt{3}}{10},$$

$$r_{n-1} = \dfrac{2p^n}{1-p} < 3^{\frac{n+1}{2}} \times 10^{-n} < 10^{-\frac{3n-1}{4}}.$$

$5°.\ \dfrac{1}{1-bx^2} = \dfrac{1+p}{1-p} \left(1 + 2 \sum_{k=1}^{\infty} p^k T_{2k}(x) \right), \quad |b| < 1,\ |x| \leqslant 1,$

$$p = 2 - b - 2\sqrt{1-b}, \qquad r_{n-1} = \dfrac{2(1+p)}{(1-p)^2} p^n.$$

$6°.\ \dfrac{1}{(a-bx)^2} = \dfrac{2}{b\sqrt{a^2-b^2}} \sum_{k=0}^{\infty} (k+1) p^k U_k(x),$

$$p = \dfrac{a - \sqrt{a^2 - b^2}}{b}.$$

$7°.\ \dfrac{1}{x^2} = 2\sqrt{2} \sum_{k=0}^{\infty} (k+1)\, p^k U_k(3-2x), \quad 1 \leqslant x \leqslant 2,$

$$p = 3 - 2\sqrt{2} = 0{\cdot}1715728\ldots$$

2.3. Infinite products.

$1°.\ \dfrac{1}{1-u} = \prod_{j=0}^{\infty} (1 + u^{2^j}), \quad |u| < 1.$

If $u = 1 - xy_0$, this formula assumes the form

$2°.\ \dfrac{1}{x} = y_0 \prod_{j=0}^{\infty} [1 + (1 - xy_0)^{2^j}].$ 18(93)

(Such formulae are used for division on certain machines.)

2.4. Iterative processes. There is an iterative formula for computing the reciprocal of a quantity $y = \dfrac{1}{x}$:

$$y_{i+1} = y_i(2 - xy_i) \quad (i = 0, 1, 2, \ldots), \quad \lim_{i \to \infty} y_i = \frac{1}{x}. \qquad 18(92, 93)$$

The process converges to $1/x$, if the modulus of the relative error $\varepsilon_0(x)$ of the initial approximation satisfies the inequality

$$|\varepsilon_0(x)| = |1 - xy_0| < 1.^\dagger$$

If $\frac{1}{2} \leqslant x < 1$, we get that
(a) The best constant to take as an initial approximation is

$$y_0 = \frac{4}{3}, \qquad \varepsilon_0 = \frac{1}{3}.$$

(b) The best linear approximation is

$$y_0 = \frac{1}{17}(48 - 32x), \qquad \varepsilon_0 = \frac{1}{17}.$$

(c) The best quadratic approximation is

$$y_0 = 0{\cdot}45469 + (1{\cdot}71285 - x)^2, \qquad \varepsilon_0 = 0{\cdot}03715$$

Three iterations starting from this approximation give an error less than 2^{-38}.

§ 3. Power functions

3.1. Power series expansions.

$$1°. \ (1 + x)^\nu = 1 + \nu x + \frac{\nu(\nu - 1)}{2!}x^2 + \ldots$$

$$\ldots + \frac{\nu(\nu - 1) \ldots (\nu - k + 1)}{k!}x^k + \ldots$$

If ν is neither a positive integer nor zero, then the series converges absolutely for $|x| < 1$ and diverges for $|x| > 1$: if $x = -1$ the series

---

† This iterative process for inverting the scalar x is a particular case of the well-known iterative procedure of Hotelling for improving an approximation Y_0 to the inverse $Y = X^{-1}$ of a non-singular matrix X. Cf. V. N. Faddeeva, *Computational Methods of Linear Algebra* (translated from the Russian by C. D. Benster), Dover, New York 1959, pp. 99—101. (G. J. T.)

converges for $\nu > -1$ and diverges for $\nu \leqslant -1$: if $x = 1$ it converges for $\nu > 0$, and if ν is a positive integer ($\nu = n$), then it reduces to a finite sum.

$$2^\circ. \quad (1 \pm x)^{\frac{1}{2}} = 1 \pm \frac{1}{2} x - \frac{1.1}{2.4} x^2 \pm \frac{1.1.3}{2.4.6} x^3$$

$$- \frac{1.1.3.5}{2.4.6.8} x^4 \pm \ldots \quad 26(35)$$

$$3^\circ. \quad (1 \pm x)^{-\frac{1}{2}} = 1 \mp \frac{1}{2} x + \frac{1.3}{2.4} x^2 \mp \frac{1.3.5}{2.4.6} x^3$$

$$+ \frac{1.3.5.7}{2.4.6.8} x^4 \mp \ldots \quad 26(35)$$

3.2. Expansions in polynomials, orthogonal and otherwise.

$$1^\circ. \quad \frac{1}{\sqrt{1 - 2px + p^2}} = \sum_{k=0}^{\infty} p^k P_k(x)$$

$$\left[|p| < \min \left|x \pm \sqrt{x^2 - 1}\right|\right]; \quad 26(396); \quad 30(91); \quad 27(489)$$

$$= \sum_{k=0}^{\infty} \frac{1}{p^{k+1}} P_k(x)$$

$$\left[|p| > \max \left|x \pm \sqrt{x^2 - 1}\right|\right]. \quad 26(396); \quad 66(70)$$

$$\text{(a)} \quad \frac{1}{\sqrt{1 - px}} = \alpha \sum_{k=0}^{\infty} h^k P_k(x), \quad 0 \leqslant p < 1,$$

$$h = \frac{1}{p} - \sqrt{\frac{1}{p^2} - 1}, \quad \alpha = \frac{1}{1 + h^2}, \quad |x| \leqslant 1.$$

$$\text{(b)} \quad \frac{1}{\sqrt{x}} = \beta \sum_{k=0}^{\infty} \varrho^k P_k(3 - 2x), \quad \varrho = 3 - 2\sqrt{2} \approx 0{\cdot}1715728,$$

$$\beta = \sqrt{\frac{2}{3[1 + (3 - \sqrt{2})^2]}} = \frac{1}{3} \sqrt{1 + \frac{1}{\sqrt{2}}} \approx 0{\cdot}4355210,$$

$$1 \leqslant x \leqslant 2.$$

$2°. \dfrac{1}{\sqrt{1-x^2}} = \dfrac{\pi}{2} \displaystyle\sum_{k=0}^{\infty} (4k+1) \left\{ \dfrac{(2k-1)!!}{2^k . k!} \right\}^2 P_{2k}(x)$

$(|x| < 1, \quad (-1)!! \equiv 1)$.   26(396);   66(72);   61(385)

$3°. \dfrac{x}{\sqrt{1-x^2}} = \dfrac{\pi}{2} \displaystyle\sum_{k=0}^{\infty} (4k+3) \dfrac{(2k-1)!!(2k+1)!!}{2^{k+1} . k!(k+1)!} P_{2k+1}(x)$

$(|x| < 1, \quad (-1)!! \equiv 1)$.   26(396);   61(385)

$4°. \sqrt{1-x^2} = \dfrac{\pi}{2} \left\{ \dfrac{1}{2} - \displaystyle\sum_{k=1}^{\infty} (4k+1) \dfrac{(2k-3)!!(2k-1)!!}{2^{2k+1} . k!(k+1)!} \times \right.$

$\left. \times P_{2k}(x) \right\} \quad (|x| < 1, \quad (-1)!! \equiv 1)$.   26(396);   61(385)

$5°. \; y = \sqrt{x} \quad (0 \leqslant x \leqslant 1)$.

An approximation y_n is given by the formula

$$y_n = \dfrac{\displaystyle\sum_{k=0}^{n} \dfrac{c_n^k}{2k-1} x^k}{\displaystyle\sum_{k=0}^{n} \dfrac{c_n^k}{2k-1}}, \quad r_n = \dfrac{1}{n\pi} \quad (0 \leqslant x \leqslant 1),$$

where the c_n^k are the coefficients of the Chebyshev polynomial $T_n(x)$, expanded in powers of x (cf. Appendix I, § 4·5, 3°).

3.3. Polynomial approximations.

1°. *The computation of* $\sqrt{A+Bi}$.
If $A > B$, then

$$\sqrt{A+Bi} = \sqrt{A} \sqrt{1 + \dfrac{B}{A} i};$$

and if $A < B$, then

$$\sqrt{A+Bi} = \sqrt{B} \sqrt{\dfrac{A}{B} + i},$$

after which the problem reduces to computing the following quantities:

$$x = \frac{B}{A}, \quad y = \sqrt{1 + ix} \quad (0 \leqslant x \leqslant 1),$$

$$x = \frac{A}{B}, \quad y = \sqrt{i + x} \quad (0 \leqslant x \leqslant 1),$$

for which we have the following approximations:

$$\sqrt{1 + ix} = 1 + 0{\cdot}0184x + 0{\cdot}0810x^2 + i(0{\cdot}5201x - 0{\cdot}0653x^2);$$
$$= 1 + x(0{\cdot}0184 + 0{\cdot}0810x) \quad (r = 0{\cdot}002)$$
$$+ ix(0{\cdot}5201 - 0{\cdot}0653x) \quad (ri = 0{\cdot}002i);$$

$$\sqrt{1 + ix} = 1 - 0{\cdot}00316x + 0{\cdot}14237x^2 - 0{\cdot}04079x^3 \quad (r = 0{\cdot}0002)$$
$$+ ix(0{\cdot}50637 - 0{\cdot}03108x - 0{\cdot}02020x^2)$$
$$(ri = 0{\cdot}0002i);$$

$$\sqrt{i + x} = 0{\cdot}7071 + x(0{\cdot}3807 + 0{\cdot}0111x)$$
$$+ i[0{\cdot}7071 - x(0{\cdot}3548 - 0{\cdot}1035x)];$$

$$\sqrt{-1 + ix} = x(0{\cdot}5201 - 0{\cdot}0653x) + i[1 + x(0{\cdot}0184 + 0{\cdot}0810x)];$$

$$\sqrt{i - x} = 0{\cdot}7071 - x(0{\cdot}3548 - 0{\cdot}1035x)$$
$$+ i[0{\cdot}7071 + x(0{\cdot}3807 + 0{\cdot}0111x)]. \quad 17(490\text{–}493)$$

2°. $y = \sqrt{x}$.

The number x is represented as the sum of two numbers A_i^2 and B^2, where A_i^2 is a known square, and $B^2 < A_i^2$.

Notation: $\dfrac{B^2}{A_i^2} = k$, y^* is an approximation to y.

(a) $y^* = A(1{\cdot}0075 + 0{\cdot}4173k)$, $\varepsilon = 7{\cdot}5 \times 10^{-3}$.
(b) $y^* = A(1{\cdot}000625 + 0{\cdot}485025k - 0{\cdot}07232k^2)$, $\varepsilon = 6{\cdot}4 \times 10^{-4}$.

3.4. Continued fraction expansions.

1°. $$(1 + x)^\nu = \frac{1}{1} - \frac{\nu x}{1 + x} - \frac{(1 - \nu)x}{2} - \frac{(1 + \nu)x}{3(1 + x)}$$

$$- \frac{(2 - \nu)x}{2} - \dots - \frac{(n - \nu)x}{2} - \frac{(n + \nu)x}{(2n + 1)(1 + x)} - \dots \quad 34(101)$$

$2°.$ $(1+x)^\nu = \cfrac{1}{1} - \cfrac{\nu x}{1} + \cfrac{(1+\nu)x}{2} + \cfrac{(1-\nu)x}{3} + \cfrac{(2+\nu)x}{2}$

$$+ \cfrac{(2-\nu)x}{5} + \ldots + \cfrac{(n+\nu)x}{2} + \cfrac{(n-\nu)x}{2n+1} + \ldots \qquad 34(101)$$

The continued fraction converges on the plane of the complex variable x, cut on the real axis from $x = -\infty$ to $x = -1$.

$3°.$ $(1+x)^\nu = \cfrac{1}{1} - \cfrac{\nu x}{1+(1+\nu)x} - \cfrac{(1+\nu)x(1+x)}{2+(3+\nu)x}$

$$- \cfrac{2(2+\nu)x(1+x)}{3+(5+\nu)x} - \ldots - \cfrac{n(n+\nu)x(1+x)}{n+1+(2n+1+\nu)x} - \ldots \qquad 34(102)$$

$4°.$ $(1+x)^\nu = \cfrac{1}{1} - \cfrac{\nu x}{1+\nu x} + \cfrac{(1-\nu)x}{2-(1-\nu)x} + \cfrac{2(2-\nu)x}{3-(2-\nu)x} + \ldots$

$$\ldots + \cfrac{n(n-\nu)x}{n+1-(n-\nu)x} + \ldots \qquad 34(102)$$

$5°.$ $(1+x)^\nu = 1 + \cfrac{\nu x}{1+x} - \cfrac{(1+\nu)x}{2} - \cfrac{(1-\nu)x}{3(1+x)} - \cfrac{(2+\nu)x}{2}$

$$\ldots - \cfrac{(n+\nu)x}{2} - \cfrac{(n-\nu)x}{(2n+1)(1+x)} - \ldots \qquad 34(102)$$

$6°.$ $(1+x)^\nu = 1 + \cfrac{\nu x}{1} + \cfrac{(1-\nu)x}{2} + \cfrac{(1+\nu)x}{3} + \cfrac{(2-\nu)x}{2} + \ldots$

$$\ldots + \cfrac{(n-\nu)x}{2} + \cfrac{(n+\nu)x}{2n+1} + \ldots \qquad 34(102)$$

The fraction converges on the plane of the complex variable x, cut on the real axis from $x = -\infty$ to $x = -1$.

$7°.$ $(1+x)^\nu = 1 + \cfrac{\nu x}{1+(1-\nu)x} - \cfrac{(1-\nu)x(1+x)}{2+(3-\nu)x} - \ldots$

$$\ldots - \cfrac{n(n-\nu)x(1+x)}{n+1+(2n+1-\nu)x} - \ldots \qquad 34(102)$$

$8°.$ $(1+x)^\nu = 1 + \cfrac{\nu x}{1-\nu x} + \cfrac{(1+\nu)x}{2-(1+\nu)x} + \cfrac{2(2+\nu)x}{3-(2+\nu)x} + \ldots$

$$\ldots + \cfrac{n(n+\nu)x}{n+1-(n+\nu)x} + \ldots \qquad 34(102)$$

$9°.$ $(1+x)^\nu = 1 + \cfrac{2\nu x}{2+(1-\nu)x} - \cfrac{(1-\nu^2)x^2}{3(2+x)} - \cfrac{(4-\nu^2)x^2}{5(2+x)}$

$$\ldots - \cfrac{(n^2-\nu^2)x^2}{(2n+1)(2+x)} - \ldots \qquad 34(104)$$

$10°.$ $\left(\dfrac{x+1}{x-1}\right)^{\nu} = 1 + \dfrac{2\nu}{x-\nu} + \dfrac{\nu^2-1}{3x} + \dfrac{\nu^2-4}{5x} + \ldots$

$$\ldots + \dfrac{\nu^2-n^2}{(2n+1)x} + \ldots \qquad 34(106)$$

$11°.$ Let $\sqrt{x} \approx a.$ Then

$$\sqrt{x} = a + \dfrac{x-a^2}{2a} + \dfrac{x-a^2}{2a} + \ldots$$

The continued fraction converges on the plane of the complex variable x, except for that part of the real axis satisfying the inequality $-\infty < x \leqslant 0$. In particular, for $a = 1$:

$$\sqrt{x} = 1 + \dfrac{x-1}{2} + \dfrac{x-1}{2} + \dfrac{x-1}{2} + \dfrac{x-1}{2} + \ldots$$

$$\dfrac{1}{1} \quad \dfrac{x+1}{2} \quad \dfrac{3x+1}{x+3} \quad \dfrac{x^2+6x+1}{4x+4} \quad \dfrac{5x^2+10x+1}{x^2+10x+5} \qquad 34(108)$$

$12°.$ *Series of rational approximations.*

(a) $\quad x^n \approx \dfrac{\displaystyle\sum_{\nu=0}^{m} \dfrac{C_m^{\nu} C_n^{\nu}}{C_{m+k}^{\nu}} (x-1)^{\nu}}{\displaystyle\sum_{\nu=0}^{k} (-1)^{\nu} \dfrac{C_k^{\nu} C_n^{\nu}}{C_{m+k}^{\nu}} \dfrac{(x-1)^{\nu}}{x^{\nu}}} \qquad I(310)$

where n is any real number. If $m = k$, this equation assumes the form

(b) $\quad x^n \approx \dfrac{\displaystyle\sum_{\nu=0}^{k} \dfrac{C_k^{\nu} C_n^{\nu}}{C_{2k}^{\nu}} (x-1)^{\nu}}{\displaystyle\sum_{\nu=0}^{k} (-1)^{\nu} \dfrac{C_k^{\nu} C_n^{\nu}}{C_{2k}^{\nu}} \dfrac{(x-1)^{\nu}}{x^{\nu}}}.$

3.5. Rational approximations.

$1°.$ Within a relative error less than $\dfrac{1}{12}$, over the range $0 \cdot 1 \leqslant x \leqslant 10$;

$$\sqrt{x} \approx \dfrac{1+4x}{4+x} \qquad 48(68)$$

$2°.$ $\sqrt{x} \approx \dfrac{A + yB}{A - yB},$ $\quad y = \dfrac{1}{2}\dfrac{(x-1)}{(x+1)}$ $\quad (0{\cdot}1 \leqslant x \leqslant 10{\cdot}0),$

$$A = \sum_{k=0}^{3} (-1)^k a_{2k} y^{2k}, \qquad B = \sum_{k=0}^{3} (-1)^k b_{2k} y^{2k},$$

$$a_0 = 1, \qquad b_0 = 1,$$
$$a_2 = 6, \qquad b_2 = 5,$$
$$a_4 = 10, \qquad b_4 = 6,$$
$$a_6 = 4, \qquad b_6 = 1. \qquad\qquad 60(85)$$

$3°.$ *Application of "Padé rational approximations".* A variety of rational approximations for the functions $\sqrt[n]{x}$ are given below for various intervals. These approximations may be improved by means of Heron's iterative process (cf. § 3.6, 1°) when $n = 2$, or by Newton's general formula (cf. § 3.6, 6°) for $n > 2$. The choice of intervals is determined by the system of computation (binary or decimal).

(a) *Extraction of the square root* (*in binary arithmetic*)

$N = 2^{2m}x,$ $\ 0{\cdot}25 < x \leqslant 1,$ $\ \sqrt{N} = 2^m \cdot \sqrt{x},$ where m is an integer.

The interval $(0{\cdot}25, 1)$ is divided into two intervals: $0{\cdot}25 < x \leqslant 0{\cdot}5$ and $0{\cdot}5 < x \leqslant 1.$

$$\sqrt{x} \approx y_0 = c_{10} - \frac{c_{11}}{x + c_{12}}.$$

	$0{\cdot}25 < x \leqslant 0{\cdot}5$	$0{\cdot}5 < x \leqslant 1$
c_{10}	$1{\cdot}792\ 843$	$2{\cdot}535\ 463$
c_{11}	$1{\cdot}707\ 469$	$4{\cdot}829\ 452$
c_{12}	$1{\cdot}071\ 429$	$2{\cdot}142\ 858$

$57(151)$

The initial approximation is taken as:

$$y_0 = c_{10} - c_{11}(x + c_{12})^{-1}.$$

Over the range $0{\cdot}25 < x \leqslant 0{\cdot}5$, we have $\varepsilon = 1{\cdot}4 \times 10^{-3}$. Next, Heron's method is applied to the initial approximation y_0. Two iterations give $\varepsilon_2 \leqslant 5 \times 10^{-13}.$

$$\sqrt{x} \approx y_0 = c_{20} - \frac{c_{21}}{x + c_{22}} - \frac{c_{23}}{x + c_{24}}.$$

	$0.25 < x \leqslant 0.5$	$0.5 < x < 1$
c_{20}	$5\left(\dfrac{5}{14}\right)^{\frac{1}{2}}$	$5\left(\dfrac{5}{7}\right)^{\frac{1}{2}}$
c_{21}	$\dfrac{20c_{20}}{7}$	$\dfrac{40\sqrt{2}}{7}$
c_{22}	$\dfrac{47}{14}$	$\dfrac{47}{7}$
c_{23}	$\dfrac{4}{49}$	$\dfrac{16}{49}$
c_{24}	$\dfrac{3}{14}$	$\dfrac{3}{7}$

57(151)

Over the range $0.25 < x \leqslant 0.5$ we have $\varepsilon_0 = 10^{-5}$. Next Heron's method is applied to the initial approximation y_0. The application of a single iteration gives $\varepsilon_1 \leqslant 5 \times 10^{-11}$.

(b) *Square root (for decimal arithmetic)*

$$N = 10^{2m}.x, \quad 10^{-2} < x \leqslant 1.$$

The interval $(10^{-2}, 1)$ is divided into four sub-intervals

$$(10^{-2}r^{k-1}, \quad 10^{-2}r^k), \quad k = 1, 2, 3, 4; \quad r = 10^{\frac{1}{2}}.$$

$$\sqrt{x} \approx y_0 = d_0 - \frac{d_1}{x + d_2} - \frac{d_3}{x + d_4} \quad (1 < 100x \leqslant r). \tag{α}$$

For the first subinterval (in which $k = 1$) we have

d_0	0·674 055	d_3	0·000 211
d_1	0·098 002	d_4	0·010 904
d_2	0·170 836		

57(151)

and $\varepsilon_0 = 1.7 \times 10^{-5}$. Next, Heron's method is applied to the initial approximation y_0. A single iteration ensures accuracy to nine significant figures, and two iterations give eighteen correct significant figures.

For the interval $(10^{-2}r^{k-1}, 10^{-2}r^k)$ where $k = 2, 3$ or 4, the coefficients d_0, d_1, d_2, d_3, and d_4 in the formula (α) are to be replaced by

$$d_0 r^{k/2}, \quad d_1 r^{3k/2}, \quad d_2 r^k, \quad d_3 r^{2k} \text{ and } d_4 r^k$$

respectively.

(c) *Cube roots (in binary arithmetic)*

$$N = 2^{3m}.x, \qquad N^{\frac{1}{3}} = 2^m.x^{\frac{1}{3}}, \qquad 2^{-3} < x < 1.$$

The interval $(2^{-3}, 1)$ is to be subdivided into three sub-intervals:

$$(2^{-3}, 2^{-2}), \left(2^{-2}, \frac{1}{2}\right) \text{ and } \left(\frac{1}{2}, 1\right).$$

$$\sqrt[3]{x} \approx y_0 = a_0 - \frac{a_1}{x + b_1}$$

	$2^{-3} < x \leqslant 2^{-2}$	$2^{-2} < x \leqslant 2^{-1}$	$2^{-1} < x < 1$
a_0	1·126 25	1·418 986	1·787 81
a_1	0·301 67	0·760 160 7	1·915 48
b_1	0·357 14	0·714 28	1·428 56

57(152)

where $\varepsilon_0 = 1\cdot2 \times 10^{-3}$ for $2^{-3} < x \leqslant 2^{-2}$. A single iteration by Newton's formula (§ 3.6, 6°) gives the first eight significant figures correct.

$$\sqrt[3]{x} \approx y_0 = a_0 - \frac{a_1}{x + b_1} - \frac{a_2}{x + b_2}$$

	$2^{-3} < x \leqslant 2^{-2}$	$2^{-2} < x \leqslant 2^{-1}$	$2^{-1} < x < 1$
a_0	1·576 745	1·986 574	2·502 926
a_1	1·267 028	3·192 710	8·045 125
b_1	1·153 061	2·306 122	4·612 244
a_2	0·022 490 6	0·089 962 4	0·359 849 6
b_2	0·096 938 8	0·193 877 6	0·387 755 2

57(152)

where $\varepsilon_0 = 7\cdot5 \times 10^{-6}$ for $2^{-3} \leqslant x \leqslant 2^{-2}$. The first four significant figures are found by means of only two divisions. A single iteration by Newton's formula increases the number of correct significant figures to fifteen.

3.6. Iterative processes. 1°. Heron's iterative formula for extraction of the square root

$$y = \sqrt{x},$$

which is a particular case of Newton's formula, is:

$$y_{i+1} = \frac{1}{2}\left(y_i + \frac{x}{y_i}\right) \quad (i = 0, 1, \ldots).$$

The iterates produced by Heron's formula satisfy the relation

$$\frac{y_i - \sqrt{x}}{y_i + \sqrt{x}} = \left(\frac{y_0 - \sqrt{x}}{y_0 + \sqrt{x}}\right)^{2^i}.$$

Over the range $\frac{1}{2} \leqslant x < 1$, the best linear approximation is

$$y_0 = \frac{1}{\sqrt{\sqrt[4]{8} + \sqrt[4]{2}}}\left(x + \frac{\sqrt{2}}{2}\right) \approx 0{\cdot}5903x + 0{\cdot}4173.$$

Starting from this initial linear approximation, two iterations give $r = 2^{-31}$.

Over the range $1 \leqslant x \leqslant 2$,

$$\left|\frac{r_{i+1}(x)}{2}\right| < \left(\frac{r_0(x)}{2}\right)^{2^{i+1}},$$

$$\varepsilon_i(x) = y_i x^{-\frac{1}{2}} - 1, \qquad |\varepsilon_{i+1}| \approx \frac{1}{2}\,\varepsilon_i^2. \hspace{2cm} 19(17);\ 18(94);$$

$$5(227);\ 57(150)$$

Supplement to 1°. Tables are given below of the coefficients a and b for the initial approximation $y_0 = ax + b$, to be used in Heron's method for computing $y = \sqrt{x}$ over the interval $(0{\cdot}01, 1)$ when the decimal system is being used. The coefficients are so chosen for the various sub-intervals that the second iterate y_2 gives the value of $\sqrt{x}$ with 8, 10 or 12 correct significant figures. When y_0 is being computed, the value of x need be taken with only three significant figures.

8 figures			10 figures		
Interval	a	b	Interval	a	b
0·01–0·02	4·1	0·060	0·01–0·02	4·2	0·0585
0·02–0·03	3·2	0·078	0·02–0·03	3·1	0·0803
0·03–0·08	2·2	0·110	0·03–0·05	2·5	0·0991
0·08–0·18	1·4	0·174	0·05–0·08	2·0	0·1240
0·18–0·30	1·0	0·247	0·08–0·13	1·6	0·1545
0·30–0·60	0·8	0·304	0·13–0·23	1·2	0·2060
0·60–1·0	0·6	0·409	0·23–0·39	0·9	0·2749
			0·39–0·60	0·7	0·3550
			0·60–0·84	0·6	0·4148
			0·84–1·0	0·5	0·5005

12 figures			12 figures		
Interval	a	b	Interval	a	b
0·010–0·014	4·58	0·05439	0·145–0·195	1·21	0·20596
0·014–0·020	3·84	0·06482	0·195–0·260	1·05	0·23745
0·020–0·028	3·23	0·07712	0·260–0·350	0·91	0·27395
0·028–0·040	2·72	0·09153	0·350–0·470	0·78	0·31953
0·040–0·056	2·29	0·10876	0·470–0·630	0·68	0·36649
0·056–0·076	1·95	0·12781	0·630–0·820	0.59	0·42301
0·076–0·105	1·66	0·15004	0·820–1·0	0·52	0·48005
0·105–0·145	1·42	0·17548			

$2°$. Iterative formula without division, for computing $y = \dfrac{1}{\sqrt{x}}$

$\left(\text{and also } \sqrt{x} = xy\right)$.

$$y_{i+1} = \frac{3}{2} y_i - \frac{1}{2} x y_i^3 \quad (i = 0, 1, \ldots),$$

$$\varepsilon_{i+1}(x) = -\frac{1}{2} \sqrt{x} \varepsilon_i^2(x) \left(3 + \varepsilon_i(x)\sqrt{x}\right).$$

Over the range $\frac{1}{2} \leqslant x < 1$, the best constant initial approximation is

$$y_0 = 2(2 - \sqrt{2}) \approx 1\cdot1715729, \quad \varepsilon_0 < 0\cdot172;$$

and the best linear initial approximation is

$$y_0 = \frac{2}{(3 + \sqrt{2})\left(\dfrac{1}{2} + \dfrac{1}{3}\sqrt{\dfrac{3 + \sqrt{2}}{6}}\right) - 1} \cdot \left(\frac{3 + \sqrt{2}}{2} - x\right)$$

$$\approx -0\cdot80999x + 1\cdot78773, \quad \varepsilon_0 < 0\cdot022. \quad 18(96)$$

$3°$. The iterative formula

$$y_{i+1} = y_i\left(\frac{3}{2} - \frac{y_i^2}{2x}\right),$$

for computing $\sqrt{x}$, requires no divisions, apart from inversion of the quantity $2x$. When $x = 2^n x_1$, the initial approximation can be taken as

$$y_0 = 2^{E\left(\frac{n}{2}\right)}. \quad\quad 5(230); \ 20(135)$$

$4°. \; y = \sqrt{x},$

$$y_{i+1} = \frac{y_i(y_i^2 + 3x)}{3y_i^2 + x}.$$

$5°. \; y = \sqrt{x}.$ An iterative formula without division, suitable for binary arithmetic, is:

$$y_{i+1} = y_i - \frac{1}{2} y_i z_i, \quad z_{i+1} = \frac{1}{4} z_i^2 (z_i - 3),$$

where $y_0 = x$, $z_0 = x - 1$ $\quad (\lim_{i \to \infty} z_i = 0).$ 5(230)

$6°.$ Newton's rule: $y = \sqrt[n]{x},$

$$y_{i+1} = \frac{1}{n} \left[(n-1)y_i + \frac{x}{y_i^{n-1}} \right].$$ 12(180)

$7°.$ Generalized Newton's method for $y = \sqrt[n]{x}$, applicable to values n of the order of 10 or greater:

$$y_{i+1} = \frac{(n-1)y_i^n + (n+1)x}{(n+1)y_i^n + (n-1)x} \, y_i.$$ 12(181)

$8°. \; y = \sqrt[n]{x}.$ First we replace y by the variable z, where $z = 10^k y$ and k is an integer (positive or negative), thereby reducing the problem to that of finding $z = \sqrt[n]{X}$, where $0 < X < 1$. The replacement should be done in such a manner that X is as close as possible to 1. Next, the number $l = \dfrac{1}{n}$ is to be computed with a relative error $\varepsilon \leqslant 0 \cdot 1 X$. Then we have the following iterative formula without division:

$$z_{i+1} = z_i + l(X - z_i^n) \; (X \leqslant z_0 \leqslant 1).$$ 12(182)

$9°. \; y = \sqrt[n]{x}$ (Iteration with quadratic convergence).

$$y_{i+1} = y_i + l(y_i - my_i^{n+1}),$$

where $l = \dfrac{1}{n}$, $m = \dfrac{1}{x}$.   12(184)

In contrast to the method of $8°$, the values of l and m must here be computed to high accuracy.

10°. Iterative formula for extraction of the cube root $y = \sqrt[3]{x}$:

$$y_{i+1} = \frac{1}{2}y_i + \frac{x + \dfrac{1}{2}x}{2y_i^2 + xy_i^{-1}},$$

$$|\varepsilon_{j+1}| \leqslant \frac{2|\varepsilon_j|^3}{3}. \qquad 57(150)$$

11°. Iterative formula for extraction of the fifth root $y = \sqrt[5]{x}$:

$$y_{i+1} = y_i\left[2\left(y_i^4 + \frac{x}{y_i}\right) + \frac{x}{y_i}\right]\left[2\left(y_i^4 + \frac{x}{y_i}\right) + y_i^4\right]^{-1},$$

$$|\varepsilon_{j+1}| \leqslant 2 \times |\varepsilon_j|^3. \qquad 57(152)$$

12°. $\sqrt{a^2 + x} = a\left(1 + \dfrac{x}{2a^2}\right)\left(1 + \dfrac{x'}{2a'^2}\right)\left(1 + \dfrac{x''}{2a''^2}\right)\cdots,$

where

$$x^{(n)} = -[x^{(n-1)}]^2, \quad a^{(n)} = 2[a^{(n-1)}]^2 + x^{(n-1)}. \qquad 33(10);$$
$$59(304,\ 354);\ 68(455)$$

Here,

$$\frac{2a(a^2 + x)}{2a^2 + x} < \sqrt{a^2 + x} < \frac{2a^2 + x}{2a};$$

$$\frac{2a(a^2 + x)}{2a^2 + x} < \sqrt{a^2 + x} < \frac{2a^2 + x}{4a} + a \cdot \frac{a^2 + x}{2a^2 + x}. \qquad 33(10)$$

3.7. Various formulae. Poncelet's formula. Historically, the earliest of the best approximations by linear functions were the so-called Poncelet formulae, which we give here.

1°. $\sqrt{a^2 + b^2} \approx \alpha a + \beta b,$

$$|a| > |b| \quad (kb \leqslant a \leqslant \infty \cdot b, \quad k = 0,\ 1,\ 2,\ \ldots);$$

$$\alpha = \frac{2}{1 + \sqrt{2(1 + k^2) - 2k\sqrt{1 + k^2}}},$$

$$\beta = \frac{2(\sqrt{1 + k^2} - k)}{1 + \sqrt{2(1 + k^2) - 2k\sqrt{1 + k^2}}},$$

$$\varepsilon = 1 - \alpha \qquad 70;\ 71(318\text{--}321);\ 72(279)$$

We give below a table of numerical values for the coefficients of the linear function $\alpha a + \beta b$, and the error bounds.

	k	α	β	$\varepsilon = 1 - \alpha$
a and b arbitrary with	0	0·82840	0·82840	0·17160 or $\dfrac{1}{6}$
$a > b$	1	0·96046	0·39783	0·03954 or $\dfrac{1}{25}$
$a > 2b$	2	0·98592	0·23270	0·01408 or $\dfrac{1}{71}$
$a > 3b$	3	0·99350	0·16123	0·00650 or $\dfrac{1}{154}$
$a > 4b$	4	0·99625	0·12260	0·00375 or $\dfrac{1}{266}$
$a > 5b$	5	0·99757	0·09878	0·00243 or $\dfrac{1}{417}$
$a > 6b$	6	0·99826	0·08261	0·00174 or $\dfrac{1}{589}$
$a > 7b$	7	0·99875	0·07098	0·00125 or $\dfrac{1}{800}$
$a > 8b$	8	0·99905	0·06220	0·00095 or $\dfrac{1}{1049}$
$a > 9b$	9	0·99930	0·05535	0·00070 or $\dfrac{1}{1428}$
$a > 10b$	10	0·99935	0·04984	0·00065 or $\dfrac{1}{1538}$

70; 71(323); 72(280)

2°. (a) $\sqrt{a^2 - b^2} \approx 6{\cdot}097a - 6{\cdot}02b$ $(1{\cdot}01b \leqslant a \leqslant 1{\cdot}02b)$,

$$\varepsilon = 0{\cdot}0309 \text{ or } \frac{1}{32}.$$

(b) $\sqrt{a^2 - b^2} \approx 1{\cdot}1319a - 0{\cdot}72636b$ $(0 \leqslant b \leqslant 0{\cdot}91a)$,

$$\varepsilon = 0{\cdot}1319 \text{ or } \frac{1}{7}.$$

(c) $\sqrt{a^2 - b^2} \approx 1{\cdot}018623a - 0{\cdot}272944b$

$$\left(0 \leqslant b \leqslant \frac{a}{2}, \text{ or } 2b \leqslant a < \infty\right).$$

$$\varepsilon = 0{\cdot}0186 \text{ or } \frac{1}{53}.$$ 70; 71(334, 335); 72(290)

$3°.\ \sqrt{a^2 + b^2 + c^2} \approx \alpha_1 a + \beta_1 \sqrt{b^2 + c^2}$ (1st operation);

$$= \alpha_1 a + \beta_1(\alpha_2 b + \beta_2 c) \text{ (2nd operation);}$$

$$= \alpha_1 a + \beta_1 \alpha_2 b + \beta_1 \beta_2 c;$$

where α_1, α_2, β_1 and β_2 are determined as in 4°, and ε_1, ε_2 are the relative error bounds corresponding to the first and second iterations respectively;

$$r = \sqrt{a^2 + b^2 + c^2}\left(\varepsilon_1 + \beta_1\varepsilon_2 \sqrt{\frac{b^2 + c^2}{a^2 + b^2 + c^2}}\right) < (\varepsilon_1 + \beta_1\varepsilon_2)\sqrt{a^2 + b^2 + c^2}.$$

In particular, if $a^2 > b^2 + c^2$ and $b^2 > c^2$, we have $\alpha_1 = \alpha_2 = 0.96$,

$$\beta_1 = \beta_2 = 0.4;\ \varepsilon_1 = \varepsilon_2 = 0.03954;\ r < \sqrt{a^2 + b^2 + c^2}\left(\varepsilon_1 + \frac{1}{2}\sqrt{2\beta_1\varepsilon_1}\right)$$

$$= 0.0507\sqrt{a^2 + b^2 + c^2}. \qquad 70;\ 71(335);\ 72(291)$$

4°. *Horvath's formula:*

$$\sqrt{a^2 + b^2 + c^2} \approx \alpha a + \beta b + \gamma c.$$

(a) If no assumptions are made concerning the relative magnitudes of the numerical values of a, b or c, then

$$\alpha = \beta = \gamma = 0.732, \quad \varepsilon = 0.268,$$

$$\sqrt{a^2 + b^2 + c^2} \approx 0.732(a + b + c), \quad \varepsilon = 0.27. \qquad 51(68)$$

(b) If $|a| > |b| > |c|$, then

$$\alpha = 0.939,\ \beta = 0.389,\ \gamma = 0.297,$$

$$\sqrt{a^2 + b^2 + c^2} \approx 0.939a + 0.389b + 0.297c, \quad \varepsilon = 0.06. \qquad 51(69)$$

CHAPTER II

EXPONENTIAL AND LOGARITHMIC FUNCTIONS

§1. The exponential function

1.1. General information. 1°. The exponential function a^x $(a > 0, a \neq 1)$ is defined everywhere on the real axis, it is continuous, convex and monotonically increasing for $a > 1$ (or decreasing for $a < 1$). If $a > 1$, then a^x increases more rapidly than any power of x, i.e. for any value of α,

$$\lim_{x \to +\infty} a^x x^{-\alpha} = \infty .$$

For any arbitrary base $a > 0$, the exponential function a^x is connected with the exponential function e^x (with the base $e = 2 \cdot 718281828459045 \ldots$) by the identity

$$a^x = e^{x \ln a} .$$

The principal relations for the exponential function are:

$$a^x \cdot a^y = a^{x+y}, \; \frac{a^x}{a^y} = a^{x-y}, \; (a^x)^y = a^{xy}, \; \sqrt[y]{a^x} = a^{\frac{x}{y}},$$

where x and y may have any numerical values.

Exponential functions with different bases may be transformed to functions with a common base, by using the identity

$$b = a^{\log_a b} .$$

Any number x may be represented in the form

$$x = n + y, \text{ where } n = E(x), \; y = \{x\}, \; 0 \leqslant y < 1.$$

Hence,

$$a^x = a^n \cdot a^y .$$

Accordingly, the computation of an exponential function may always be reduced to a computation for an argument y in the range $(0,1)$.

Furthermore,

$$a^y = (a^{y \cdot 2^{-m}})^{2^m} = \underbrace{((\ldots (a^{y \cdot 2^{-m}})^2)^2 \ldots)^2}_{m \text{ times}}.$$

In this manner, the computation of the exponential function is reduced to a computation for an argument y in the range $(0, 2^{-m})$, where m can be any positive integer.

2°. The exponential function as the limit of powers:

$$e^x = \lim_{n \to \infty} \left(1 + \frac{x}{n}\right)^n = \lim_{h \to 0} (1 + hx)^{\frac{1}{h}}.$$

The approach to the limit is uniform, so that the derivative of the power function $\left[\left(1 + \dfrac{x}{n}\right)^n\right]' = \left(1 + \dfrac{x}{n}\right)^{n-1}$ also tends to e^x as $n \to \infty$, i.e. $(e^x)' = e^x$.

3°. The function $y = Ce^{kx}$ satisfies the differential equation of "organic growth"

$$y' = ky.$$

More generally, if λ is a root of the nth-degree algebraic equation

$$\sum_{k=0}^{n} a_k \lambda^k = 0, \tag{2.1}$$

then the function $y = Ce^{\lambda x}$ satisfies the differential equation

$$\sum_{k=0}^{n} a_k y^{(k)} = 0.$$

4°. If λ is a solution of equation (2.1) and if $a = \lambda^{1/h}$, then the function $y = Ca^x$ is a solution of the difference equation

$$\sum_{k=0}^{n} a_k y(x + kh) = 0.$$

5°. Euler's formula gives a definition for the exponential function e^z everywhere in the plane of z (where $z = x + iy$):

$$e^z = e^x (\cos y + i \sin y).$$

For the imaginary arguments $z = \pm 2\pi i$, $\pm \pi i$ or $\pm \frac{1}{2}\pi i$, the function e^z assumes the form

$$e^{\pm 2\pi i} = 1, \quad e^{\pm \pi i} = -1, \quad e^{\pm \frac{\pi}{2}i} = \pm i.$$

In the complex plane the function e^z is periodic with the imaginary period $2\pi i$:

$$e^{z+n.2\pi i} = e^z.$$

1.2. Power series expansions.

$1°$. $e^x = \sum_{k=0}^{\infty} \dfrac{x^k}{k!}$.   26(36)

$2°$. $a^x = \sum_{k=0}^{\infty} \dfrac{(x \ln a)^k}{k!}$.   26(36)

$3°$. $\dfrac{x}{e^x - 1} = 1 - \dfrac{x}{2} + \sum_{k=1}^{\infty} \dfrac{B_{2k} x^{2k}}{(2k)!} \quad (x < 2\pi)$.   26(36); 32(520)

$4°$. $e^{e^x} = e\left(1 + x + \dfrac{2x^2}{2!} + \dfrac{5x^3}{3!} + \dfrac{15x^4}{4!} + \ldots\right)$.   26(36); 39(126)

$5°$. $e^{\frac{p(x+x^{-1})}{2}} = I_0(p) + 2 \sum_{n=1}^{\infty} (x^n + x^{-n}) I_n(p)$.

1.3. Expansions in polynomials, orthogonal and otherwise.

A. *Expansions in Chebyshev polynomials.*

$1°$. $e^{ax} = I_0(a) + 2 \sum_{k=1}^{\infty} I_k(a) \cdot T_k(x) \quad (|x| \leqslant 1)$,

$|r_{n-1}(a, x)| \leqslant \dfrac{2I_n(a)}{1 - \dfrac{(n+1)^{-1} \cdot a}{2}} \approx \dfrac{a^n}{2^{n-1} n!} \quad (|x| \leqslant 1)$.

19(6); 55(110, 114)

$2°$. $e^x = e^{\frac{1}{2}}\left[I_0\left(\dfrac{1}{2}\right) + 2 \sum_{k=1}^{\infty} I_k\left(\dfrac{1}{2}\right) T_k(2x-1)\right]$

$(0 \leqslant x \leqslant 1)$.   18(101)

3°. $2^x = 2^{\frac{1}{2}}\left[I_0\left(\frac{1}{2}\ln 2\right) + 2\sum_{k=1}^{\infty} I_k\left(\frac{1}{2}\ln 2\right) T_k\left(2x-1\right)\right]$

$$(0 \leqslant x \leqslant 1),$$

if $k > 4$ then $|r_{k-1}(x)| < \dfrac{3^{\frac{k}{2}+1}\cdot 10^{-k}}{k!}.$ 18(102); 19(7)

k	$I_k\left(\frac{1}{2}\right)$	$I_k\left(\frac{1}{2}\ln 2\right)$	
0	1·063 483 370 74	1·030 254 491 81	
1	0·257 894 305 39	0·175 901 603 92	
2	0·031 906 149 18	0·015 165 005 18	
3	0·002 645 111 97	0·000 873 781 81	18(102)
4	0·000 164 805 55	0·000 037 797 02	
5	0·000 008 223 17	0·000 001 308 64	
6	0·000 000 342 12	0·000 000 037 77	
7	0·000 000 012 21	0·000 000 000 93	
8	0·000 000 000 38	0·000 000 000 02	
9	0·000 000 000 01		

4°. $e^x = \left(e^{\frac{x}{2}}\right)^2 = e^{\frac{1}{2}}\left[I_0\left(\frac{1}{4}\right) + 2\sum_{k=1}^{\infty} I_k\left(\frac{1}{4}\right) T_k\left(4x-1\right)\right]^2$

$$\left(0 \leqslant x \leqslant \frac{1}{2}\right).$$ 18(102)

5°. $2^x = 2^{\frac{1}{2}}\left[I_0\left(\frac{1}{4}\ln 2\right) + 2\sum_{k=1}^{\infty} I_k\left(\frac{1}{4}\ln 2\right) T_k\left(4x-1\right)\right]^2$

$$\left(0 \leqslant x \leqslant \frac{1}{2}\right).$$ 18(102)

k	$I_k\left(\frac{1}{4}\right)$	$I_k\left(\frac{1}{4}\ln 2\right)$	
0	1·015 686 141 22	1·007 521 170 16	
1	0·125 979 108 95	0·086 969 024 12	
2	0·007 853 269 66	0·003 762 940 69	18(102)
3	0·000 326 794 39	0·000 108 610 07	
4	0·000 010 204 36	0·000 002 351 70	
5	0·000 000 254 98	0·000 000 040 74	
6	0·000 000 005 31	0·000 000 000 59	
7	0·000 000 000 09	0·000 000 000 01	

$6°.\quad 10^{\frac{x}{4}} = e^{\frac{x}{4M}} = \frac{a_0}{2} + \sum_{k=0}^{\infty} a_k T_k(x) \quad (|x| \leqslant 1),$

$$a_k = 2I_k\left(\frac{1}{4M}\right),$$

$$r_n \leqslant \frac{a_{n+1}}{1 - \dfrac{a_{n+2}}{a_{n+1}}}, \quad M = \log e.$$

k	a_k	r_k
0	2·169 147 476 660 513 190 741 362	
1	0·599 821 658 383 255 642 328 086	
2	0·085 153 585 765 270 650 944 524	88×10^{-4}
3	0·008 113 939 789 138 247 927 893	63×10^{-5}
4	0·000 581 443 119 239 232 582 513	36×10^{-6}
5	0·000 033 378 565 899 425 867 451	18×10^{-7}
6	0·000 001 598 039 880 644 344 284	69×10^{-9}
7	0·000 000 065 610 602 217 712 768	25×10^{-10}
8	0·000 000 002 357 820 784 237 217	79×10^{-12}
9	0·000 000 000 075 334 639 407 421	23×10^{-13}
10	0·000 000 000 002 166 674 498 582	59×10^{-15}
11	0·000 000 000 000 056 657 102 243	15×10^{-16}
12	0·000 000 000 000 001 358 214 469	32×10^{-18}
13	0·000 000 000 000 000 030 057 520	64×10^{-20}
14	0·000 000 000 000 000 000 617 703	13×10^{-21}
15	0·000 000 000 000 000 000 011 849	23×10^{-23}
16	0·000 000 000 000 000 000 000 213	$<5 \times 10^{-24}$

78(88)

$7°.\quad e^{-x} = \sum_{k=0}^{\infty} a_k T_k(2x - 1) \quad (0 \leqslant x \leqslant 1).$

a_0	0·645 035 270	a_4	0·000 199 919	
a_1	−0·312 841 606	a_5	−0·000 009 975	47(145)
a_2	0·038 704 116	a_6	0·000 000 415	
a_3	−0·003 208 683	a_7	−0·000 000 015	

B. *Expansions in Legendre polynomials.*

$8°. \quad e^x = \sum_{k=0}^{\infty} a_k P_k(x) \quad (|x| < 1).$

a_0	1·175 201 193 644	a_6	0·000 099 454 339 113
a_1	1·103 638 323 514	a_7	0·000 007 620 541 309
a_2	0·357 814 350 647	a_8	0·000 000 506 471 974
a_3	0·070 455 633 668	a_9	0·000 000 029 718 142
a_4	0·009 965 128 149	a_{10}	0·000 000 001 560 868
a_5	0·001 099 586 127	a_{11}	0·000 000 000 074 628

$9°. \quad y = e^x = \lim_{n \to \infty} y_n(x), \qquad y_n = \dfrac{\sum_{k=0}^{n} c_n^k k!\, S_k(x)}{\sum_{k=0}^{n} c_n^k k!}, \qquad 17(468)$

where the

$$S_k(x) = 1 + x + \frac{x^2}{2!} + \dots + \frac{x^k}{k!}$$

are the successive "partial sums" of the Taylor series, and the c_n^k are defined on pp. 449 and 503 of reference [17].

The successive approximations over the interval (0,1) are:

$$y_0 = 1,$$
$$y_1 = \frac{1 + 2x}{1},$$
$$y_2 = \frac{9 + 8x + 8x^2}{9},$$
$$y_3 = \frac{113 + 114x + 48x^2 + 32x^3}{113},$$
$$y_4 = \frac{1825 + 1824x + 928x^2 + 256x^3 + 128x^4}{1825}.$$

The y_n converge to e^x more rapidly than do the partial sums of the Taylor series.

$10°. \quad y = e^x, \qquad y_n(x) = \dfrac{\sum_{k=0}^{n} \bar{c}_n^k k!\, S_k(x)}{(-1)^{n+1} + \sum_{k=0}^{n} \bar{c}_n^k k!}, \qquad 17(469)$

where

$$S_k(x) = 1 + x + \frac{x^2}{2!} + \ldots + \frac{x^k}{k!}, \qquad 17(468)$$

$$\bar{c}_n^k = 2^{2k-1}\left[2\binom{n+k}{n-k} - \binom{n+k-1}{n-k} \right](-1)^{k+n}, \qquad 17(450)$$

and the $\bar{c}_n^k$ are coefficients of the powers of x' in the expansion of the Chebyshev polynomial $T_n(2x - 1)$ (cf. Appendix 1, § 4.5, 4°).

The successive approximations in the range $(0, 1)$ are:

$$y_1 = \frac{8 + 16x}{9},$$

$$y_2 = \frac{114 + 96x + 96x^2}{113} \qquad (r = 0.01),$$

$$y_3 = \frac{1824 + 1856x + 768x^2 + 512x^3}{1825} \qquad (r = 0.0006),$$

$$y_4 = \frac{36690 + 36640x + 18720x^2 + 5120x^3 + 2560x^4}{36689}.$$

The maximal error does not exceed the inverse of the denominator.

1.4. Polynomial approximations.
1°. *Approximations for* e^x.

(a) $e^x \approx \sum_{k=0}^{4} a_k x^k \quad \left(-\frac{1}{2} \leqslant x \leqslant 0 \right), \quad r = 5 \times 10^{-7}.$

a_0	0·999 999 6	a_3	0·162 842 7
a_1	0·999 958 6	a_4	0·032 534 0
a_2	0·499 330 9		

(b) $e^x \approx \sum_{k=0}^{6} a_k x^k \quad (-1 \leqslant x \leqslant 0), \quad r = 2.4 \times 10^{-8}.$

a_0	0·999 999 98	a_4	0·041 223 25
a_1	0·999 998 45	a_5	0·076 543 11
a_2	0·499 975 05	a_6	0·000 849 01
a_3	0·166 515 09		

(c) $e^x \approx \sum_{k=0}^{7} a_k x^k \quad (|x| \leqslant 1), \quad r = 2 \times 10^{-7}.$

a_0	0·999 999 8	a_4	0·041 635 0
a_1	1·000 000 0	a_5	0·008 329 8
a_2	0·500 006 3	a_6	0·001 439 3
a_3	0·166 667 4	a_7	0·000 204 0

(d) $\dfrac{1}{4} e^x \approx \sum_{k=0}^{10} a_k x^k \quad (|x| < 1).$

a_0	0·250 000 000	a_6	0·000 347 223
a_1	0·250 000 000	a_7	0·000 049 587
a_2	0·125 000 000	a_8	0·000 006 199
a_3	0·041 666 666	a_9	0·000 000 706
a_4	0·010 416 666	a_{10}	0·000 000 070
a_5	0·002 083 340		

3(282)

2°. *Approximations for 2^x over the range $0 \leqslant x \leqslant 1$.*

(a) $2^x \approx \sum_{k=0}^{7} a_k x^k \quad (0 \leqslant x \leqslant 1).$

a_0	0·999 999 999 93	a_4	0·009 613 530 02
a_1	0·693 147 187 87	a_5	0·001 342 985 66
a_2	0·240 226 356 70	a_6	0·000 142 992 74
a_3	0·055 505 295 42	a_7	0·000 021 651 59

7(5,6)

(b) $2^x \approx \sum_{k=0}^{8} a_k x^k \quad (0 \leqslant x \leqslant 1).$

a_0	1·000 000 000 040	a_5	0·001 301 780 490 28
a_1	0·693 147 151 142	a_6	0·000 191 629 879 96
a_2	0·240 227 029 850	a_7	0·000 008 390 778 29
a_3	0·055 500 205 505 4	a_8	0·000 007 561 668 20
a_4	0·009 633 032 340 04		

(c) $\quad 2^x = \left\{\left[\left(\sum_{k=0}^{4} a_k x^k\right)^2\right]^2\right\}^2 \quad (0 \leqslant x \leqslant 1), \quad r = O(10^{-9}).$

a_0	1	a_3	0·000 108 419 178 11
a_1	0·086 643 396 773	a_4	0·000 023 481 760 517
a_2	0·003 753 591 712		

$3°.$ *Approximations for 10^x.* The following formulae (a) to (d) are a series of best approximations to 10^x, in the form of squares of polynomials of degrees from 4 to 7, over the range $(0, 1)$. (cf. [49], pp. 141–144).

(a) $\quad 10^x \approx \left[\sum_{k=0}^{4} a_k x^k\right]^2 \quad (0 \leqslant x \leqslant 1), \quad \varepsilon = 8 \times 10^{-5}.$

a_0	1	a_3	0·208 003 0
a_1	1·149 919 6	a_4	0·126 808 9
a_2	0·677 432 3		

(b) $\quad 10^x \approx \left[\sum_{k=0}^{5} a_k x^k\right]^2 \quad (0 \leqslant x \leqslant 1), \quad \varepsilon = 3·5 \times 10^{-6}.$

a_0	1	a_3	0·261 306 50
a_1	1·151 384 24	a_4	0·058 906 81
a_2	0·661 308 51	a_5	0·029 366 22

(c) $\quad 10^x \approx \left[\sum_{k=0}^{6} a_k x^k\right]^2 \quad (0 \leqslant x \leqslant 1), \quad \varepsilon = 1·5 \times 10^{-7}.$

a_0	1	a_4	0·075 467 547
a_1	1·151 287 586	a_5	0·013 420 940
a_2	0·662 843 149	a_6	0·005 654 902
a_3	0·253 603 317		

(d) $\quad 10^x \approx \left[\sum_{k=0}^{7} a_k x^k\right]^2 \quad (0 \leqslant x \leqslant 1), \quad \varepsilon = 5 \times 10^{-9}.$

a_0	1	a_4	0·072 951 736 66
a_1	1·151 292 776 03	a_5	0·017 421 119 88
a_2	0·662 730 884 29	a_6	0·002 554 917 96
a_3	0·254 393 574 84	a_7	0·000 932 642 67

4°. *Approximations for $10^{x/4}$*. The formulae (a) to (n) are a series of approximations to $10^{x/4}$ (which equals $e^{x/4M}$) by polynomials of degrees from 2 to 15 for $|x| \leqslant 1$ (cf. [78], pp. 89, 90). Note that $10^x = [(10^{x/4})^2]^2$.

(a) $10^{x/4} \approx \sum_{k=0}^{2} a_k x^k$, $r = 88 \times 10^{-4}$.

a_0	0·999 4
a_1	0·599 8
a_2	0·170 3

(b) $10^{x/4} \approx \sum_{k=0}^{3} a_k x^k$, $r = 61 \times 10^{-5}$.

a_0	0·999 42	a_2	0·170 31
a_1	0·575 48	a_3	0·032 46

(c) $10^{x/4} \approx \sum_{k=0}^{4} a_k x^k$, $r = 33 \times 10^{-6}$.

a_0	1·000 002	a_3	0·032 456
a_1	0·575 480	a_4	0·004 652
a_2	0·165 656		

(d) $10^{x/4} \approx \sum_{k=0}^{5} a_k x^k$, $r = 17 \times 10^{-7}$.

a_0	1·000 001 6	a_3	0·031 788 2
a_1	0·575 646 7	a_4	0·004 651 5
a_2	0·165 655 6	a_5	0·000 534 1

(e) $10^{x/4} \approx \sum_{k=0}^{6} a_k x^k$, $r = 68 \times 10^{-9}$.

a_0	0·999 999 998	a_4	0·004 574 839
a_1	0·575 646 732	a_5	0·000 534 057
a_2	0·165 684 391	a_6	0·000 051 137
a_3	0·031 788 188		

(f) $10^{x/4} \approx \sum\limits_{k=0}^{7} a_k x^k, \qquad r = 24 \times 10^{-10}.$

a_0	0·999 999 997 6	a_4	0·004 574 839 0
a_1	0·575 646 272 6	a_5	0·000 526 708 7
a_2	0·165 684 391 3	a_6	0·000 051 137 3
a_3	0·031 791 862 0	a_7	0·000 004 199 1

(g) $10^{x/4} \approx \sum\limits_{k=0}^{8} a_k x^k, \qquad r = 77 \times 10^{-12}.$

a_0	1·000 000 000 002	a_5	0·000 526 706 667
a_1	0·575 646 272 571	a_6	0·000 050 533 674
a_2	0·165 684 315 844	a_7	0·000 004 199 079
a_3	0·031 791 862 032	a_8	0·000 000 301 801
a_4	0·004 575 216 291		

(h) $10^{x/4} \approx \sum\limits_{k=0}^{9} a_k x^k, \qquad r = 22 \times 10^{-13}.$

a_0	1·000 000 000 002 2	a_5	0·000 526 741 211 5
a_1	0·575 646 273 249 1	a_6	0·000 050 533 674 1
a_2	0·165 684 315 844 2	a_7	0·000 004 155 685 8
a_3	0·031 791 852 992 1	a_8	0·000 000 301 801 1
a_4	0·004 575 216 291 0	a_9	0·000 000 019 285 7

(i) $10^{x/4} \approx \sum\limits_{k=0}^{10} a_k x^k, \qquad r = 57 \times 10^{-15}.$

a_0	0·999 999 999 999 999	a_6	0·000 050 536 100 735
a_1	0·575 646 273 249 134	a_7	0·000 004 155 685 790
a_2	0·165 684 315 952 548	a_8	0·000 000 299 027 717
a_3	0·031 791 852 992 132	a_9	0·000 000 019 285 668
a_4	0·004 575 215 424 299	a_{10}	0·000 000 001 109 337
a_5	0·000 526 741 211 507		

(j) $\quad 10^{x/4} \approx \sum_{k=0}^{11} a_k x^k, \qquad r = 15 \times 10^{-16}.$

a_0	0·999 999 999 999 998 6	a_6	0·000 050 536 100 735 3
a_1	0·575 646 273 248 511 0	a_7	0·000 004 155 845 336 0
a_2	0·165 684 315 952 547 7	a_8	0·000 000 299 027 717 0
a_3	0·031 791 853 004 596 5	a_9	0·000 000 019 126 121 3
a_4	0·004 575 215 424 298 6	a_{10}	0·000 000 001 109 337 3
a_5	0·000 526 741 141 705 1	a_{11}	0·000 000 000 058 016 9

(k) $\quad 10^{x/4} \approx \sum_{k=0}^{12} a_k x^k, \qquad r = 30 \times 10^{-18}.$

a_0	1·000 000 000 000 000 001	a_7	0·000 004 155 845 336 035
a_1	0·575 646 273 248 511 030	a_8	0·000 000 299 037 105 003
a_2	0·165 684 315 952 449 877	a_9	0·000 000 019 126 121 288
a_3	0·031 791 853 004 596 500	a_{10}	0·000 000 001 100 992 474
a_4	0·004 575 215 425 439 511	a_{11}	0·000 000 000 058 016 873
a_5	0·000 526 741 141 705 104	a_{12}	0·000 000 000 002 781 623
a_6	0·000 050 536 095 867 452		

(l) $\quad 10^{x/4} \approx \sum_{k=0}^{13} a_k x^k, \qquad r = 64 \times 10^{-20}.$

a_0	1·000 000 000 000 000 000 62	a_7	0·000 004 155 845 035 940 58
a_1	0·575 646 273 248 511 421 18	a_8	0·000 000 299 037 105 002 59
a_2	0·165 684 315 952 449 877 32	a_9	0·000 000 019 126 621 445 52
a_3	0·031 791 853 004 585 558 94	a_{10}	0·000 000 001 100 992 473 58
a_4	0·004 575 215 425 439 510 81	a_{11}	0·000 000 000 057 616 746 99
a_5	0·000 526 741 141 792 631 59	a_{12}	0·000 000 000 002 781 623 23
a_6	0·000 050 536 095 867 452 04	a_{13}	0·000 000 000 000 123 115 60

(m) $\quad 10^{x/4} \approx \sum_{k=0}^{14} a_k x^k, \qquad r = 12 \times 10^{-21}.$

a_0	1	a_8	0·000 000 299 037 088 398 732
a_1	0·575 646 273 248 511 421 182	a_9	0·000 000 019 126 621 445 516
a_2	0·165 684 315 952 449 937 857	a_{10}	0·000 000 001 101 016 825 900
a_3	0·031 791 853 004 585 558 943	a_{11}	0·000 000 000 057 616 746 991
a_4	0·004 575 215 425 438 542 252	a_{12}	0·000 000 000 002 763 912 452
a_5	0·000 526 741 141 792 631 590	a_{13}	0·000 000 000 000 123 115 602
a_6	0·000 050 536 095 873 263 394	a_{14}	0·000 000 000 000 005 060 223
a_7	0·000 004 155 845 035 940 579		

(n) $10^{x/4} \approx \sum\limits_{k=0}^{15} a_k x^k, \quad r = 21 \times 10^{-23}$.

a_0	0·99999999999999999999979	a_8	0·000000029903708739873190
a_1	0·5756462732485114210 0473	a_9	0·0000000019126620611 34669
a_2	0·16568431595244993785734	a_{10}	0·0000000001101016825 89952
a_3	0·03179185300458556557866	a_{11}	0·00000000000576178389 9443
a_4	0·00457521542543854225205	a_{12}	0·000000000000276391245210
a_5	0·00052674114179255992718	a_{13}	0·0000000000000122387 59936
a_6	0·00005053609587326339430	a_{14}	0·000000000000000506022298
a_7	0·00000415584503628183046	a_{15}	0·000000000000000019413402

1.5. Continued fraction expansions.

1°. $e^x = \dfrac{1}{1} - \dfrac{x}{1} + \dfrac{x}{2} - \dfrac{x}{3} + \dfrac{x}{2}$

$$\dfrac{1}{1} \quad \dfrac{1}{1-x} \quad \dfrac{2+x}{2-x} \quad \dfrac{6+2x}{6-4x+x^2} \quad \dfrac{12+6x+x^2}{12-6x+x^2}$$

$$- \dfrac{x}{5} + \dots + \dfrac{x}{2} - \dfrac{x}{2n+1} + \dots \qquad 34(111)$$

$$\dfrac{60+24x+3x^2}{60-36x+9x^2-x^3}$$

The continued fraction converges everywhere in the plane of the complex variable x.

2°. $e^x = \dfrac{1}{1} - \dfrac{x}{1+x} - \dfrac{x}{2+x} - \dfrac{2x}{3+x} - \dots - \dfrac{nx}{n+1+x} -$

$$\qquad 34(111)$$

3°. $e^x = 1 + \dfrac{x}{1} - \dfrac{x}{2} + \dfrac{x}{3} - \dfrac{x}{2}$

$$\dfrac{1}{1} \quad \dfrac{1+x}{1} \quad \dfrac{2+x}{2-x} \quad \dfrac{6+4x+x^2}{6-2x} \quad \dfrac{12+6x+x^2}{12-6x+x^2}$$

$$+ \dfrac{x}{5} - \dots - \dfrac{x}{2} + \dfrac{x}{2n+1} - \dots \qquad 34(112)$$

$$\dfrac{60+36x+9x^2+x^3}{60-24x+3x^2}$$

The continued fraction converges everywhere in the plane of the complex variable x.

$4°.$ $\quad e^x = 1 + \dfrac{x}{1-x} + \dfrac{x}{2-x} + \dfrac{2x}{3-x} + \ldots + \dfrac{nx}{n+1-x} + \ldots$

$$34(112)$$

$5°.$ $\quad e^x = 1 + \dfrac{2x}{2-x} + \quad \dfrac{x^2}{6} \quad + \quad \dfrac{x^2}{10}$

$$\dfrac{1}{1} \quad \dfrac{2+x}{2-x} \quad \dfrac{12+6x+x^2}{12-6x+x^2} \quad \dfrac{120+60x+12x^2+x^3}{120-60x+12x^2-x^3}$$

$$+ \qquad\qquad \dfrac{x^2}{14}$$

$$\dfrac{1680 + 840x + 180x^2 + 20x^3 + x^4}{1680 - 840x + 180x^2 - 20x^3 + x^4}$$

$$+ \qquad\qquad \dfrac{x^2}{18} \qquad\qquad +\ldots$$

$$\dfrac{30240 + 15120x + 3360x^2 + 420x^3 + 30x^4 + x^5}{30240 - 15120x + 3360x^2 - 420x^3 + 30x^4 - x^5}$$

$$\ldots + \dfrac{x^2}{2(2n+1)} + \ldots \qquad 34(112)$$

$6°.$ $\quad e^x = \dfrac{1}{1} - \dfrac{2x}{2+x} + \dfrac{x^6}{6} + \dfrac{x^2}{10} + \ldots + \dfrac{x^2}{2(n+1)} + \ldots$

$$34(113)$$

$7°.$ $\quad e^x = 1 + \dfrac{x}{1 - \dfrac{x}{2} + F},$

where

$$F = \dfrac{x^2/4.3}{1} + \dfrac{x^2/4.15}{1} + \dfrac{x^2/4.35}{1} + \ldots + \dfrac{x^2/4.[4(n-1)^2 - 1]}{1} + \ldots,$$

$$|r_{n-1}(x)| \leqslant \dfrac{\left(\dfrac{x}{2}\right)^{2n}}{D_{n-1} D_n \prod\limits_{i=1}^{n} (4i^2 - 1)}, \qquad 65(264)$$

with equality occurring only at the point $x = 0$.

An equivalent form for expressing F is:

$$F = \dfrac{x^2/4.4}{3/4} + \dfrac{x^2/4.4.8}{5/8} + \dfrac{x^2/4.8.8}{7/8} + \dfrac{x^2/4.8.16}{9/16} + \ldots$$

$$65(265)$$

The number of terms needed to give 12 correct significant figures is listed in the table:

x	F in the form 7°
0·1	4
1	6
10	17

8°. $e^x = 1 + \dfrac{x}{1 - \dfrac{x}{2}} + \dfrac{x^2/4}{3} + \dfrac{x^2/4}{5} + \ldots + \dfrac{x^2/4}{2n - 1} + \ldots$

With $|x| \leqslant 1$, we have $r_4 = 0.84 \times 10^{-4}$, $r_5 = 0.33 \times 10^{-7}$, $r_6 = 0.81 \times 10^{-10}$.

64(194)

9°. $e^x = -1 + \dfrac{2}{1} - \dfrac{x}{2} + \dfrac{x^2}{6} + \dfrac{x^2}{10} + \dfrac{x^2}{14} + \dfrac{x^2}{18} + \ldots$

$r_6 < 10^{-11}$ if $0 < x < 1$.   20(134)

10°. $e^x = \dfrac{y + x}{y - x}$ $(|x| \leqslant 1)$,

where

$$y = 2 + \dfrac{x^2}{6} + \dfrac{x^2}{10} + \dfrac{x^2}{14} + \dfrac{x^2}{18} + \ldots$$ 20(249)

$$r_6 < 10^{-11}.$$

A series of rational approximations is given by:

11°. $e^x \approx \dfrac{\sum\limits_{\nu=0}^{m} \dfrac{C_m^\nu}{C_{m+k}^\nu} \dfrac{x^\nu}{\nu!}}{\sum\limits_{\nu=0}^{k} (-1)^\nu \dfrac{C_k^\nu}{C_{m+k}^\nu} \dfrac{x^\nu}{\nu!}}$.   I(310)

With $m = k$ we get

12°. e^x

$$\approx \frac{2k(2k-1)\ldots(k+1) + C_k^1(2k-1)(2k-2)\ldots(k+1)x + \ldots + x^k}{2k(2k-1)\ldots(k+1) - C_k^1(2k-1)(2k-2)\ldots(k+1)x + \ldots + (-1)^k x^k}$$

I(310); 34(152)

where the C_n^k are the binomial coefficients.

This expansion contains all the convergents of the expansion (cf. § 1.5, 5°).

Another representation is:

$$e^x \approx \frac{\sum\limits_{k=0}^{n} c_k^n x^k}{\sum\limits_{k=0}^{n} c_k^n (-x)^k}, \qquad \text{17(422)}$$

where

$$c_k^n = \frac{(2n-k)!}{(n-k)!\,k!}.$$

The numerical values of the coefficients are given in Table XV on p. 516 of reference [17]. The first four approximations (for $n = 1, 2, 3$ and 4) are:

$$\frac{2+x}{2-x}, \qquad \frac{12+6x+x^2}{12-6x+x^2}, \qquad \frac{120+60x+12x^2+x^3}{120-60x+12x^2-x^3},$$

$$\frac{1680+840x+180x^2+20x^3+x^4}{1680-840x+180x^2-20x^3+x^4}, \qquad r = 1 \cdot 1 \times 10^{-7}\ (|x| \leqslant 1).$$

13°. $e^x \approx \dfrac{P_m(x)}{P_m(-x)} \qquad (|x| \leqslant 2^{-k} \ln 2).$

Here

$$(2m)!\,P_m(x) = m!\sum_{k=0}^{m} (2m-k)!\,\frac{x^k}{[k!\,(m-k)!]^2},$$

$$|\varepsilon_n(x)| < (2n+1)^{-1}\left(\frac{n!}{(2n)!}\right)^2 |x|^{2n+1} e^{-\frac{x}{2}+\frac{x^2}{8(2n+3)}}. \qquad \text{55(111)}$$

14°. $e^x = \dfrac{1+\tanh\left(\dfrac{x}{2}\right)}{1-\tanh\left(\dfrac{x}{2}\right)} \approx \dfrac{D_n(x)+A_n(x)}{D_n(x)-A_n(x)},$

where $\dfrac{A_n(x)}{D_n(x)}$ is the nth convergent of the expansion of the hyperbolic tangent:

$$\tanh\left(\frac{x}{2}\right) = \frac{\dfrac{x}{2}}{1} + \frac{\left(\dfrac{x}{2}\right)^2}{3} + \frac{\left(\dfrac{x}{2}\right)^2}{5} + \ldots + \frac{\left(\dfrac{x}{2}\right)^2}{2n+1} + \ldots \qquad \text{55(111)}$$

(cf. Ch. III, § 3.6, 6°).

1.6. Rational approximations.

$1°.\quad e^x = \dfrac{\left[\displaystyle\sum_{k=0}^{3} a_{2k}\left(\dfrac{x}{3}\right)^{2k}\right] + \left[\dfrac{x}{3}\displaystyle\sum_{k=0}^{3} b_{2k}\left(\dfrac{x}{3}\right)^{2k}\right]}{\left[\displaystyle\sum_{k=0}^{3} a_{2k}\left(\dfrac{x}{3}\right)^{2k}\right] - \left[\dfrac{x}{3}\displaystyle\sum_{k=0}^{3} b_{2k}\left(\dfrac{x}{3}\right)^{2k}\right]},\quad |x| < \pi.$

a_0	0·864 864	b_0	1·297 296
a_2	0·898 128	b_2	0·374 22
a_4	0·102 06	b_4	0·018 370 8
a_6	0·002 041 2	b_6	0·000 109 35

$$r = 10^{-9}.$$

Each of the expressions within square brackets is a very good approximation either to

$$\cosh\frac{x}{2} \quad\text{or}\quad \sinh\frac{x}{2}. \qquad 60(84)$$

$2°.$ Table of rational approximations (Padè approximations) for

$$e^x \approx \frac{N_p(x)}{D_q(x)}, \qquad p+q \leqslant 2$$

(where p and q are the degrees of the polynomials N_p and D_q respectively).

q \ p	0	1	2	Numerical values resulting for $x=1$		
0	1	$1+x$	$1+x+\dfrac{x^2}{2}$	1·0	2·0	2·5
1	$\dfrac{1}{1-x}$	$\dfrac{1+\dfrac{x}{2}}{1-\dfrac{x}{2}}$	$\dfrac{1+\dfrac{2}{3}x+\dfrac{x^2}{12}}{1-\dfrac{x}{3}}$		3·0	2·75
3	$\dfrac{1}{1-x+\dfrac{x^2}{2}}$	$\dfrac{1+\dfrac{x}{3}}{1-\dfrac{2}{3}x+\dfrac{x^2}{6}}$	$\dfrac{1+\dfrac{x}{2}+\dfrac{x^2}{12}}{1-\dfrac{x}{2}+\dfrac{x^2}{12}}$	2·0	2·6	2·714 286

3°. The formulae (a) to (e) are a series of rational approximations to e^{-x} over the range $[0, \infty)$ (cf. [49], pp. 181–184, and [48] p. 68).

(a) $\quad e^{-x} \approx \dfrac{1}{\left[\sum\limits_{k=0}^{3} a_k x^k\right]^4}, \quad r = 2{\cdot}4 \times 10^{-4} \quad (0 \leqslant x \leqslant 16).$

a_0	1	a_2	0·029 273 2
a_1	0·250 721 3	a_3	0·003 827 8

(b) $\quad e^{-x} \approx \dfrac{1}{\left[\sum\limits_{k=0}^{4} a_k x^k\right]^4}, \quad r = 2{\cdot}3 \times 10^{-5} \quad (0 \leqslant x \leqslant 16).$

a_0	1	a_3	0·002 277 23
a_1	0·249 910 35	a_4	0·000 266 95
a_2	0·031 585 65		

(c) $\quad e^{-x} \approx \dfrac{1}{\left[\sum\limits_{k=0}^{5} a_k x^k\right]^4}, \quad r = 2{\cdot}4 \times 10^{-6} \quad (0 \leqslant x \leqslant 16).$

a_0	1	a_3	0·002 673 255
a_1	0·250 010 936	a_4	0·000 127 992
a_2	0·031 198 056	a_5	0·000 014 876

(d) $\quad e^{-x} \approx \dfrac{1}{\left[\sum\limits_{k=0}^{6} a_k x^k\right]^4}, \quad r = 2{\cdot}5 \times 10^{-7} \quad (0 \leqslant x \leqslant 16).$

a_0	1	a_4	0·000 171 562 0
a_1	0·249 998 684 2	a_5	0·000 005 430 2
a_2	0·031 257 583 2	a_6	0·000 000 690 6
a_3	0·002 591 371 2		

(e) $\quad e^{-x} \approx \dfrac{1}{\left[\sum\limits_{k=0}^{5} a_k x^k\right]^8}, \qquad r = 1 \cdot 1 \times 10^{-7}.$

a_0	1	a_3	0·000 326 627
a_1	0·125 000 204	a_4	0·000 009 652
a_2	0·007 811 604	a_5	0·000 000 351

4°. The formulae (a) to (c) are rational approximations to

$$\frac{1 - e^{-x}}{x}$$

over the range $[0, \infty)$ (cf. [49], pp. 129–131).

(a) $\quad \dfrac{1 - e^{-x}}{x} \approx \dfrac{\sum\limits_{k=1}^{2} a_k \xi^k}{\sum\limits_{k=0}^{2} b_k \xi^k}, \quad$ $r = 2 \times 10^{-3}\left(0 \leqslant \dfrac{1}{\sqrt{1+x}} \leqslant 1 \cdot 0\right),$

$\xi = \dfrac{1}{1 + px}, \qquad p = 0 \cdot 47698.$

a_0	—	b_0	1
a_1	0·428 50	b_1	−0·579 53
a_2	0·569 65	b_2	0·579 53

(b) $\quad \dfrac{1 - e^{-x}}{x} \approx \dfrac{\sum\limits_{k=1}^{3} a_k \xi^k}{\sum\limits_{k=0}^{3} b_k \xi^k}, \quad$ $r = 1 \cdot 5 \times 10^{-4}\left(0 \leqslant \dfrac{1}{\sqrt{1+x}} < 1 \cdot 0\right),$

$\xi = \dfrac{1}{1 + px}, \qquad p = 0 \cdot 3606032.$

a_0	—	b_0	1
a_1	0·367 162 6	b_1	−1·356 271 0
a_2	−0·227 223 2	b_2	1·614 808 7
a_3	0·860 199 6	b_3	−0·258 537 7

(c) $\quad \dfrac{1 - e^{-x}}{x} \approx \dfrac{\sum\limits_{k=1}^{4} a_k \xi^k}{\sum\limits_{k=0}^{4} b_k \xi^k}, \quad$ $r = 1 \cdot 2 \times 10^{-5}\left(0 \leqslant \dfrac{1}{\sqrt{1+x}} \leqslant 1 \cdot 0\right),$

$\xi = \dfrac{1}{1 + px}, \qquad p = 0 \cdot 28989933.$

a_0	—	b_0	1
a_1	0·289 053 86	b_1	−2·217 814 31
a_2	−0·332 404 94	b_2	3·331 319 12
a_3	0·455 484 98	b_3	−1·627 814 95
a_4	0·587 854 66	b_4	0·514 310 14

5°. The formulae (a) to (c) are a series of rational approximations to

$$\frac{1}{\sqrt{2\pi}} e^{-\frac{1}{2}x^2}$$

(cf. [49], pp. 151–153).

(a) $\dfrac{1}{\sqrt{2\pi}} e^{-\frac{1}{2}x^2} \approx \dfrac{1}{\sum\limits_{k=0}^{3} b_{2k} x^{2k}}$ $(|x| < \infty)$, $r = 3 \times 10^{-3}$ $(0 \leqslant x \leqslant 5)$.

b_0	2·490 895	b_4	−0·024 393
b_2	1·466 003	b_6	0·178 257

(b) $\dfrac{1}{\sqrt{2\pi}} e^{-\frac{1}{2}x^2} \approx \dfrac{1}{\sum\limits_{k=0}^{4} b_{2k} x^{2k}}$ $(|x| < \infty)$, $r = 8 \times 10^{-4}$ $(0 \leqslant x \leqslant 5)$.

b_0	2·511 261	b_6	−0·063 417
b_2	1·172 801	b_8	0·029 461
b_4	0·494 618		

(c) $\dfrac{1}{\sqrt{2\pi}} e^{-\frac{1}{2}x^2} \approx \dfrac{1}{\sum\limits_{k=0}^{5} b_{2k} x^{2k}}$ $(|x| < \infty)$, $r = 2\cdot2 \times 10^{-4}$ $(0 \leqslant x \leqslant 5)$

b_0	2·505 236 7	b_6	0·130 646 9
b_2	1·283 120 4	b_8	−0·020 249 0
b_4	0·226 471 8	b_{10}	0·003 913 2

1.7. Iterative processes.

1°. Modified Briggs' method for computing 2^x (where $0 < x < 1$). Let

$$c_k = \log_2(1 + 2^{-k}) \quad (k = 1, 2, \ldots, n, \ldots).$$

Putting $x_0 = x$, we construct successively x_k, a_k, (for $k = 1, 2, \ldots$), where

$$x_{i+1} = x_i \text{ and } a_{i+1} = 0, \text{ if } x_i < c_{i+1},$$

$$x_{i+1} = x_i - c_i \text{ and } a_{i+1} = 1, \text{ if } x_i \geqslant c_{i+1}.$$

Then

$$2^x = \prod_{k=1}^{\infty} (1 + 2^{-k})^{a_k}.$$

$$2^x \approx \prod_{k=1}^{n} (1 + 2^{-k})^{a_k}, \quad \varepsilon_n = 2^{2^{-n}} - 1 \approx \ln 2 \times 2^{-n}. \quad 55(115)$$

§ 2. The logarithmic function

2.1. General information. 1°. The logarithmic function $\log_a x$, i.e. the logarithm of x to the base a (where $a > 0$ and $a \neq 1$), is the inverse of the exponential function:

$$a^{\log_a x} = x, \qquad \log_a a^y = y.$$

The *natural logarithm* of x is its logarithm to the base e:

$$\ln x = \log_e x,$$

$$e^{\ln x} = x, \qquad \ln e^y = y.$$

The *decimal logarithm* of x is its logarithm to the base 10:

$$\log x = \log_{10} x.$$

The logarithmic function is defined everywhere in the interval $(0, +\infty)$, and is everywhere continuous. If $a > 1$, then $\log_a x$ is a concave monotonically increasing function, with $\log_a x < 0$ if $x < 1$ and $\log_a x > 0$ if $x > 1$; but if $0 < a < 1$ then $\log_a x$ is a convex monotonically decreasing function, with $\log_a x > 0$ if $x < 1$ and $\log_a x < 0$ if $x > 1$.

2°. The connection between logarithms to different bases is as follows:

(a) $\quad \log_b a = \dfrac{1}{\log_a b}$,

(b) $\quad \log_a x = -\log_{\frac{1}{a}} x$.

The latter relation enables us to express a logarithm to base $a_1 \left(\text{where } a_1 = \dfrac{1}{a} < 1\right)$ in terms of a logarithm to base $a > 1$. In view of this, we shall hereafter always consider the base to be $a > 1$.

(c) $\quad \log_a x = \log_b x \log_a b = \dfrac{\log_b x}{\log_b a}$.

In particular,

$$\log_a x = \ln x \log_a e = \frac{\ln x}{\ln a}.$$

For instance,

$$\log x = M \ln x, \qquad \ln x = \frac{1}{M} \log x,$$

where

$$M = \log e = 0 \cdot 43429448190325182765\ldots,$$

$$\frac{1}{M} = \ln 10 = 2 \cdot 30258509299404568402\ldots$$

(here, M is called the *modulus of the transformation from natural to decimal logarithms*),

$$\log_2 x = M_1 \ln x, \quad \ln x = \frac{1}{M_1} \log_2 x,$$

$$M_1 = \log_2 e = 1 \cdot 44269504088893407360\ldots,$$

$$\frac{1}{M_1} = \ln 2 = 0 \cdot 69314718055994530942\ldots$$

3°. The principal relations are the following:

$$\log_a(xy) = \log_a x + \log_a y,$$

$$\log_a x^\alpha = \alpha \log_a x.$$

For any number $x > 0$, there is a unique integer $n \geqslant 0$ such that

$$a^n \leqslant x < a^{n+1} \quad (n = E(\log_a x)).$$

Then

$$x = a^n y = a^{n+1} y_1, \quad 1 \leqslant y \leqslant a, \quad \frac{1}{a} \leqslant y_1 = \frac{1}{a} y < 1,$$

$$\log_a x = n + \log_a y = (n+1) + \log_a y_1.$$

The problem of evaluating a logarithm to base a for any positive number has thus been reduced to that of finding the logarithm of a number in the range $(1, a)$ (or the range $(1/a, 1)$):

$$\lim_{x \to +\infty} \log_a x = +\infty, \quad \lim_{x \to +0} \log_a x = -\infty.$$

4°. For any $\alpha > 0$,

$$\lim_{x \to +\infty} ((\log_a x) \cdot x^{-\alpha}) = 0,$$

i.e. the logarithmic function increases more slowly than any power of x:

$$\lim_{x \to +0} ((\log_a x) \cdot x^\alpha) = 0.$$

Furthermore, if $\alpha > n > 0$, then for any derivative of order k, where $k < n$,

$$\lim_{x \to +0} ((\log_a x) . x^\alpha)^{(k)} = 0.$$

5°. The logarithmic function can be expressed as a limit:

$$\ln x = \lim_{n \to \infty} n\left(\sqrt[n]{x} - 1\right) = \lim_{h \to 0} \frac{1}{h}(x^h - 1).$$

Convergence to the limit is uniform over any interval $[a, b]$, where $0 < a < b$. Hence the derivative

$$\left[\frac{1}{h}(x^h - 1)\right]'$$

converges to $(\ln x)' = 1/x$ as $h \to 0$, uniformly over the interval (a, b).

6°. Logarithms in the complex plane. Let

$$z = x + iy = \varrho(\cos\varphi + i\sin\varphi),$$

Then

$$\ln z = \ln \varrho + i\varphi;$$

and since φ is determined apart from an additive term $2\pi k$ (where k is any integer), then $\ln z$ is determined apart from an additive constant $2\pi ki$, i.e. the logarithmic function is multi-valued in the complex plane. In particular,

$$\ln 1 = k.2\pi i, \qquad \ln(-1) = \pi + k.2\pi i,$$

$$\ln i = \frac{\pi}{2} + k.2\pi i, \qquad \ln(-i) = \frac{3\pi}{2} + k.2\pi i.$$

2.2. Power series expansions.

1°. $$\ln(1 + x) = \sum_{k=1}^{\infty} (-1)^{k+1} \frac{x^k}{k} \qquad (-1 < x \leqslant 1). \qquad 26(57)$$

(a) $$\ln x = \sum_{k=1}^{\infty} (-1)^{k+1} \frac{(x - 1)^k}{k} \qquad (0 < x < 2).$$

(b) $$\ln(1 + x) = \frac{1}{1 + x}\left[x + \sum_{k=2}^{\infty}(-1)^k \frac{x^k}{k(k-1)}\right] \quad (-1 < x < 2).$$

$2°.$ $\ln x = 2 \sum_{k=1}^{\infty} \frac{1}{2k-1} \left(\frac{x-1}{x+1} \right)^{2k-1}$ $(0 < x)$. $26(58)$

$3°.$ $\ln x = \sum_{k=1}^{\infty} \frac{1}{k} \left(\frac{x-1}{x} \right)^{k}$ $\left(x \geqslant \frac{1}{2} \right)$. $26(58);\ 39(124)$

$4°.$ $\ln \frac{1+x}{1-x} = 2 \sum_{k=1}^{\infty} \frac{1}{2k-1} x^{2k-1}$ $(|x| < 1)$. $26(58);\ 32(421)$

$5°.$ $\ln \frac{x+1}{x-1} = 2 \sum_{k=1}^{\infty} \frac{1}{(2k-1)x^{2k-1}}$ $(|x| > 1)$. $26(58);\ 39(124)$

$6°.$ $\ln \frac{x}{1-x} = \sum_{k=1}^{\infty} \frac{1}{kx^k}$ $(|x| > 1)$. $26(58);\ 52(25)$

$7°.$ $\frac{1}{2} \{\ln(1 \pm x)\}^2 = \sum_{k=1}^{\infty} \frac{(\mp 1)^{k+1}x^{k+1}}{k+1} \sum_{n=1}^{k} \frac{1}{n}$

$$(|x| < 1). \quad 26(59);\ 52(23)$$

2.3. Expansions in polynomials, orthogonal and otherwise.
A. *Expansions in Chebyshev polynomials.*

$1°.$ $\ln \frac{1+p^2+2px}{1+p^2-2px} = 4 \sum_{k=0}^{\infty} \frac{p^{2k+1}}{2k+1} T_{2k+1}(x)$ $(|x| < 1)$,

$$r_{n-1} < \frac{4p^{2k+1}}{(2k+1)(1-p^2)} \ . \qquad 19(10)$$

(a) $\ln x = \frac{\ln 2}{2} + \sum_{k=0}^{\infty} \frac{4p^{2k+1}}{2k+1} T_{2k+1} \left((\sqrt{2}+1)^2 \frac{x-\sqrt{2}}{x+\sqrt{2}} \right)$

$$(1 \leqslant x \leqslant 2), \quad p = \frac{\sqrt[4]{2}-1}{\sqrt[4]{2}+1} \approx 0{\cdot}08642723372,$$

$$r_{n-1} < \frac{4p^{2k+1}}{(2k+1)(1-p^2)}. \qquad 19(11,\ 12)$$

(b) $\ln x = -\dfrac{1}{2}\ln 2 - \sum\limits_{k=0}^{\infty}\dfrac{4p^{2k+1}}{2k+1}\,T_{2k+1}\left[(\sqrt{2}+1)^2\dfrac{1-\sqrt{2}\,x}{1+\sqrt{2}\,x}\right]$

$\left(\dfrac{1}{2}\leqslant x\leqslant 1\right),\qquad r_{n-1}<\dfrac{4p^{2n+1}}{(2n+1)(1-p^2)}\;.$

n	$\dfrac{4p^n}{n}$	n	$\dfrac{4p^n}{n}$
1	0·345 708 934 90	7	0·000 000 020 58
3	0·000 860 776 94	9	0·000 000 000 12
5	0·000 003 857 93		

18(105)

$2°$. $\ln(1+x)=\sum\limits_{k=0}^{\infty}A_k T_k(1+4x)\quad\left(-\dfrac{1}{2}\leqslant x\leqslant 0\right);$

$\ln(1+x)=\sum\limits_{k=0}^{\infty}A'_k T_k[1+(4+2\sqrt{2})x]$

$\left(\dfrac{\sqrt{2}}{2}-1\leqslant x\leqslant 0\right).$

k	A_k	A'_k
0	−0·316 694 367 64	−0·165 789 090 74
1	0·343 145 750 51	0·172 854 467 45
2	−0·029 437 251 52	−0·007 469 666 73
3	0·003 367 089 26	0·000 430 388 42
4	−0·000 433 275 89	−0·000 027 897 96
5	0·000 059 470 71	0·000 001 928 91
6	−0·000 008 502 97	−0·000 000 138 93
7	0·000 001 250 47	0·000 000 010 29
8	−0·000 000 187 73	−0·000 000 000 78
9	0·000 000 028 63	0·000 000 000 06
10	−0·000 000 004 42	
11	0·000 000 000 69	
12	−0·000 000 000 11	
13	0·000 000 000 02	

18(104)

$3°.\ \log(1+x) = \sum_{k=0}^{\infty} A_k T_k(2x-1) \quad (0 \leqslant x \leqslant 1).$

k	A_k	k	A_k
0	0·376 452 813	6	−0·000 008 503
1	0·343 145 750	7	0·000 001 250
2	−0·029 437 252	8	−0·000 000 188
3	0·003 367 089	9	0·000 000 029
4	−0·000 433 276	10	−0·000 000 004
5	0·000 059 471	11	0·000 000 001

47(146)

$$4°.\ \log(x+a) - \log a = 2 \sum_{k=1}^{\infty} \frac{q^k}{k}\left\{1 - (-1)^k T_k\!\left(\frac{x+1}{2}\right)\right\}$$

$$= -2\log(1-q) - 2\sum_{k=1}^{\infty} \frac{(-1)^k q^k}{k}\, T_k\!\left(\frac{x+1}{2}\right),$$

$$q = 2a + 1 - 2(a^2+a)^{\frac{1}{2}} \quad (0 \leqslant x \leqslant 1),$$

$$r_n = \frac{4\,|q^{n+1}|}{(n+1)\,|1-q|}. \qquad 63(16)$$

This formula is valid for complex a with $a \neq 0$, $\arg a \leqslant \frac{1}{2}\pi$.

B. *Expansions in Legendre polynomials.*

$5°.\ \ \ln\frac{x+3}{3-x} = \sum_{k=1}^{\infty} A_{2k-1} P_{2k-1}(x) \quad (|x| < 1).$

k	A_{2k-1}	k	A_{2k-1}
1	0·682 233 833 281	5	0·000 000 152 405
2	0·010 668 387 537	6	0·000 000 004 046
3	0·000 238 906 394	7	0·000 000 000 109
4	0·000 005 896 784		

2.4. Polynomial approximations. Approximations to $\ln(1+x)$ are given by the following formulae.

1°. $\ln(1+x) \approx \displaystyle\sum_{k=0}^{3} a_k x^k, \quad r = 5.3 \times 10^{-4} \quad (0 \leqslant x \leqslant 1).$

a_0	0.000 49	a_2	−0.397 28	47(144)
a_1	0.982 48	a_3	0.107 84	

2°. The formulae (a) to (e) are a series of best approximations to $\ln(1+x)$ over the range $(0,1)$ (cf. [49], pp. 176–180):

(a) $\ln(1+x) \approx \displaystyle\sum_{k=1}^{4} a_k x^k, \quad r = 7.5 \times 10^{-5} \quad (0 \leqslant x \leqslant 1).$

a_1	0.997 444 2	a_3	0.225 668 5
a_2	−0.471 283 9	a_4	−0.058 752 7

(b) $\ln(1+x) \approx \displaystyle\sum_{k=1}^{5} a_k x^k, \quad r = 10^{-5} \quad (0 \leqslant x \leqslant 1).$

a_1	0.999 495 56	a_4	−0.136 062 75
a_2	−0.491 908 96	a_5	0.032 158 45
a_3	0.289 474 78		

(c) $\ln(1+x) \approx \displaystyle\sum_{k=1}^{6} a_k x^k, \quad r = 1.5 \times 10^{-6} \quad (0 \leqslant x \leqslant 1).$

a_1	0.999 901 67	a_4	−0.193 761 49
a_2	−0.497 875 44	a_5	0.085 569 27
a_3	0.317 650 05	a_6	−0.018 338 31

(d) $\ln(1+x) \approx \displaystyle\sum_{k=1}^{7} a_k x^k, \quad r = 2.2 \times 10^{-7} \quad (0 \leqslant x \leqslant 1).$

a_1	0.999 981 028	a_5	0.134 639 267
a_2	−0.499 470 150	a_6	−0.055 119 959
a_3	0.328 233 122	a_7	0.010 757 369
a_4	−0.225 873 284		

(e) $\ln(1+x) \approx \displaystyle\sum_{k=1}^{8} a_k x^k$, $r = 3\cdot2 \times 10^{-8}$ $(0 \leqslant x \leqslant 1)$.

a_1	0·999 996 423 9	a_5	0·167 654 071 1
a_2	−0·499 874 123 8	a_6	−0·095 329 389 7
a_3	0·331 799 025 8	a_7	0·036 088 493 7
a_4	−0·240 733 808 4	a_8	−0·006 453 544 2

3°. $\ln(1+x) \approx \displaystyle\sum_{k=0}^{12} a_k x^k$ $\left(-\dfrac{1}{2} \leqslant x \leqslant 0\right)$.

a_0	−0·000 000 000 01	a_6	−0·276 111 962 93
a_1	0·999 999 990 26	a_7	−0·459 239 902 41
a_2	−0·500 001 065 85	a_8	−2·352 660 611 07
a_3	0·333 287 735 65	a_9	−5·397 653 173 04
a_4	−0·251 007 902 11	a_{10}	−8·894 125 650 74
a_5	0·186 831 717 99	a_{11}	−8·211 977 469 95
		a_{12}	−3·724 595 639 09

18(118)

4°. $\ln(1-x) \approx \displaystyle\sum_{k=1}^{5} a_k x^k$, $r = 4\cdot11 \times 10^{-7}$

$$\left(0 \leqslant x \leqslant 1 - \frac{\sqrt{2}}{2}\right).$$

a_1	−1·000 029 4	a_4	−0·151 410 4
a_2	−0·498 850 1	a_5	−0·455 877 5
a_3	−0·349 443 8		

5°. $\ln(1-x) \approx \displaystyle\sum_{k=1}^{5} a_k x^k$, $r = 4\cdot11 \times 10^{-7}$

$$\left(1 - \frac{\sqrt{2}}{2} \leqslant x \leqslant \frac{1}{2}\right).$$

a_0	0·008 002 0	a_3	−2·491 775 5
a_1	−1·118 249 4	a_4	3·171 873 2
a_2	0·207 236 6	a_5	−2·579 317 0

6°. $\ln(1-x) \approx \sum\limits_{k=1}^{9} a_k x^k,$ $r = 10^{-6}$ $\left(0 \leqslant x \leqslant \dfrac{1}{2}\right).$

a_1	$-1\cdot000\,002$	a_6	$0\cdot623\,373$
a_2	$-0\cdot499\,919$	a_7	$-2\cdot122\,103$
a_3	$-0\cdot335\,428$	a_8	$2\cdot649\,698$
a_4	$-0\cdot223\,585$	a_9	$-1\cdot877\,585$
a_5	$-0\cdot387\,483$		

7°. $\ln\dfrac{a+x}{a-x} \approx 0\cdot4483470\,x + 0\cdot0510518\,x^3,$

$$a = \dfrac{10^{\frac{1}{2}}+1}{10^{\frac{1}{2}}-1},\quad r = 6\cdot012\times10^{-4}\quad(|x|\leqslant1).\qquad 67(189)$$

8°. $\ln\dfrac{a+x}{a-x} \approx \sum\limits_{k=0}^{2} a_{2k+1} x^{2k+1},$ $r = 3\cdot37\times10^{-6}$ $(|x|\leqslant1).$

a_1	$0\cdot869\,028\,5$
a_3	$0\cdot277\,386\,4$
a_5	$0\cdot254\,319\,5$

67(190)

9°. $\ln(1+e^{-x}) \approx \left(\sum\limits_{k=0}^{4} a_k x^k\right)^{-2}\ln2,$

$$r = 2\cdot6\times10^{-4}\quad(0\leqslant x<\infty).$$

a_0	1	a_3	$0\cdot0094$
a_1	$0\cdot3581$	a_4	$0\cdot0052$
a_2	$0\cdot1151$		

50(46)

10°. $\ln(1+e^{-x}) \approx \left(\sum\limits_{k=0}^{5} a_k x^k\right)^{-2}\ln2,$

$$r = 4\cdot5\times10^{-5}\quad(0\leqslant x<\infty).$$

a_0	1	a_3	$0\cdot024\,11$
a_1	$0\cdot361\,23$	a_4	$-0\cdot000\,55$
a_2	$0\cdot102\,04$	a_5	$0\cdot000\,69$

50(46)

$11°.$ $\ln(1 + e^{-x}) \approx \left(\displaystyle\sum_{k=0}^{6} a_k x^k\right)^{-2} \ln 2,$

$$r = 8 \times 10^{-6} \quad (0 \leqslant x < \infty).$$

a_0	1	a_4	0·002 654
a_1	0·360 571	a_5	−0·000 100
a_2	0·105 546	a_6	0·000 066
a_3	0·018 760		

50(46)

2.5. Continued fraction expansions.

$1°.$ $\ln(1 + x) = \cfrac{x}{1+x} - \cfrac{x}{2} - \cfrac{x}{3(1+x)} - \cfrac{2x}{2}$

$$- \cfrac{2x}{5(1+x)} - \ldots - \cfrac{nx}{2} - \cfrac{nx}{(2n+1)(1+x)} - \ldots$$ 34(109)

$2°.$ $\ln(1 + x) = \cfrac{x}{1} + \cfrac{x}{2} + \cfrac{x}{3} + \cfrac{2x}{2} + \cfrac{2x}{5} + \ldots$

$$+ \cfrac{nx}{2} + \cfrac{nx}{2n+1} + \ldots$$ 34(109)

This fraction converges in the plane of the complex variable x, cut on the real axis from $x = -\infty$ to $x = -1$.

$3°.$ $\ln(1 + x) = \cfrac{x}{1+x} - \cfrac{x(1+x)}{2+3x} - \cfrac{4x(1+x)}{3+5x} - \ldots$

$$\ldots - \cfrac{n^2 x(1+x)}{n+1+(2n+1)x} - \ldots$$ 34(110)

$4°.$ $\ln(1 + x) = \cfrac{x}{1} + \cfrac{x}{2-x} + \cfrac{4x}{3-2x} + \ldots$

$$\ldots + \cfrac{n^2 x}{n+1-nx} + \ldots$$ 34(110)

This is an *equivalent fraction*[†] for $\ln(1 + x)$.

[†] An *equivalent fraction* for a power series is defined to be a continued fraction, whose successive convergents are equal to the sequence of partial sums of the series.

$5°.$ $\ln(1+x) = \dfrac{2x}{2+x} - \dfrac{x^2}{3(2+x)} - \dfrac{4x^2}{5(2+x)} - \ldots$

$$\ldots - \frac{n^2x^2}{(2n+1)(2+x)} - \ldots . \qquad 34(110)$$

$6°.$ $\ln x = \dfrac{x-1}{1} + \dfrac{1^2(x-1)}{2} + \dfrac{1^2(x-1)}{3} + \dfrac{2^2(x-1)}{4}$

$$+ \frac{2^2(x-1)}{5} + \frac{3^2(x-1)}{6} + \ldots . \qquad 77(128)$$

The following numbers of terms need to be taken for various values of x, in order to compute $\ln x$ with nine correct significant figures: 16 terms for $x = 0{\cdot}5108$, 11 for $x = 0{\cdot}6931$, 7 for $x = 0{\cdot}9163$ and 6 for $x = 2{\cdot}3026$.

$7°.$ $\ln x = \dfrac{2(x-1)}{x+1} - \dfrac{(x-1)^2}{3(x+1)} - \dfrac{4(x-1)^2}{5(x+1)}$

$$\frac{0}{1} \; \frac{2(x-1)}{x+1} \quad \frac{6(x^2-1)}{2x^2+8x+2} \quad \frac{2(x-1)(11x^2+38x+11)}{6(x+1)(x^2+8x+1)}$$

$$- \frac{9(x-1)^2}{7(x+1)} - \ldots - \frac{n^2(x-1)^2}{(2n+1)(x+1)} - \ldots .$$

$$\frac{20(x^2-1)(5x^2+32x+5)}{24(x^4+16x^3+36x^2+16x+11)} \qquad 34(110)$$

The following chain of inequalities holds for $x \geqslant 1$:

$$\ln x \geqslant \ldots \geqslant \frac{5(x^2-1)(5x^2+32x+5)}{6(x^4+16x^3+36x^2+16x+11)}$$

$$\geqslant \frac{(x-1)(11x^2+38x+11)}{3(x+1)(x^2+8x+1)} \geqslant \frac{3(x^2-1)}{x^2+4x+1} \geqslant 2\frac{x-1}{x+1}.$$

$$34(111)$$

$8°.$ A series of rational approximation can be obtained by means of Obreshkov's formula:

$$\ln x \approx \sum_{\nu=1}^{m} (-1)^{\nu-1} \frac{C_m^\nu}{C_{m+k}^\nu} \frac{(x-1)^\nu}{\nu} + \sum_{\nu=1}^{k} \frac{C_k^\nu}{C_{m+k}^\nu} \frac{(x-1)^\nu}{\nu x^\nu}.$$

In particular, for $m = k$,

$$\ln x \approx \sum_{\nu=1}^{k} \frac{C_k^\nu}{C_{2k}^\nu} \left[(-1)^{\nu-1} + \frac{1}{x^\nu} \right] \frac{(x-1)^\nu}{\nu}.$$

For instance, with $k = 1$,

$$\ln x \approx \frac{1}{2}\left(x - \frac{1}{x}\right),$$

and for $k = 2$,

$$\ln x \approx \frac{x^2 - 1}{12x^2}(8x - x^2 - 1). \qquad \text{I(311)}$$

2.6. Rational approximations. 1°. The formulae (a) to (e) are a set of rational approximations to $y = \log x$ over the interval $(10^{-\frac{1}{2}}, 10^{\frac{1}{2}})$. If we replace $\left(\dfrac{x-1}{x+1}\right)$ in these formulae by $\left(\dfrac{x-\sqrt{10}}{x+\sqrt{10}}\right)$, then we get formulae of the same accuracy for $\left(\log x - \dfrac{1}{2}\right)$ over the interval $(1, 10)$ (for the formula (e), cf. [48], p. 68; cf. [49], pp. 125–128 for the remaining formulae).

(a) $\quad \log x \approx \displaystyle\sum_{k=1}^{2} a_{2k-1}\left(\frac{x-1}{x+1}\right)^{2k-1} \quad \left(\frac{1}{\sqrt{10}} \leqslant x \leqslant \sqrt{10}\right),$

$\qquad r = 7 \times 10^{-4} \quad (1 \leqslant x \leqslant \sqrt{10}).$

a_1	0·863 04	a_3	0·364 15

(b) $\quad \log x \approx \displaystyle\sum_{k=1}^{3} a_{2k-1}\left(\frac{x-1}{x+1}\right)^{2k-1} \quad \left(\frac{1}{\sqrt{10}} \leqslant x \leqslant \sqrt{10}\right),$

$\qquad r = 4 \times 10^{-5} \quad (1 \leqslant x \leqslant \sqrt{10}).$

a_1	0·869 028 6	a_3	0·277 383 9	a_5	0·254 327 5

(c) $\quad \log x \approx \displaystyle\sum_{k=1}^{4} a_{2k-1}\left(\frac{x-1}{x+1}\right)^{2k-1} \quad \left(\frac{1}{\sqrt{10}} \leqslant x \leqslant \sqrt{10}\right),$

$\qquad r = 2 \times 10^{-6} \quad (1 \leqslant x \leqslant \sqrt{10}).$

a_1	0·868 554 34	a_5	0·153 613 71
a_3	0·291 150 68	a_7	0·211 394 97

(d) $\log x \approx \sum_{k=1}^{5} a_{2k-1}\left(\dfrac{x-1}{x+1}\right)^{2k-1}$ $\left(\dfrac{1}{\sqrt{10}} \leqslant x \leqslant \sqrt{10}\right)$,

$$r = 1\cdot5\times10^{-7}   (1 \leqslant x \leqslant \sqrt{10}).$$

a_1	0·868 591 718	a_7	0·094 376 476
a_3	0·289 335 524	a_9	0·191 337 714
a_5	0·177 522 071		

(e) $\log x \approx \sum_{k=1}^{6} a_{2k-1}\left(\dfrac{x-1}{x+1}\right)^{2k-1}$,

$$r = 1\cdot5\times10^{-8}.$$

a_1	0·868 588 8	a_7	0·131 438 1
a_3	0·289 549 7	a_9	0·054 756 2
a_5	0·173 115 9	a_{11}	0·183 241 5

Next, we consider approximations to $\ln x$.

2°. $\ln x \approx -\dfrac{1}{2}\ln 2 + \sum_{k=0}^{2} a_{2k+1} u^{2k+1}$, $u = \dfrac{x - \dfrac{\sqrt{2}}{2}}{x + \dfrac{\sqrt{2}}{2}}$

$$\left(\dfrac{1}{2} \leqslant x < 1\right),   r = 3\times10^{-8}.$$

| a_1 | 2·000 000 815 | a_3 | 0·666 445 069 | a_5 | 0·415 054 254 |

11(170)

3°. $\ln x \approx -\dfrac{1}{2}\ln 2 + \sum_{k=0}^{3} a_{2k+1} u^{2k+1}$, $u = \dfrac{x - \dfrac{\sqrt{2}}{2}}{x + \dfrac{\sqrt{2}}{2}}$

$$\left(\dfrac{1}{2} \leqslant x < 1\right).$$

| a_1 | 1·999 999 993 788 | a_5 | 0·399 659 100 019 |
| a_3 | 0·666 669 470 507 | a_7 | 0·300 974 506 336 |

7(4,5)

$4°$. $\ln x \approx \ln 2\left[-\dfrac{1}{2} + \displaystyle\sum_{k=0}^{3} a_{2k+1} u^{2k+1}\right]$, $\qquad u = \dfrac{x - \dfrac{\sqrt{2}}{2}}{x + \dfrac{\sqrt{2}}{2}}$

$$\left(\frac{1}{2} \leqslant x < 1\right), \qquad r = 2^{-32}.$$

a_1	2·885 390 072 74	a_5	0·576 584 342 06
a_3	0·961 800 762 29	a_7	0·434 259 751 29

$5°$. $\ln x = u \displaystyle\sum_{k=0}^{5} a_{2k} u^{2k}$, $\qquad u = 3\dfrac{x-1}{x+1}$ $\qquad (2^{-35} < x < 1)$.

a_0	0·666 666 666	a_6	0·000 130 642	
a_2	0·024 691 358	a_8	0·000 011 290	3(286)
a_4	0·001 616 092	a_{10}	0·000 001 132	

$6°$. $\ln x \approx \ln a + \displaystyle\sum_{k=1}^{7} a_{2k-1}\left(\dfrac{x-a}{x+a}\right)^{2k-1}$, $\qquad a = 10^{n+\frac{1}{2}}$ with

$$10^n \leqslant x \leqslant 10^{n+1}, \quad n = 0, \pm 1, \ldots, \quad r < 3 \times 10^{-10}.$$

a_1	2·000 000 036 6	a_9	0·250 341 093 0	
a_3	0·666 661 710 0	a_{11}	0·057 228 326 5	60(88)
a_5	0·400 193 032 6	a_{13}	0·410 597 043 8	
a_7	0·282 433 571 2			

$7°$. $\ln x \approx z \displaystyle\sum_{k=0}^{6} a_k (z^2)^k$, $\qquad z = \dfrac{x-1}{x+1}$ $\qquad \left(\dfrac{1}{2} \leqslant x < 1\right)$.

a_0	2·000 000 000 00	a_4	0·223 206 676 54
a_1	0·666 666 656 95	a_5	0·170 167 231 05
a_2	0·400 000 986 83	a_6	0·221 370 154 23
a_3	0·285 670 543 63		

$8°$. A number of rational approximations (or Padè approximations) for

$$\frac{\ln(1+x)}{x} \approx \frac{N_p(x)}{D_q(x)}$$

are listed in the following table, with $p+q \leqslant 2$, where p and q are the degrees of the polynomials N_p and D_q respectively.

q \ p	0	1	2
0	1	$1-\dfrac{1}{2}x$	$1-\dfrac{1}{2}x+\dfrac{1}{3}x^2$
1	$\dfrac{1}{1+\dfrac{1}{2}x}$	$\dfrac{1+\dfrac{1}{6}x}{1+\dfrac{2}{3}x}$	$\dfrac{1+\dfrac{1}{4}x-\dfrac{1}{24}x^2}{1+\dfrac{3}{4}x}$
2	$\dfrac{1}{1+\dfrac{1}{2}x+\dfrac{1}{12}x^2}$	$\dfrac{1+\dfrac{1}{2}x}{1+x+\dfrac{1}{6}x^2}$	$\dfrac{1+\dfrac{7}{10}x+\dfrac{1}{30}x^2}{1+\dfrac{6}{5}x+\dfrac{3}{10}x^2}$

81(169)

Binary logarithms

9°. The formulae (a) to (c) are a set of rational approximations to $y = \log_2 x$ for the interval $\left(\dfrac{1}{\sqrt{2}}, \sqrt{2}\right)$. If we replace $\left(\dfrac{x-1}{x+1}\right)$ in these formulae by $\left(\dfrac{x-\sqrt{2}}{x+\sqrt{2}}\right)$ then we get formulae of the same accuracy for $\left(\log_2 x - \dfrac{1}{2}\right)$ over the interval $(1, 2)$ (cf. [49], pp. 164–166).

(a) $\quad \log_2 x \approx \sum_{k=1}^{2} a_{2k-1}\left(\dfrac{x-1}{x+1}\right)^{2k-1} \quad \left(\dfrac{1}{\sqrt{2}} \leqslant x \leqslant \sqrt{2}\right),$

$$r = 6 \times 10^{-6} \quad (1 \leqslant x \leqslant \sqrt{2}).$$

a_1	2·885 228 73	a_3	0·983 528 29

(b) $\log_2 x \approx \sum_{k=1}^{3} a_{2k-1}\left(\dfrac{x-1}{x+1}\right)^{2k-1} \quad \left(\dfrac{1}{\sqrt{2}} \leqslant x \leqslant \sqrt{2}\right),$

$$r = 3 \times 10^{-8} \quad (1 \leqslant x \leqslant \sqrt{2}).$$

a_1	2·885 391 290 3	a_5	0·598 978 649 6
a_3	0·961 470 632 3		

(c) $\log_2 x \approx \sum_{k=1}^{4} a_{2k-1}\left(\dfrac{x-1}{x+1}\right)^{2k-1} \quad \left(\dfrac{1}{\sqrt{2}} \leqslant x \leqslant \sqrt{2}\right),$

$$r = 1 \cdot 8 \times 10^{-10} \quad (1 \leqslant x \leqslant \sqrt{2}).$$

a_1	2·885 390 072 738	a_5	0·576 584 342 056
a_3	0·961 800 762 286	a_7	0·434 259 751 292

10°. $\ln\dfrac{1-x}{1+x} \approx \dfrac{\sum_{k=0}^{2} a_{2k+1} x^{2k+1}}{\sum_{k=0}^{2} b_{2k} x^{2k}} \quad \left(0 \leqslant x \leqslant \dfrac{1}{3}\right), \quad r = 4 \times 10^{-7}.$

a_1	−1890	b_0	945
a_3	1470	b_2	−1050
a_5	−128	b_4	225

11°. $\log x \approx -0 \cdot 076 + 0 \cdot 281 x - \dfrac{0 \cdot 238}{x + 0 \cdot 15} \quad (0 \cdot 1 \leqslant x \leqslant 1 \cdot 0),$

$$r = 0 \cdot 005. \qquad\qquad 48(68)$$

12°. $\ln(1+x) \approx \dfrac{13 \cdot 5294048 x^2 - 8 \cdot 6147976 x + 0 \cdot 0000108}{0 \cdot 4 x^2 + 3 \cdot 1280130 x + 3 \cdot 5622914},$

$$r = 5 \times 10^{-6} \quad (0 \leqslant x < 1). \qquad 28(119)$$

13°. $\ln(1+x) = \dfrac{x}{2}\left(\dfrac{1}{1+\alpha x} + \dfrac{1}{1+\beta x}\right) + r \quad (|x| < 1),$

$$r = \dfrac{x^5}{180} - \dfrac{x^6}{72} + \dfrac{17 x^7}{756} - \dots + (-1)^n\left(\dfrac{1}{n} - a_n\right) x^n + \dots,$$

$$\alpha = \frac{1}{2} + \frac{1}{\sqrt{12}}, \quad \beta = \frac{1}{2} - \frac{1}{\sqrt{12}}, \quad a_n = \frac{1}{2}(\alpha^{n-1} + \beta^{n-1}),$$

$$a_n = a_{n-1} - \frac{1}{6}a_{n-2}.$$

14°. Rational approximations (or Padè approximations) for

$$\frac{-\ln(1-x)}{x} \approx \frac{N_p(x)}{D_q(x)}$$

are listed in the following tables for $p + q \leqslant 6$, where p and q are the degrees of the polynomials N_p and D_q respectively (cf. [58]).

(a) $p = 0$

$q = 0$	1
$q = 1$	$\dfrac{1}{1 - \dfrac{1}{2}x}$
$q = 2$	$\dfrac{1}{1 - \dfrac{1}{2}x - \dfrac{1}{12}x^2}$
$q = 3$	$\dfrac{1}{1 - \dfrac{1}{2}x - \dfrac{1}{12}x^2 - \dfrac{1}{24}x^3}$
$q = 4$	$\dfrac{1}{1 - \dfrac{1}{2}x - \dfrac{1}{12}x^2 - \dfrac{1}{24}x^3 - \dfrac{19}{720}x^4}$
$q = 5$	$\dfrac{1}{1 - \dfrac{1}{2}x - \dfrac{1}{12}x^2 - \dfrac{1}{24}x^3 - \dfrac{19}{720}x^4 - \dfrac{3}{160}x^5}$
$q = 6$	$\dfrac{1}{1 - \dfrac{1}{2}x - \dfrac{1}{12}x^2 - \dfrac{1}{24}x^3 - \dfrac{19}{720}x^4 - \dfrac{3}{160}x^5 - \dfrac{863}{60\,480}x^6}$

(b) $p = 1$

$q = 0$	$1 + \dfrac{1}{2}x$
$q = 1$	$\dfrac{6 - x}{6 - 4x}$
$q = 2$	$\dfrac{6 - 3x}{6 - 6x + x^2}$
$q = 3$	$\dfrac{90 - 57x}{90 - 102x + 21x^2 + x^3}$
$q = 4$	$\dfrac{3420 - 2430x}{3420 - 4140x + 930x^2 + 60x^3 + 11x^4}$
$q = 5$	$\dfrac{102\,060 - 77\,670x}{102\,060 - 128\,700x + 30\,330x^2 + 2220x^3 + 543x^4 + 136x^5}$

(c) $p = 2$

$q = 0$	$1 + \dfrac{1}{2}x + \dfrac{1}{3}x^2$
$q = 1$	$\dfrac{24 - 6x - x^2}{24 - 18x}$
$q = 2$	$\dfrac{30 - 21x + x^2}{30 - 36x + 9x^2}$
$q = 3$	$\dfrac{60 - 60x + 11x^2}{60 - 90x + 36x^2 - 3x^3}$
$q = 4$	$\dfrac{4620 - 5430x + 1360x^2}{4620 - 7740x - 3690x^2 - 420x^3 - 9x^4}$

(d) $p = 3$

$q = 0$	$1 + \dfrac{1}{2}x + \dfrac{1}{3}x^2 + \dfrac{1}{4}x^3$
$q = 1$	$\dfrac{60 - 18x - 4x^2 - x^3}{60 - 48x}$
$q = 2$	$\dfrac{180 - 150x + 12x^2 + x^3}{180 - 240x + 72x^2}$
$q = 3$	$\dfrac{420 - 510x + 140x^2 - 3x^3}{420 - 720x + 360x^2 - 48x^3}$

(e) $p = 4$

$q = 0$	$1 + \dfrac{1}{2}x + \dfrac{1}{3}x^2 + \dfrac{1}{4}x^3 + \dfrac{1}{5}x^4$
$q = 1$	$\dfrac{360 - 120x - 30x^2 - 10x^3 - 3x^4}{360 - 300x}$
$q = 2$	$\dfrac{1260 - 1170x + 120x^2 + 15x^3 + 2x^4}{1260 - 1800x + 600x^2}$

(f) $p = 5$

$q = 0$	$1 + \dfrac{1}{2}x + \dfrac{1}{3}x^2 + \dfrac{1}{4}x^3 + \dfrac{1}{5}x^4 + \dfrac{1}{6}x^5$
$q = 1$	$\dfrac{420 - 150x - 40x^2 - 15x^3 - 6x^4 - 2x^5}{420 - 360x}$

(g) $p = 6$

$q = 0$	$1 + \dfrac{1}{2}x + \dfrac{1}{3}x^2 + \dfrac{1}{4}x^3 + \dfrac{1}{5}x^4 + \dfrac{1}{6}x^5 + \dfrac{1}{7}x^6$

$$58(42)$$

15°. Rational approximations or Padè approximations for

$$\frac{(x-1)\ln(1-x)}{x} \approx \frac{N_p(x)}{D_q(x)}$$

are listed in the following tables for $p+q \leqslant 5$, where p and q are the degrees of the polynomials N_p and D_q respectively (cf. [58]).

(a) $p = 0$

$q = 0$	1
$q = 1$	$\dfrac{1}{1 + \dfrac{1}{2}x}$
$q = 2$	$\dfrac{1}{1 + \dfrac{1}{2}x + \dfrac{5}{12}x^2}$
$q = 3$	$\dfrac{1}{1 + \dfrac{1}{2}x + \dfrac{5}{12}x^2 + \dfrac{3}{8}x^3}$
$q = 4$	$\dfrac{1}{1 + \dfrac{1}{2}x + \dfrac{5}{12}x^2 + \dfrac{3}{8}x^3 + \dfrac{251}{720}x^4}$
$q = 5$	$\dfrac{1}{1 + \dfrac{1}{2}x + \dfrac{5}{12}x^2 + \dfrac{3}{8}x^3 + \dfrac{251}{720}x^4 + \dfrac{95}{288}x^5}$

(b) $p = 1$

$q = 0$	$1 - \dfrac{1}{2}x$
$q = 1$	$\dfrac{6 - 5x}{6 - 2x}$
$q = 2$	$\dfrac{30 - 27x}{30 - 12x - x^2}$
$q = 3$	$\dfrac{810 - 753x}{810 - 348x - 39x^2 - 10x^3}$
$q = 4$	$\dfrac{45\,180 - 42\,750x}{45\,180 - 20\,160x - 2550x^2 - 870x^3 - 281x^4}$

(c) $p = 2$

$q = 0$	$1 - \dfrac{1}{2}x - \dfrac{1}{6}x^2$
$q = 1$	$\dfrac{12 - 12x + x^2}{12 - 6x}$
$q = 2$	$\dfrac{30 - 39x + 10x^2}{30 - 24x + 3x^2}$
$q = 3$	$\dfrac{600 - 870x + 281x^2}{600 - 570x + 96x^2 + 3x^3}$

(d) $p = 3$

$q = 0$	$1 - \dfrac{1}{2}x - \dfrac{1}{6}x^2 - \dfrac{1}{12}x^3$
$q = 1$	$\dfrac{60 - 66x + 8x^2 + 8x^3}{60 - 36x}$
$q = 2$	$\dfrac{60 - 90x + 32x^2 - x^3}{60 - 60x + 12x^2}$

(e) $p = 4$

$q = 0$	$1 - \dfrac{1}{2}x - \dfrac{1}{6}x^2 - \dfrac{1}{12}x^3 - \dfrac{1}{20}x^4$
$q = 1$	$\dfrac{180 - 210x + 30x^2 + 5x^3 + x^4}{180 - 120x}$

(f) $p = 5$

$q = 0$	$1 - \dfrac{1}{2}x - \dfrac{1}{6}x^2 - \dfrac{1}{12}x^3 - \dfrac{1}{20}x^4 - \dfrac{1}{30}x^5$

2.7. Iterative processes. 1°. There exists an iterative process for computing the value of

$$x = \log_2 y \quad (1 \leqslant y < 2)$$

"digit by digit". The value of x is found in the binary scale:

$$x = \alpha_0 \cdot \alpha_1 \alpha_2 \ldots \alpha_n \ldots \qquad (\alpha_i = 0, 1).$$

We evaluate successively the x_n, y_n and α_n $(n = 0, 1, \ldots)$

$$\alpha_0 = 0, \qquad y_0 = y;$$
$$\alpha_1 = 0, \text{ if } y_0^2 < 2,$$
$$\alpha_1 = 1, \text{ if } y_0^2 \geqslant 2.$$

Let $\alpha_1, \alpha_2, \ldots, \alpha_{i-1}$ be computed already, and let y_i have been found.

If $y_i^2 < 2$, then $\alpha_i = 0$ and $y_{i+1} = y_i^2$, but if $y_i^2 \geqslant 2$, then $\alpha_i = 1$ and $y_{i+1} = \frac{1}{2} y_i^2$.

After n steps, we have found n digits of the binary representation

$$x = \log_2 y \approx 0 \cdot \alpha_1 \alpha_2 \ldots \alpha_n \ldots \qquad 19(65)$$

Another variant of this method is given in [18].

2°. Iterative process for expansion as a continued fraction. Let $a_0 > a_1 > 1$. In order to compute $\log_{a_0} a_1$, we construct the two sequences

$$a_2, a_3, \ldots,$$
$$n_1, n_2, \ldots,$$

where the n_i are positive integers, by means of the relations

$$a_i^{n_i} < a_{i-1} < a_i^{n_i+1},$$

$$a_{i+1} = \frac{a_{i-1}}{a_i^{n_i}}$$

Then

$$\log_{a_0} a_1 = \frac{1}{n_1 +} \frac{1}{n_2 +} \frac{1}{n_3 + \ldots} \cdot$$

The numerators A_i and the denominators D_i of the convergents may readily be computed by the recurrence relations

$$A_{i+1} = A_{i-1} + n_{i+1} A_i,$$
$$D_{i+1} = D_{i-1} + n_{i+1} D_i.$$

NOTE TO APPENDIX I ADDED IN PROOF

During the printing of this English edition, Dr. O. A. Chervonen-kis kindly supplied a list of the misprints in the Russian text. The necessary corrections have now been inserted into the text, except for the following table, which should have followed immediately after section 10° on p. 174. (G. J. T.)

§ 4.5. 11°. Hermite polynomials $h_n(x)$.

$$h_0(x) = 1.$$
$$h_1(x) = x.$$
$$h_2(x) = x^2 - 1.$$
$$h_3(x) = x^3 - 3x.$$
$$h_4(x) = x^4 - 6x^2 + 3.$$
$$h_5(x) = x^5 - 10x^3 + 15x.$$
$$h_6(x) = x^6 - 15x^4 + 45x^2 - 15.$$
$$h_7(x) = x^7 - 21x^5 + 105x^3 - 105x.$$
$$h_8(x) = x^8 - 28x^6 + 210x^4 - 420x^2 + 105.$$

TRIGONOMETRIC, HYPERBOLIC, INVERSE TRIGONOMETRIC AND INVERSE HYPERBOLIC FUNCTIONS

§ 1. Trigonometric functions

1.1. General information. 1°. *Trigonometric functions.* The functions $\sin x$ and $\cos x$ are defined everywhere on the real axis, and they are everywhere continuous and bounded. The function $\tan x$ is defined and is continuous everywhere on the real axis, except at the points

$$x = (n + \tfrac{1}{2})\pi \quad (n = 0, \ \pm 1, \ \pm 2, \ldots).$$

The function $\cot x$ is defined and continuous everywhere on the real axis, except at the points

$$x = n\pi \ (n = 0, \pm 1, \pm 2, \ldots).$$

The function $\sec x$ and $\operatorname{cosec} x$ are the reciprocals of the functions $\cos x$ and $\sin x$ respectively, i.e.

$$\sec x = 1/\cos x, \ \operatorname{cosec} x = 1/\sin x.$$

Furthermore,

$$\lim_{x \to \frac{1}{2}\pi - 0} \tan x = +\infty, \quad \lim_{x \to \frac{1}{2}\pi + 0} \tan x = -\infty,$$

$$\lim_{x \to +0} \cot x = +\infty, \quad \lim_{x \to -0} \cot x = -\infty.$$

The argument x of the trigonometric functions $\sin x$, $\cos x$, etc., may be regarded as a measure in radians of an arc or an angle.

The trigonometric functions are periodic: $\sin x$ and $\cos x$ have a period of 2π, but $\tan x$ and $\cot x$ have a period of π.

2°. The function $\cos x$ is an even function, but $\sin x$, $\tan x$ and $\cot x$ are odd functions.

$$\sin x = \operatorname{sign} x \sin |x|, \qquad \cos x = \cos |x|,$$

$$\tan x = \operatorname{sign} x \tan |x|, \qquad \cot x = \operatorname{sign} x \cot |x|.$$

3°. **Addition formulae and functional equations.**

$$\sin(x \pm y) = \sin x \cos y \pm \cos x \sin y,$$

$$\cos(x \pm y) = \cos x \cos y \mp \sin x \sin y,$$

$$\tan(x \pm y) = \frac{\tan x \pm \tan y}{1 \mp \tan x \tan y}.$$

It follows from these formulae that

(a) $\Delta_h \cos x = \cos(x + h) - 2 \cos x + \cos(x - h) = -\pi_h \cos x,$

$\Delta_h \sin x = \sin(x + h) - 2 \sin x + \sin(x - h) = -\pi_h \sin x,$

where

$$\pi_h = 4 \sin^2 \frac{1}{2} h;$$

and also that

(b) $a \cos x + b \sin x = \varrho \sin(x + \varphi),$

$$\varrho = \sqrt{a^2 + b^2}, \qquad \varphi = \arctan \frac{b}{a}.$$

The addition formulae are sufficient to define the trigonometric functions.

Indeed, the functions $f_1(x) = \sin x$, $f_2(x) = \cos x$, are the unique continuous solutions of the functional equations

$$f_1(x + y) = f_1(x) f_2(y) + f_1(y) f_2(x),$$

$$f_2(x + y) = f_2(x) f_2(y) - f_1(x) f_1(y)$$

under the conditions that these functions are positive over the range $\left(0, \dfrac{1}{2}\pi\right)$, and that

$$f_1\left(\frac{1}{2}\pi\right) = 1, \qquad f_2\left(\frac{1}{2}\pi\right) = 0.$$

The function $f(x) = \tan x$ is the unique continuous solution of the functional equation

$$f(x + y) = \frac{f(x) + f(y)}{1 - f(x) f(y)}$$

under the conditions that $f(x)$ is positive over the range $\left(0, \frac{1}{4}\pi\right)$, and that $f\left(\frac{1}{4}\pi\right) = 1$.

$4°$. The general formula for multiple angles are known as de Moivre's formulae.

$$(\cos x + i \sin x)^n = \cos nx + i \sin nx,$$

$$\cos nx = \mathrm{Re}(\cos x + i \sin x)^n = H_n^{(0)}(\cos x, \sin x),$$

$$\sin nx = \mathrm{Im}(\cos x + i \sin x)^n = H_n^{(1)}(\cos x, \sin x),$$

$$\tan nx = \frac{H_n^{(1)}(1, \tan x)}{H_n^{(0)}(1, \tan x)}, \qquad \cot nx = \frac{H_n^{(0)}(\cot x, 1)}{H_n^{(1)}(\cot x, 1)},$$

where $H_n^{(0)}$ and $H_n^{(1)}$ are the harmonic polynomials (cf. Appendix I, § 2.1).

Also we have

$$\cos nx = T_n(\cos x), \qquad \sin nx = \sin x\, U_{n-1}(\cos x),$$

$$\cos 2kx = (-1)^k T_{2k}(\sin x),$$

$$\sin 2kx = (-1)^{k+1} \cos x\, U_{2k-1}(\sin x),$$

$$\sin(2k+1)\, x = (-1)^k T_{2k+1}(\sin x),$$

$$\cos(2k+1)\, x = (-1)^{k+1} \cos x\, U_{2k}(\sin x).$$

$5°$. The formulae

$$\sin x = \frac{2\tan \dfrac{1}{2}x}{1 + \tan^2 \dfrac{1}{2}x}, \qquad \cos x = \frac{1 - \tan^2 \dfrac{1}{2}x}{1 + \tan^2 \dfrac{1}{2}x}$$

enable us to reduce simultaneously the computation of both $\sin x$ and $\cos x$ to the computation of $\tan \dfrac{1}{2}x$.

$6°$. *Some reduction formulae.*

(a) Reduction of $\sin \dfrac{1}{2}\pi x$ to the interval $(-1, 1)$:

$$z = \left|\left|\left|\left\{\frac{x-1}{4}\right\}\right| 4 - 2\right| - 1\right|, \quad |z| \leqslant 1,$$

$$\sin\frac{\pi}{2}z = \sin\frac{\pi}{2}x. \qquad\qquad 18(98)$$

The formula holds for arbitrary real x.

(b) If $|x| < 2$, then $z = ||x - 1| - 2| - 1$.

(c) If $|x| < 4$, then $z = 1 - |||x - 1| - 2| - 2|$.

(d) Reduction of $\sin x$ to the interval $\left(-\frac{1}{2}\pi, \frac{1}{2}\pi\right)$. Let

$$|x| = 2\pi\alpha + \pi\beta + \frac{\pi}{2}\gamma + \frac{\pi}{2}\delta, \qquad\qquad 18(98)$$

where α is the (integer) number of periods, $\beta = 0$ or 1, $\gamma = 0$ or 1, $0 \leqslant \delta \leqslant 1$. Then

$$\sin x = \sin\frac{1}{2}\pi t,$$

where

$$t = (-1)^\beta \operatorname{sign} x \, [\gamma + (-1)^\gamma \delta],$$

so that

$$|t| < 1.$$

The formula holds for arbitrary real x.

(e) $\qquad\qquad t = 2\left[\dfrac{x}{\pi}\right] - \dfrac{2x}{\pi} \quad$ if $\quad \beta \neq \gamma$,

(f) $\qquad\qquad t = \dfrac{2x}{\pi} - 2\left[\dfrac{x}{\pi}\right] \quad$ if $\quad \beta = \gamma$,

where

$$2\left[\frac{x}{\pi}\right] = 2\operatorname{sign}x \, . \, (2\alpha + \beta + \gamma)$$

is twice the integer which is closest to $\dfrac{x}{\pi}$.

(g) Reduction of $\tan x$ to the interval $\left(-\frac{1}{4}\pi, \frac{1}{4}\pi\right)$. Let

$$u = \left\{\frac{x}{\pi} - \frac{1}{4}\right\},$$

$$v = |u| - \frac{1}{2},$$

$$z = |v| - \frac{1}{4}\left|\left|\left\{\frac{x}{\pi} - \frac{1}{4}\right\}\right| - \frac{1}{2}\right| - \frac{1}{4}, \quad |z| < \frac{1}{4},$$

Then

$$\tan x = \begin{cases} \tan \pi z, & \text{if} \quad uv \geqslant 0, \\ \dfrac{1}{\tan \pi z}, & \text{if} \quad uv < 0. \end{cases} \qquad 18(99)$$

(h) Reduction of $\tan x$ to the interval $\left(-\dfrac{1}{2}\pi, \dfrac{1}{2}\pi\right)$. Let

$$z = \pi \left\{ \frac{x}{\pi} + \frac{1}{2} \right\} - \frac{\pi}{2},$$

Then

$$\tan x = \tan z. \qquad 18(99)$$

7°. *Connection with the exponential function.* Euler's formulae are:

$$\cos x = \frac{e^{ix} + e^{-ix}}{2}, \; \sin x = \frac{e^{ix} - e^{-ix}}{2i}$$

The trigonometric functions of complex argument are defined on the basis of Euler's formulae.

8°. *Connection between the trigonometric and hyperbolic functions.*

(a) $\sin x = -i \sinh ix$.

(b) $\cos x = \cosh ix$.

(c) $\tan x = \dfrac{1}{i} \tanh ix$.

(d) $\cot x = i \coth ix$.

1.2. Power series expansions.

1°. $\quad \sin x = \displaystyle\sum_{k=0}^{\infty} (-1)^k \frac{x^{2k+1}}{(2k+1)!}$.

2°. $\quad \cos x = \displaystyle\sum_{k=0}^{\infty} (-1)^k \frac{x^{2k}}{(2k)!}$.

The formulae 1° and 2° may be written in the form

$$\sin x = \sum_{k=0}^{\infty} u_k, \quad \cos x = \sum_{k=0}^{\infty} u'_k,$$

where

$$u_0 = x, \quad u_0' = 1,$$

$$u_{k+1} = -\frac{x^2}{(2k+3)(2k+2)} u_k, \quad u_{k+1}' = -\frac{x^2}{(2k+2)(2k+1)} u_k'.$$

20(237)

3°. $\sin \pi x = \sum_{k=1}^{\infty} \frac{A_k}{k!} [x(1-x)]^k,$

$$A_k = \left[\frac{d^{k-1}(1-x)\pi \cos \pi x}{dx^{k-1}} \right]_{x=0}.$$

24(362)

4°. $\tan x = \sum_{k=1}^{\infty} \frac{2^{2k}(2^{2k}-1)}{(2k)!} |B_{2k}| x^{2k-1} \quad \left(|x| < \frac{\pi}{2} \right).$ 26(48);
32(523)

5°. $\cot x = \frac{1}{x} - \sum_{k=1}^{\infty} \frac{2^{2k} |B_{2k}|}{(2k)!} x^{2k-1} \quad (|x| < \pi).$ 26(48);
32(523)

6°. $\sec x = \sum_{k=0}^{\infty} \frac{E_{2k}}{(2k)!} x^{2k} \quad \left(|x| \leqslant \frac{\pi}{2} \right).$ 26(49)

7°. $\operatorname{cosec} x = \frac{1}{x} + \sum_{k=1}^{\infty} \frac{2(2^{2k-1}-1)|B_{2k}| x^{2k-1}}{(2k)!} \quad (|x| < \pi).$ 26(49)

8°. $e^{\sin x} = 1 + x + \frac{x^2}{2!} - \frac{3x^4}{4!} - \frac{8x^5}{5!} + \frac{3x^6}{6!} + \frac{56x^7}{7} + \cdots$ 26(36); 39

9°. $e^{\cos x} = e \left(1 - \frac{x^2}{2!} + \frac{4x^4}{4!} - \frac{31x^6}{6!} + \cdots \right).$ 26(36); 39

10°. $e^{\tan x} = 1 + x + \frac{x^2}{2!} + \frac{3x^3}{3!} + \frac{9x^4}{4!} + \frac{37x^5}{5!} + \cdots$ 26(36); 39

11°. $\ln \sin x = \ln x - \frac{x^2}{6} - \frac{x^4}{180} - \frac{x^6}{2835} - \cdots$

$$= \ln x + \sum_{k=1}^{\infty} \frac{(-1)^k 2^{2k-1} B_{2k} x^{2k}}{k(2k)!} \quad (|x| < \pi).$$ 26(59); 39

12°. $\ln \cos x = -\frac{x^2}{2} - \frac{x^4}{12} - \frac{x^6}{45} - \frac{17x^8}{2520} - \cdots$

$$= \sum_{k=1}^{\infty} (-1)^k \frac{2^{2k-1}(2^{2k}-1)B_{2k}}{k(2k)!} x^{2k}$$

$$= -\frac{1}{2} \sum_{k=1}^{\infty} \frac{\sin^{2k} x}{k} \quad \left(|x| < \frac{\pi}{2} \right).$$ 26(59); 32(524)

13°. $\ln \tan x = \ln x + \dfrac{x^2}{3} + \dfrac{7}{90}\, x^4 + \dfrac{62}{2835}\, x^6 + \dfrac{127}{18\,900}\, x^8 + \cdots$

$\qquad = \ln x + \displaystyle\sum_{k=1}^{\infty} (-1)^{k+1}\, \dfrac{(2^{2k-1}-1)\,2^{2k}B_{2k}\,x^{2k}}{k\,(2k)!} \ \left(|x| < \dfrac{\pi}{2}\right).$ 26(59); 39

1.3. Infinite products.

1°. $\sin x = x \displaystyle\prod_{k=1}^{\infty} \left(1 - \dfrac{x^2}{k^2\pi^2}\right).$ 26(51); 36(149)

2°. $\cos x = \displaystyle\prod_{k=0}^{\infty} \left(1 - \dfrac{4x^2}{(2k+1)^2\pi^2}\right).$ 26(51); 36(149)

3°. $\cos\dfrac{\pi x}{4} - \sin\dfrac{\pi x}{4} = \displaystyle\prod_{k=1}^{\infty} \left[1 + \dfrac{(-1)^k x}{2k-1}\right].$ 26(51); 43(189)

4°. $1 + \sin x$

$\qquad = \dfrac{1}{8}\,(\pi + 2x)^2 \displaystyle\prod_{k=1}^{\infty} \left[1 - \left(\dfrac{\pi + 2x}{2k\pi}\right)^2\right]^2.$ 26(51); 66(216)

5°. $\dfrac{\sin\pi(x+a)}{\sin\pi a}$

$\qquad = \dfrac{x+a}{a} \displaystyle\prod_{k=1}^{\infty} \left(1 - \dfrac{x}{k-a}\right)\left(1 + \dfrac{x}{k+a}\right).$ 26(51); 66(216)

6°. $1 - \dfrac{\sin^2\pi x}{\sin^2\pi a} = \displaystyle\prod_{k=-\infty}^{\infty} \left[1 - \left(\dfrac{x}{k-a}\right)^2\right].$ 26(51); 66(216)

7°. $\sin x = x \displaystyle\prod_{k=1}^{\infty} \cos\dfrac{x}{2^k}\ (|x| < 1).$ 26(51); 39(130); 66(216)

8°. $\dfrac{\sin x}{x} = \displaystyle\prod_{k=1}^{\infty} \left[1 - \dfrac{4}{3}\sin^2\left(\dfrac{x}{3^k}\right)\right].$ 26(51); 66(216)

1.4. Expansions in elementary rational functions.

1°. $\tan\dfrac{\pi x}{2} = \dfrac{4x}{\pi} \displaystyle\sum_{k=1}^{\infty} \dfrac{1}{(2k-1)^2 - x^2}.$ 26(50); 43(191); 39(129)

$2°.\quad \cot \pi x = \dfrac{1}{\pi x} + \dfrac{2x}{\pi} \displaystyle\sum_{k=1}^{\infty} \dfrac{1}{x^2 - k^2}$

$$= \dfrac{1}{\pi x} + \dfrac{x}{\pi} \sum_{k=-\infty}^{\infty} \dfrac{1}{k(x-k)}. \quad 26(50); \ 39(129); \ 52(137)$$

$3°.\quad \tan^2 \dfrac{\pi x}{2}$

$$= x^2 \sum_{k=1}^{\infty} \dfrac{2(2k-1)^2 - x^2}{(1^2 - x^2)^2 (3^2 - x^2)^2 \cdots [(2k-1)^2 - x^2]^2}. \quad 26(50); \ 52(135)$$

$4°.\quad \sec \dfrac{\pi x}{2} = \dfrac{4}{\pi} \displaystyle\sum_{k=1}^{\infty} (-1)^{k+1} \dfrac{2k-1}{(2k-1)^2 - x^2}.$ $\qquad 26(50);$ $\qquad 39(129)$

$5°.\quad \sec^2 \dfrac{\pi x}{2} = \dfrac{4}{\pi^2} \displaystyle\sum_{k=1}^{\infty} \left\{ \dfrac{1}{(2k-1-x)^2} + \dfrac{1}{(2k-1+x)^2} \right\}.$

$$26(50); \ 52(137)$$

$6°.\quad \operatorname{cosec} \pi x = \dfrac{1}{\pi x} + \dfrac{2x}{\pi} \displaystyle\sum_{k=1}^{\infty} \dfrac{(-1)^k}{x^2 - k^2}$

$$= \dfrac{1}{\pi x} + \dfrac{1}{\pi} \sum_{k=-\infty}^{\infty} (-1)^k \left(\dfrac{1}{x-k} + \dfrac{1}{k} \right). \quad 26(50); \ 39(129); \ 52(137)$$

$7°.\quad \operatorname{cosec}^2 \pi x = \dfrac{1}{\pi^2} \displaystyle\sum_{k=-\infty}^{\infty} \dfrac{1}{(x-k)^2}$

$$= \dfrac{1}{\pi^2 x^2} + \dfrac{2}{\pi^2} \sum_{k=1}^{\infty} \dfrac{x^2 + k^2}{(x^2 - k^2)^2}. \quad 26(50); \ 52(134)$$

1.5. Expansions in polynomials, orthogonal and otherwise.

A. *Expansions in Chebyshev polynomials.*

$1°.\quad \sin \dfrac{\pi}{4} x = 2 \displaystyle\sum_{k=0}^{\infty} (-1)^k J_{2k+1}\left(\dfrac{\pi}{4} \right) T_{2k+1}(x) \qquad (|x| \leqslant 1),$

$$|r_m(x)| \leqslant \dfrac{\left(\dfrac{\pi}{8} \right)^{2m+1} \left(1 + \dfrac{\pi}{16m} \right)}{(2m+1)!}. \qquad 19(13)$$

k	$2(-1)^k J_{2k+1}\left(\dfrac{\pi}{4}\right)$	r_k
0	0·726 375 676 693 734 663 591 187	
1	−0·019 420 029 053 201 506 305 923	16×10^{-5}
2	0·000 151 692 922 851 073 994 812	6×10^{-7}
3	−0·000 000 560 580 468 412 001 104	13×10^{-10}
4	0·000 000 001 205 324 167 854 356	17×10^{-13}
5	−0·000 000 000 001 694 139 308 710	17×10^{-16}
6	0·000 000 000 000 001 677 809 317	13×10^{-19}
7	−0·000 000 000 000 000 001 233 791	8×10^{-22}
8	0·000 000 000 000 000 000 000 700	$<10^{-24}$

78(79)

$2°.$ $\dfrac{\sin \dfrac{\pi}{4} x}{x} = \sum_{k=0}^{\infty} a_{2k} T_{2k}(x) \qquad (|x| \leqslant 1).$

k	a_{2k}	r_{2k}
0	0·745 947 960 457 275 642 099 900	
1	−0·039 144 567 527 081 957 017 426	31×10^{-5}
2	0·000 304 509 420 678 944 405 580	12×10^{-7}
3	−0·000 001 123 574 976 796 415 956	25×10^{-10}
4	0·000 000 002 414 039 972 413 748	34×10^{-13}
5	−0·000 000 000 003 391 636 705 036	34×10^{-16}
6	0·000 000 000 000 003 358 087 616	25×10^{-19}
7	−0·000 000 000 000 000 002 468 982	15×10^{-22}
8	0·000 000 000 000 000 000 001 400	1×10^{-24}

78(83)

$3°.$ $\cos \dfrac{\pi}{4} x = J_0\left(\dfrac{\pi}{4}\right) + 2\sum_{k=1}^{\infty} (-1)^k J_{2k}\left(\dfrac{\pi}{4}\right) T_{2k}(x)$

$$(|x| \leqslant 1),$$

$$J_0\left(\dfrac{\pi}{4}\right) = 0·851 631 913 704 808 012 700 406\ldots,$$

$$|r_m(x)| \leqslant \dfrac{\left(\dfrac{\pi}{8}\right)^{2(m+1)}\left(1 + \dfrac{\pi}{16m}\right)}{[2(m+1)]!}. \quad 19(13);\ 78(85)$$

k	$2(-1)^k J_{2k}\left(\dfrac{\pi}{4}\right)$	r_{2k}
1	$-0\cdot146\ 436\ 144\ 390\ 836\ 863\ 320\ 797$	20×10^{-4}
2	$0\cdot001\ 921\ 449\ 311\ 814\ 646\ 796\ 907$	10×10^{-6}
3	$-0\cdot000\ 009\ 964\ 968\ 489\ 829\ 300\ 069$	28×10^{-9}
4	$0\cdot000\ 000\ 027\ 576\ 595\ 607\ 187\ 395$	48×10^{-12}
5	$-0\cdot000\ 000\ 000\ 047\ 399\ 498\ 081\ 648$	56×10^{-15}
6	$0\cdot000\ 000\ 000\ 000\ 055\ 495\ 485\ 415$	48×10^{-18}
7	$-0\cdot000\ 000\ 000\ 000\ 000\ 047\ 097\ 049$	31×10^{-21}
8	$0\cdot000\ 000\ 000\ 000\ 000\ 000\ 030\ 298$	16×10^{-24}
9	$-0\cdot000\ 000\ 000\ 000\ 000\ 000\ 000\ 015$	10^{-24}

78(85)

$4°.$ $\sin\dfrac{\pi}{2}x = 2\sum_{k=0}^{\infty}(-1)^k J_{2k+1}\left(\dfrac{\pi}{2}\right)T_{2k+1}(x)$

$$(|x|\leqslant 1).\qquad 18(97);\ 42(22);\ 5(251)$$

$5°.$ $\cos\dfrac{\pi}{2}x = J_0\left(\dfrac{\pi}{2}\right) + 2\sum_{k=1}^{\infty}(-1)^k J_{2k}\left(\dfrac{\pi}{2}\right)T_{2k}(x)$

$$(|x|\leqslant 1).\qquad 18(97);\ 42(22);\ 5(251)$$

k	$J_k\left(\dfrac{\pi}{2}\right)$	k	$J_k\left(\dfrac{\pi}{2}\right)$
0	$0\cdot47200\ 121\ 577$	7	$0\cdot00003\ 385\ 064$
1	$0\cdot56682\ 408\ 891$	8	$0\cdot00000\ 335\ 220$
2	$0\cdot24970\ 162\ 914$	9	$0\cdot00000\ 029\ 457$
3	$0\cdot06903\ 588\ 829$	10	$0\cdot00000\ 002\ 327$
4	$0\cdot01399\ 603\ 981$	11	$0\cdot00000\ 000\ 167$
5	$0\cdot00224\ 535\ 712$	12	$0\cdot00000\ 000\ 011$
6	$0\cdot00029\ 834\ 760$		

$6°.$ $\sin\dfrac{\pi}{2}x = x\sum_{k=0}^{\infty}a_k T_k(2x^2-1)\qquad(|x|\leqslant 1).$

a_0	$1\cdot276\ 278\ 962$	a_3	$-0\cdot000\ 136\ 587$	
a_1	$-0\cdot285\ 261\ 569$	a_4	$0\cdot000\ 001\ 185$	47(145)
a_2	$0\cdot009\ 118\ 016$	a_5	$-0\cdot000\ 000\ 007$	

7°. $\cos \dfrac{\pi}{2} x = \displaystyle\sum_{k=0}^{\infty} a_k T_k (2x^2 - 1) \quad (|x| \leqslant 1).$

a_0	0·472 001 216	a_3	−0·000 596 695	
a_1	−0·499 403 258	a_4	0·000 006 704	47(145)
a_2	0·027 992 080	a_5	−0·000 000 047	

8°. $\tan \dfrac{\pi}{4} x = \displaystyle\sum_{k=0}^{\infty} a_{2k+1} T_{2k+1}(x) \quad (|x| \leqslant 1).$

a_1	0·93845 067 562	a_{11}	0·00000 150 310	
a_3	0·05717 001 507	a_{13}	0·00000 010 792	
a_5	0·00406 513 598	a_{15}	0·00000 000 775	18(100)
a_7	0·00029 161 838	a_{17}	0·00000 000 056	
a_9	0·00002 093 559	a_{19}	0·00000 000 004	

9°. $x \cot \dfrac{\pi}{4} x = \displaystyle\sum_{k=0}^{\infty} a_{2k} T_{2k}(x) \quad (|x| \leqslant 1).$

a_0	1·13809 362 221	a_8	−0·00000 035 763	
a_2	−0·13659 733 195	a_{10}	−0·00000 000 575	
a_4	−0·00147 349 212	a_{12}	−0·00000 000 009	18(100)
a_6	−0·00002 243 466			

B. *Expansions in Legendre polynomials.*

10°. $\sin \dfrac{\pi}{2} x = 3 . J_{\frac{3}{2}}\left(\dfrac{\pi}{2}\right) P_1(x) - 7 . J_{\frac{7}{2}}\left(\dfrac{\pi}{2}\right) P_3(x)$

$$+ 11 . J_{\frac{11}{2}}\left(\dfrac{\pi}{2}\right) P_5(x) - \dots \quad 42(22)$$

11°. $\cos \dfrac{\pi}{2} x = 1 . J_{\frac{1}{2}}\left(\dfrac{\pi}{2}\right) P_0(x) - 5 . J_{\frac{5}{2}}\left(\dfrac{\pi}{2}\right) P_2(x)$

$$+ 9 . J_{\frac{9}{2}}\left(\dfrac{\pi}{2}\right) P_4(x) - \dots \quad 42(22)$$

k	$J_k\left(\dfrac{\pi}{2}\right)$	k	$J_k\left(\dfrac{\pi}{2}\right)$
0·5	0·63661 977 237	7·5	0·00001 082 285
1·5	0·40528 473 457	8·5	0·00000 100 778
2·5	0·13741 705 403	9·5	0·00000 008 384
3·5	0·03212 733 371	10·5	0·00000 000 630
4·5	0·00575 321 708	11·5	0·00000 000 043
5·5	0·00083 617 200	12·5	0·00000 000 003
6·5	0·00010 234 280		

$12°.$ $\sin x = \displaystyle\sum_{k=1}^{\infty} a_{2k-1} P_{2k-1}(x)$ $(|x| < 1).$

a_1	0·903 506 036 819	a_7	−0·000 007 185 201 298
a_3	−0·063 046 067 820	a_9	0·000 000 028 336 153
a_5	0·001 018 172 750	a_{11}	−0·000 000 000 071 236

$13°.$ $\cos x = \displaystyle\sum_{k=0}^{\infty} a_{2k} P_{2k}(x)$ $(|x| < 1).$

a_0	0·841 470 984 808	a_6	−0·000 093 040 172
a_2	−0·310 175 260 057	a_8	0·000 000 480 504 796
a_4	0·009 099 142 276	a_{10}	−0·000 000 001 494 193

C. Expansions in Hermite polynomials.

$14°.$ $e \sin 2x = \displaystyle\sum_{k=0}^{\infty} (-1)^k \frac{1}{(2k+1)!} H_{2k+1}(x).$ 26(412); 30

$15°.$ $e \cos 2x = \displaystyle\sum_{k=0}^{\infty} (-1)^k \frac{1}{(2k)!} H_{2k}(x).$ 26(412); 30

1.6. Polynomial approximations. $1°.$ The formulae (a)–(g) are a set of best approximations for $\sin \frac{1}{4}\pi x$, with $|x| \leqslant 1$ (cf. [78], p. 81).

(a) $\quad \sin \dfrac{\pi}{4} x \approx \displaystyle\sum_{k=0}^{1} a_{2k+1} x^{2k+1}, \quad r = 15 \times 10^{-5}.$

a_1	0·78464	a_3	−0·07768

(b) $\quad \sin \dfrac{\pi}{4} x \approx \displaystyle\sum_{k=0}^{2} a_{2k+1} x^{2k+1}, \quad r = 5 \times 10^{-7}.$

a_1	0·785 394 2	a_3	−0·080 714 0	a_5	0·002 427 1

(c) $\quad \sin \dfrac{\pi}{4} x \approx \displaystyle\sum_{k=0}^{3} a_{2k+1} x^{2k+1}, \quad r = 12 \times 10^{-10}.$

a_1	0·785 398 152 5	a_5	0·002 489 871 8
a_3	−0·080 745 367 2	a_7	−0·000 035 877 1

(d) $\quad \sin \dfrac{\pi}{4} x \approx \displaystyle\sum_{k=0}^{4} a_{2k+1} x^{2k+1}, \quad r = 17 \times 10^{-13}.$

a_1	0·785 398 163 378 8	a_7	−0·000 036 571 416 7
a_3	−0·080 745 511 815 0	a_9	0·000 000 308 563 0
a_5	0·002 490 392 478 1		

(e) $\quad \sin \dfrac{\pi}{4} x \approx \displaystyle\sum_{k=0}^{5} a_{2k+1} x^{2k+1}, \quad r = 16 \times 10^{-16}.$

a_1	0·785 398 163 397 426 5	a_7	−0·000 036 576 187 395 3
a_3	−0·080 745 512 187 669 4	a_9	0·000 000 313 333 683 3
a_5	0·002 490 394 565 299 5	a_{11}	−0·000 000 001 734 798 7

(f) $\quad \sin \dfrac{\pi}{4} x \approx \displaystyle\sum_{k=0}^{6} a_{2k+1} x^{2k+1}, \quad r = 12 \times 10^{-19}.$

a_1	0·785 398 163 397 448 291 1	a_9	0·000 000 313 361 602 011 1
a_3	−0·080 745 512 188 280 090 2	a_{11}	−0·000 000 001 757 133 649 7
a_5	0·002 490 394 570 185 250 2	a_{13}	0·000 000 000 006 872 307 0
a_7	−0·000 036 576 204 146 593 7		

$$(g) \quad \sin \frac{\pi}{4} x \approx \sum_{k=0}^{7} a_{2k+1} x^{2k+1}, \quad r = 7 \times 10^{-22}.$$

a_1	0·785 398 163 397 448 309 603 7
a_3	−0·080 745 512 188 280 781 135 0
a_5	0·002 490 394 570 192 712 152 2
a_7	−0·000 036 576 204 182 126 908 8
a_9	0·000 000 313 361 688 869 963 8
a_{11}	−0·000 000 001 757 247 355 925 5
a_{13}	0·000 000 000 006 948 111 081 5
a_{15}	−0·000 000 000 000 020 214 431 7

2°. The formulae (a)–(d) are a set of best approximations to $\sin \frac{1}{2}\pi x$ for $|x| \leqslant 1$ (cf. [49] pp. 138—140).

$$(a) \quad \sin \frac{\pi}{2} x \approx \sum_{k=0}^{2} a_{2k+1} x^{2k+1} \quad (|x| \leqslant 1),$$

$$\varepsilon = 11 \times 10^{-5} \quad (0 \leqslant x \leqslant 1 \cdot 0).$$

a_1	1·570 626 8	a_3	−0·643 229 2	a_5	0·072 710 2

$$(b) \quad \sin \frac{\pi}{2} x \approx \sum_{k=0}^{3} a_{2k+1} x^{2k+1} \quad (|x| \leqslant 1),$$

$$\varepsilon = 11 \times 10^{-7} \quad (0 \leqslant x \leqslant 1 \cdot 0)$$

a_1	1·570 794 852	a_5	0·079 487 663
a_3	−0·645 920 978	a_7	−0·004 362 476

$$(c) \quad \sin \frac{\pi}{2} x \approx \sum_{k=0}^{4} a_{2k+1} x^{2k+1} \quad (|x| \leqslant 1),$$

$$\varepsilon = 55 \times 10^{-10} \quad (0 \leqslant x \leqslant 1 \cdot 0).$$

a_1	1·570 796 318 47	a_7	—0·004 673 765 57
a_3	—0·645 963 711 06	a_9	0·000 151 484 19
a_5	0·079 689 679 28		

(d) $\sin \dfrac{\pi}{2} x \approx \sum\limits_{k=0}^{5} a_{2k+1} x^{2k+1}.$

a_1	1·570 796 326 621 43	a_7	—0·004 681 620 239 10
a_3	—0·645 964 092 644 01	a_9	0·000 160 217 134 30
a_5	0·079 699 587 286 30	a_{11}	—0·000 003 418 172 25

3°. The formulae (a)–(c) are a set of approximations to $\sin x$, for $|x| \leqslant \frac{1}{2}\pi$.

(a) $\sin x \approx \sum\limits_{k=0}^{3} a_{2k+1} x^{2k+1}, \quad r = 10^{-6}.$

a_1	0·999 999 2	a_5	0·008 313 2
a_3	—0·166 656 7	a_7	—0·000 185 2

(b) $\sin x \approx \sum\limits_{k=0}^{4} a_{2k+1} x^{2k+1}, \quad r = 6 \times 10^{-9}.$

a_1	1·000 000 002	a_7	—0·000 198 107
a_3	—0·166 666 589	a_9	0·000 002 608
a_5	0·008 333 075		

(c) $\sin x \approx \sum\limits_{k=0}^{5} a_{2k+1} x^{2k+1}.$

a_1	1·000 000 000 000	a_7	—0·000 198 407 018 014
a_3	—0·166 666 665 811	a_9	0·000 002 752 239 414 7
a_5	0·008 333 320 401	a_{11}	—0·000 000 023 840 800 41

4°. The formulae (a)–(g) are a set of best approximations to

$$\frac{\sin \frac{1}{4}\pi x}{x}$$

for $|x| \leqslant 1$ (cf. [78], p. 84).

(a) $\quad \dfrac{\sin \dfrac{\pi}{4} x}{x} \approx \displaystyle\sum_{k=0}^{1} a_{2k} x^{2k}, \quad r = 31 \times 10^{-5}.$

a_0	0·785 09	a_2	−0·078 29

(b) $\quad \dfrac{\sin \dfrac{\pi}{4} x}{x} \approx \displaystyle\sum_{k=0}^{3} a_{2k} x^{2k}, \quad r = 12 \times 10^{-7}.$

a_0	0·785 397 0	a_2	−0·080 725 2	a_4	0·002 436 1

(c) $\quad \dfrac{\sin \dfrac{\pi}{4} x}{x} \approx \displaystyle\sum_{k=0}^{3} a_{2k} x^{2k}, \quad r = 24 \times 10^{-10}.$

a_0	0·785 398 161 0	a_4	0·002 490 007 0
a_2	−0·080 745 434 8	a_6	−0·000 035 954 4

(d) $\quad \dfrac{\sin \dfrac{\pi}{4} x}{x} \approx \displaystyle\sum_{k=0}^{4} a_{2k} x^{2k}, \quad r = 34 \times 10^{-13}.$

a_0	0·785 398 163 394 1	a_6	−0·000 036 572 393 5
a_2	−0·080 745 512 018 5	a_8	0·000 000 308 997 1
a_4	0·002 490 393 210 7		

(e) $\quad \dfrac{\sin \dfrac{\pi}{4} x}{x} \approx \displaystyle\sum_{k=0}^{5} a_{2k} x^{2k}, \quad r = 34 \times 10^{-16}.$

a_0	0·785 398 163 397 444 9	a_6	−0·000 036 576 192 123 5
a_2	−0·080 745 512 188 038 8	a_8	0·000 000 313 338 411 5
a_4	0·002 490 394 567 368 1	a_{10}	−0·000 000 001 736 518 0

(f) $$\frac{\sin \dfrac{\pi}{4} x}{x} \approx \sum_{k=0}^{6} a_{2k} x^{2k}, \quad r = 25 \times 10^{-19}.$$

a_0	0·785398163397448307 1	a_8	0·000000000313361622 5530
a_2	−0·080745512188280539 6	a_{10}	−0·000000000001757150 0833
a_4	0·002490394570188845 0	a_{12}	0·000000000000006877 3634
a_6	−0·000036576204158918 9		

(g) $$\frac{\sin \dfrac{\pi}{4} x}{x} \approx \sum_{k=0}^{7} a_{2k} x^{2k}, \quad r = 15 \times 10^{-22}.$$

a_0	0·785 398 163 397 448 309 614 2
a_2	−0·080 745 512 188 280 781 527 0
a_4	0·002 490 394 570 192 716 385 8
a_6	−0·000 036 576 204 182 147 068 8
a_8	0·000 000 313 361 688 919 243 8
a_{10}	−0·000 000 001 757 247 420 437 5
a_{12}	0·000 000 000 006 948 154 089 5
a_{14}	−0·000 000 000 000 020 225 900 5

5°. $$\frac{\sin \dfrac{\pi}{2} \sqrt{x}}{\sqrt{x}} \approx \sum_{k=0}^{2} \bar{a}_k^4 x^k \quad (0 \leqslant x \leqslant 1), \quad r_4 = 0·000 137 808.$$

$\bar{a}_0^4$	1·570 643 5	$\bar{a}_1^4$	−0·643 382 57	$\bar{a}_2^4$	0·072 866 729	75(34)

6°. $$\frac{\sin \dfrac{\pi}{2} \sqrt{x}}{\sqrt{x}} \approx \sum_{k=0}^{4} \bar{a}_k^4 x^k \quad (0 \leqslant x \leqslant 1), \quad r_4 = 10^{-7}.$$

$\bar{a}_0^4$	1·570 796 3	$\bar{a}_3^4$	−0·004 675 262 7	75(34)
$\bar{a}_1^4$	−0·645 964 00	$\bar{a}_4^4$	0·000 152 015 09	
$\bar{a}_2^4$	0·079 690 922			

7°. The formulae (a)–(h) are a set of best approximations to $\cos \frac{1}{4}\pi x$ for $|x| \leqslant 1$. For formula (a) cf. [67], p. 192; and for the formulae (b)–(h) cf. [78], p. 86.

(a) $\cos \dfrac{\pi}{4} x \approx \displaystyle\sum_{k=0}^{1} a_{2k} x^{2k}$, $r = 1{\cdot}9215 \times 10^{-3}$.

a_0	0·998 078 5	a_2	−0·292 893 2

(b) $\cos \dfrac{\pi}{4} x \approx \displaystyle\sum_{k=0}^{2} a_{2k} x^{2k}$, $r = 99 \times 10^{-7}$.

a_0	0·999 990 0	a_2	−0·308 245 1	a_4	0·015 371 8

(c) $\cos \dfrac{\pi}{4} x \approx \displaystyle\sum_{k=0}^{3} a_{2k} x^{2k}$, $r = 27 \times 10^{-9}$.

a_0	0·999 999 972	a_4	0·015 849 910
a_2	−0·308 424 251	a_6	−0·000 318 877

(d) $\cos \dfrac{\pi}{4} x \approx \displaystyle\sum_{k=0}^{4} a_{2k} x^{2k}$, $r = 47 \times 10^{-12}$.

a_0	0·999 999 999 953	a_6	−0·000 325 938 600
a_2	−0·308 425 135 160	a_8	0·000 003 529 804
a_4	0·015 854 325 237		

(e) $\cos \dfrac{\pi}{4} x \approx \displaystyle\sum_{k=0}^{5} a_{2k} x^{2k}$, $r = 57 \times 10^{-15}$.

a_0	0·999 999 999 999 944	a_6	−0·000 325 991 687 588
a_2	−0·308 425 137 530 042	a_8	0·000 003 590 475 595
a_4	0·015 854 344 197 125	a_{10}	−0·000 000 024 268 543

(f) $\cos \dfrac{\pi}{4} x \approx \displaystyle\sum_{k=0}^{6} a_{2k} x^{2k}$, $r = 48 \times 10^{-18}$.

a_0	0·999 999 999 999 999 953	a_8	0·000 003 590 859 180 060
a_2	−0·308 425 137 534 037 837	a_{10}	−0·000 000 024 609 507 280
a_4	0·015 854 344 243 741 571	a_{12}	0·000 000 000 113 654 754
a_6	−0·000 325 991 886 483 649		

(g) $\cos \dfrac{\pi}{4} x \approx \sum\limits_{k=0}^{7} a_{2k} x^{2k}, \quad r = 31 \times 10^{-21}.$

a_0	0·999999999999999999970	a_8	0·00000359086044 6028362
a_2	−0·3084251375340 42452958	a_{10}	−0·0000000246113 64034253
a_4	0·0158543442438 15419342	a_{12}	0·0000000000115 005120719
a_6	−0·0003259918869 26737786	a_{14}	−0·0000000000000 385819025

(h) $\cos \dfrac{\pi}{4} x \approx \sum\limits_{k=0}^{8} a_{2k} x^{2k}, \quad r = 16 \times 10^{-24}.$

a_0	0·999 999 999 999 999 999 999 983
a_2	−0·308 425 137 534 042 456 835 958
a_4	0·015 854 344 243 815 500 783 469
a_6	−0·000 325 991 886 927 389 313 737
a_8	0·000 003 590 860 448 587 936 703
a_{10}	−0·000 000 024 611 369 494 680 064
a_{12}	0·000 000 000 115 011 573 950 464
a_{14}	−0·000 000 000 000 389 790 244 864
a_{16}	0·000 000 000 000 000 992 804 864

8°. The formulae (a)–(c) are a set of best approximations for $\cos \frac{1}{2} \pi x$.

(a) $\cos \dfrac{\pi}{2} x \approx \sum\limits_{k=0}^{2} a_{2k} x^{2k}, \quad r = 5 \cdot 968 \times 10^{-4} \quad (|x| \leqslant 1).$

a_0	0·999 4032	a_2	−1·222 7967	a_4	0·223 9903

67(193)

(b) $\cos \dfrac{\pi}{2} x \approx \sum\limits_{k=0}^{4} a_{2k} x^{2k} \quad (0 \leqslant x \leqslant 1), \quad r = 5 \times 10^{-8}.$

a_0	0·999 999 95	a_6	−0·020 810 46
a_2	−1·233 698 19	a_8	0·000 858 11
a_4	0·253 650 64		

11(154)

(c) $\cos \dfrac{\pi}{2} x \approx \displaystyle\sum_{k=0}^{5} a_{2k} x^{2k}, \quad r = 7 \times 10^{-9} \quad (|x| \leqslant 1).$

a_0	0·999 999 999 8	a_6	−0·020 862 656 4
a_2	−1·233 700 533 6	a_8	0·000 917 670 3
a_4	0·253 669 314 7	a_{10}	−0·000 023 788 8

60(88)

9°. The formulae (a) and (b) are approximations for $\cos x$.

(a) $\cos x \approx \displaystyle\sum_{k=0}^{4} \bar{a}_k x^k \quad (|x| \leqslant 1), \quad r = 4·295 \times 10^{-5}.$

$\bar{a}_0$	0·999 958 87	$\bar{a}_3$	$1·159 \times 10^{-6}$
$\bar{a}_1$	$−2·5 \times 10^{-7}$	$\bar{a}_4$	0·039 632 11
$\bar{a}_2$	−0·499 246 63		

75(33)

(b) $\cos x \approx \displaystyle\sum_{k=0}^{5} a_{2k} x^{2k} \quad (|x| < 1), \quad r = 2 \times 10^{-9}.$

a_0	1·000 000 000 000	a_6	−0·001 388 885 683
a_2	−0·499 999 999 942	a_8	0·000 024 795 132
a_4	0·041 666 665 950	a_{10}	−0·000 000 269 591

10°. The formulae (a)–(d) are approximations for $\tan \frac{1}{4}\pi x$ and $\tan x$.

(a) $\tan \dfrac{\pi}{4} x \approx \displaystyle\sum_{k=0}^{8} a_{2k+1} x^{2k+1} \quad (|x| < 1), \quad r = 2 \times 10^{-10}.$

a_1	0·785 398 164 100	a_{11}	0·000 564 878 935
a_3	0·161 490 982 898	a_{13}	0·000 273 110 441
a_5	0·039 847 028 543	a_{15}	0·000 027 981 368
a_7	0·009 943 148 779	a_{17}	0·000 036 452 696
a_9	0·002 510 214 922		

(b) $\tan \dfrac{\pi}{4} x \approx \displaystyle\sum_{k=0}^{9} a_{2k+1} x^{2k+1}$ $(|x| < 1)$.

a_1	0·785 398 163 34	a_{11}	0·000 635 623 83
a_3	0·161 491 028 48	a_{13}	0·000 128 272 67
a_5	0·039 846 228 68	a_{15}	0·000 071 528 28
a_7	0·009 949 562 98	a_{17}	0·000 013 303 15
a_9	0·002 482 421 62	a_{19}	0·000 010 475 27

18(117)

(c) $\tan x \approx \displaystyle\sum_{k=0}^{5} a_{2k+1} x^{2k+1},$ $r = 2 \cdot 2 \times 10^{-7}$ $\left(|x| \leqslant \dfrac{\pi}{4}\right).$

a_1	0·999 999 8	a_7	0·057 164 8
a_3	0·333 359 1	a_9	0·012 559 5
a_5	0·132 854 1	a_{11}	0·020 373 2

(d) $\tan x \approx \displaystyle\sum_{k=0}^{6} a_{2k+1} x^{2k+1},$ $r = 2 \times 10^{-8}$ $\left(|x| \leqslant \dfrac{\pi}{4}\right).$

a_1	1·000 000 02	a_9	0·024 570 96
a_3	0·333 330 82	a_{11}	0·002 940 45
a_5	0·133 397 62	a_{13}	0·009 473 24
a_7	0·059 358 36		

11°. $\cot \dfrac{\pi}{4} x \approx \dfrac{a_{-1}}{x} + \displaystyle\sum_{k=0}^{4} a_{2k+1} x^{2k+1},$ $r = 2 \times 10^{-10}$ $(|x| < 1).$

a_{-1}	1·273 239 544 735	a_5	−0·000 632 697 788
a_1	−0·261 799 389 768	a_7	−0·000 038 528 582
a_3	−0·010 766 029 173	a_9	−0·000 002 899 234

12°. $\dfrac{1}{x} - \cot x \approx \displaystyle\sum_{k=0}^{2} a_{2k+1} x^{2k+1},$ $r = 10^{-6}$ $\left(|x| \leqslant \dfrac{\pi}{4}\right).$

a_1	0·333 335	a_3	0·022 173	a_5	0·002 327

$13°. \quad \dfrac{1}{x} - \cot x \approx \sum_{k=0}^{3} a_{2k+1} x^{2k+1},$

$$r = 2{\cdot}8 \times 10^{-8} \quad \left(|x| \leqslant \frac{\pi}{4}\right).$$

a_1	0·333 333 22	a_5	0·002 102 83
a_3	0·022 224 45	a_7	0·000 242 24

14°. The formulae (a)–(d) are a set of best polynomial approximations to $x \cot x$ for $|x| \leqslant \frac{1}{4}\pi$, with $y = (4x/\pi)^2$. They may be used for finding

$$\tan x = \frac{x}{x \cot x}$$

with an error not exceeding $1 \cdot 3r$ (cf. [73], p. 113).

(a) $x \cot x \approx 1{\cdot}0012 - 0{\cdot}2146y, \quad r = 1{\cdot}2 \times 10^{-3}.$

(b) $x \cot x \approx \sum_{k=0}^{2} a_k y^k, \quad r = 1{\cdot}8 \times 10^{-5}.$

a_0	0·999 983	a_1	−0·205 308	a_2	−0·009 258

(c) $x \cot x \approx \sum_{k=0}^{3} a_k y^k, \quad r = 2{\cdot}9 \times 10^{-7}.$

a_0	1·000 000 28	a_2	−0·008 412 46
a_1	−0·205 625 53	a_3	−0·000 563 84

(d) $x \cot x \approx \sum_{k=0}^{4} a_k y^k, \quad r = 6 \times 10^{-9}.$

a_0	0·999 999 994	a_3	−0·000 491 943
a_1	−0·205 616 537	a_4	−0·000 035 949
a_2	−0·008 457 395		

1.7. Continued fraction expansions.

1°. $\sin x = \dfrac{x}{1} + \dfrac{x^2}{6} - \dfrac{7x^2}{10} + \dfrac{11x^2}{98}$

$\dfrac{0}{1}\quad \dfrac{x}{1}\quad \dfrac{6x}{6+x^2}\quad \dfrac{60x-7x^3}{60+3x^2}\quad \dfrac{5880x-620x^3}{5880+360x^2+11x^4}$

$$-\frac{551x^2}{198}-\dots$$

34(165)

2°. $\sin x = x - \dfrac{x^3}{6} + \dfrac{3x^2}{10} - \dfrac{11x^2}{42}$

$\dfrac{x}{1}\quad \dfrac{6x-x^3}{6}\quad \dfrac{60x-7x^3}{60+3x^2}\quad \dfrac{2520x-360x^3+11x^5}{2520+60x^2}$

$$+\frac{25x^2}{66}-\dots \qquad 34(165)$$

$$\frac{166320x-22260x^3+551x^5}{166320+5460x^2+75x^4}$$

3°. $\cos x = 1 - \dfrac{x^2}{2} + \dfrac{x^2}{6} - \dfrac{3x^2}{10}$

$\dfrac{1}{1}\quad \dfrac{2-x^2}{2}\quad \dfrac{12-5x^2}{12+x}\quad \dfrac{120-5x^2+3x^4}{120+4x^2}$

$$+\frac{13x^2}{126}-\dots \qquad 34(168)$$

$$\frac{15120-6900x^2+313x^4}{15120+660x^2+13x^4}$$

4°. $\cos x = \dfrac{1}{1} + \dfrac{x^2}{2} - \dfrac{5x^2}{6} + \dfrac{3x^2}{50}$

$\dfrac{0}{1}\quad \dfrac{1}{1}\quad \dfrac{2}{2+x^2}\quad \dfrac{12-5x^2}{12+x^2}\quad \dfrac{600-244x^2}{600+56x^2+3x^4}$

$$-\frac{313x^2}{126}+\dots \qquad 34(167,\ 168)$$

$5°.\ \tan x = \dfrac{x}{1} - \dfrac{x^2}{3} - \dfrac{x^2}{5} - \dfrac{x^2}{7}$

$$\dfrac{0}{1} \quad \dfrac{x}{1} \quad \dfrac{3x}{3-x^2} \quad \dfrac{15x-x^3}{16-6x^2} \quad \dfrac{105x-10x^3}{105-45x^2+x^4}$$

$$- \ \dfrac{x^2}{9} \qquad - \ldots - \dfrac{x^2}{2n+1} - \ldots \qquad 34(120)$$

$$\dfrac{945x-105x^3+x^5}{945-420x^2+15x^4}$$

For $|x| \leqslant \frac{1}{4}\pi$ we have $|r_7(x)| < 10^{-10}$.   34(120); 11

$6°.\ \tan x = x + \dfrac{15x^3}{15-7x^2} + \dfrac{x^2}{1} + \dfrac{9x^2}{315-28x^2} + \dfrac{5x^2}{1}$

$+ \dfrac{13x^2}{1287-44x^2} + \ldots + \dfrac{(4n+1)x^2}{(4n-3)(4n-1)(4n+1)-4(4n-1)x^2}$

$$+ \dfrac{(4n-3)x^2}{1} + \ldots \qquad 34(122)$$

1.8. Rational approximations.

$1°.\ \sin x \approx \dfrac{2\left[\dfrac{x}{3}\displaystyle\sum_{k=0}^{3}(-1)^k b_{2k}\left(\dfrac{x}{3}\right)^{2k}\right]\left[\displaystyle\sum_{k=0}^{3}(-1)^k a_{2k}\left(\dfrac{x}{3}\right)^{2k}\right]}{\left[\displaystyle\sum_{k=0}^{3}(-1)^k a_{2k}\left(\dfrac{x}{3}\right)^{2k}\right]^2 + \left[\dfrac{x}{3}\displaystyle\sum_{k=0}^{3}(-1)^k b_{2k}\left(\dfrac{x}{3}\right)^{2k}\right]^2}$

$$(|x| \leqslant \pi), \quad r = 6 \times 10^{-9}$$

The values of a_{2k} and b_{2k} are given in Ch. II, § 1.6, 1°.
The expressions

$$\dfrac{x}{3}\sum_{k=0}^{3}(-1)^k b_{2k}\left(\dfrac{x}{3}\right)^{2k} \quad \text{and} \quad \sum_{k=0}^{3}(-1)^k a_{2k}\left(\dfrac{x}{3}\right)^{2k}$$

are very good approximations to $\sin \frac{1}{2}x$ and $\cos \frac{1}{2}x$ respectively.

$2°.\ \cos x \approx \dfrac{\left[\displaystyle\sum_{k=0}^{3}(-1)^k a_{2k}\left(\dfrac{x}{3}\right)^{2k}\right]^2 - \left[\dfrac{x}{3}\displaystyle\sum_{k=0}^{3}(-1)^k b_{2k}\left(\dfrac{x}{3}\right)^{2k}\right]^2}{\left[\displaystyle\sum_{k=0}^{3}(-1)^k a_{2k}\left(\dfrac{x}{3}\right)^{2k}\right]^2 + \left[\dfrac{x}{3}\displaystyle\sum_{k=0}^{3}(-1)^k b_{2k}\left(\dfrac{x}{3}\right)^{2k}\right]^2}$

$$(|x| \leqslant \pi), \quad r = 10^{-9}$$

The values of a_{2k} and b_{2k} are given in Ch. II, § 1.6, 1°. 60(83)

$3°.$ $\cos x \approx \dfrac{\sum\limits_{k=0}^{6} \bar{a}_k x^k}{g(x)}$ $(|x| \leqslant 1)$, $r = 2{\cdot}58486 \times 10^{-3}$,

$g(x) = 1 + 2{\cdot}828421929x^2 - 2x^4 + 2{\cdot}828421929x^6 + x^8.$

$\bar{a}_0$	1·002 584 8	$\bar{a}_4$	1·427 635 5	
$\bar{a}_1$	3×10^{-7}	$\bar{a}_5$	$3{\cdot}2 \times 10^{-7}$	75(33)
$\bar{a}_2$	2·201 263 5	$\bar{a}_6$	0·610 635 04	
$\bar{a}_3$	2×10^{-7}			

$4°.$ $z(x) = \cos \dfrac{\pi}{1 + x^{\frac{1}{2}}} \approx \dfrac{-1 - 4x + 5x^2}{1 + 8x + 6x^2},$

$$r = 0{\cdot}003 \quad (0 \leqslant x \leqslant 1). \quad 48(68)$$

Comment. It follows from 4° that $z(x^{-1}) = -z(x)$, so that the formula may be used also for finding the values of the function for $1 \leqslant x < \infty$.

$5°.$ $z(x) = \cos \dfrac{\pi}{1 + x^{\frac{1}{2}}} \approx \dfrac{-1 - 4{\cdot}828\eta + 7{\cdot}866\eta^2 - 2{\cdot}038\eta^3}{1 + 5{\cdot}560\eta - 4{\cdot}985\eta^2 + 0{\cdot}385\eta^3},$

$\eta = \dfrac{x}{0{\cdot}16 + 0{\cdot}84x}$ $r = 0{\cdot}00017$ $(0 \leqslant x \leqslant 1)$.   50(47)

$6°.$ $\tan x \approx \dfrac{2\left[\dfrac{x}{3} \sum\limits_{k=0}^{3} (-1)^k b_{2k} \left(\dfrac{x}{3}\right)^{2k}\right]\left[\sum\limits_{k=0}^{3} (-1)^k a_{2k} \left(\dfrac{x}{3}\right)^{2k}\right]}{\left[\sum\limits_{k=0}^{3} (-1)^k a_{2k} \left(\dfrac{x}{3}\right)^{2k}\right]^2 - \left[\dfrac{x}{3} \sum\limits_{k=0}^{3} (-1)^k b_{2k} \left(\dfrac{x}{3}\right)^{2k}\right]^2}$

$$(|x| \leqslant \pi), \quad r = 7 \times 10^{-8}.$$

The values of a_{2k} and b_{2k} are given in Ch. II, § 1.6, 1°. 60(83, 84)

$7°.$ $\tan x \approx \dfrac{945x - 105x^3 + x^5}{945 - 420x^2 + 15x^4}$, $r = 2 \times 10^{-8}$ $\left(|x| \leqslant \dfrac{\pi}{4}\right).$

34(162)

8°. $\tan \pi x \approx \dfrac{x \sum\limits_{k=0}^{2} a_k x^{2k}}{\sum\limits_{k=0}^{3} b_k x^{2k}}$ $\qquad (|x| < 1)$.

a_0	0·318 309 886 184	b_0	0·101 321 183 642
a_1	−0·380 799 109 526	b_1	−0·454 545 454 545
a_2	0·062 638 942 788	b_2	0·199 385 947 497
		b_3	−0·009 370 763 928

9°. $2 \tan \dfrac{x}{2} = \dfrac{\dfrac{x}{\pi}}{\sum\limits_{k=0}^{4} a_k \left(\dfrac{x}{\pi}\right)^{2k}}$ $\qquad \left(0 \leqslant x \leqslant \dfrac{\pi}{4}\right)$. $\qquad$ 7(7)

a_0	1·273 239 544 731	a_3	0·000 009 877 325
a_1	0·065 449 846 718	a_4	0·000 000 158 336
a_2	0·000 672 881 123		

7(8)

10°. $\tan x = x \dfrac{a_0 + (a_1 + a_2 x^2) x^2}{a_0 + [a_3 + (a_4 + a_5 x^2) x^2] x^2}$ $\qquad \left(0 \leqslant x < \dfrac{\pi}{4}\right)$.

a_0	0·500 000 000	a_3	−0·227 272 727
a_1	−0·060 606 060	a_4	0·010 101 010
a_2	0·001 010 101	a_5	−0·000 048 100

3(290)

1.9. Formulae for combinations of trigonometric functions with hyperbolic and exponential functions.

1°. $y_1 = \cosh x \cos x = \sum\limits_{k=0}^{\infty} \dfrac{(-4)^k x^{4k}}{(4k)!}$.

$y_1 \approx \sum\limits_{k=0}^{3} a_{4k} x^{4k}$ $\qquad \left(|x| \leqslant \dfrac{\pi}{2}\right)$, $\qquad r = 10^{-10}$.

a_0	0·999 999 999 9	a_8	0·014 708 143 4
a_4	−1·014 678 027 4	a_{12}	−0·000 030 116 0

60(95)

2°. $y_2 = \cosh x \sin x + \sinh x \cos x = 2 \sum_{k=0}^{\infty} \dfrac{(-4)^k x^{4k+1}}{(4k+1)!}$.

$$y_2 \approx \sum_{k=0}^{3} a_{4k+1} x^{4k+1} \quad \left(|x| \leqslant \frac{\pi}{2}\right), \quad r = 2 \times 10^{-10}.$$

a_1	3·141 592 653 6	a_9	0·005 134 114 0	60(95)
a_5	−0·637 541 009 2	a_{13}	0·000 007 279 8	

3°. $y_3 = \sinh x \sin x = 2 \sum_{k=0}^{\infty} \dfrac{(-4)^k x^{4k+2}}{(4k+2)!}$.

$$y_3 \approx \sum_{k=0}^{2} a_{4k+2} x^{4k+2} \quad \left(|x| \leqslant \frac{\pi}{2}\right), \quad r < 10^{-8}.$$

a_2	2·467 401 010 8	a_{10}	0·000 805 034 8	60(95)
a_6	−0·166 907 130 8			

4°. $y_4 = \cosh x \sin x - \sinh x \cos x = 4 \sum_{k=0}^{\infty} \dfrac{(-4)^k x^{4k+3}}{(4k+3)!}$.

$$y_4 \approx \sum_{k=0}^{2} a_{4k+3} x^{4k+3} \quad \left(|x| \leqslant \frac{\pi}{2}\right), \quad r = 3 \times 10^{-9}.$$

a_3	2·583 856 371 2	a_{11}	0·000 230 026 4	60(95)
a_7	−0·074 907 916 4			

5°. $e^{\frac{\pi}{2}x} \sin \dfrac{\pi}{2} x = \dfrac{1}{2}(y_2 + y_4) + y_3$.

The values of y_2, y_3, y_4 are given in 2°, 3° and 4°.   60(96)

6°. $e^{\frac{\pi}{2}x} \cos \dfrac{\pi}{2} x = \dfrac{1}{2}(y_2 - y_4) + y_1$.

The values of y_1, y_2, y_4 are given in 1°, 2° and 4°.   60(96)

§ 2. Inverse trigonometric functions

2.1. General information. 1°. *Definition of the inverse trigonometric functions.*

$$\text{If } x = \sin y, \text{ then } y = \text{Arcsin} x;$$

$$\text{if } x = \cos y, \text{ then } y = \text{Arccos} x;$$

$$\text{if } x = \tan y, \text{ then } y = \text{Arctan} x; \text{ and}$$

$$\text{if } x = \cot y, \text{ then } y = \text{Arccot} x.$$

The functions Arcsin x and Arccos x have real values if $-1 \leqslant x \leqslant +1$. The functions Arctan x and Arccot x have real values for any real x. The inverse trigonometric functions are multivalued functions.

The *principal values* of the inverse trigonometric functions are denoted by arcsin x, arccos x, arctan x and arccot x. They are related to all other values of the corresponding functions by the relations:

$$\text{Arcsin } x = n\pi + (-1)^n \arcsin x,$$

$$\text{Arccos } x = 2n\pi \pm \arccos x,$$

$$\text{Arctan } x = \arctan x + n\pi,$$

$$\text{Arccot } x = \text{arccot } x + n\pi.$$

The domain of definition of the function arcsin x is the interval $[-1, 1]$, and its range of values is the interval $[-\tfrac{1}{2}\pi, \tfrac{1}{2}\pi]$.

The domain of definition of the function arccos x is the interval $[-1, 1]$, and its range of values is the interval $[0, \pi]$.

The domain of definition of the function arctan x is the interval $(-\infty, +\infty)$, and its range of values is the interval $(-\tfrac{1}{2}\pi, \tfrac{1}{2}\pi)$.

The domain of definition of the function arccot x is the interval $(-\infty, +\infty)$, and its range of values is the interval $(0, \pi)$.

$$\lim_{x \to +\infty} \arctan x = \tfrac{1}{2}\pi, \quad \lim_{x \to -\infty} \arctan x = -\tfrac{1}{2}\pi;$$

$$\lim_{x \to +\infty} \text{arccot } x = 0, \quad \lim_{x \to -\infty} \text{arccot } x = \pi.$$

2°. *Functional relations.*

Both arc sin x and arc tan x are odd functions.

$$\arcsin x = \text{sign } x \cdot \arcsin |x|.$$

$$\arctan x = \operatorname{sign} x \cdot \arctan |x|.$$
$$\arccos (-x) = \pi - \arccos x.$$
$$\operatorname{arccot} (-x) = \pi - \operatorname{arccot} x.$$

3°. *Relations between the various inverse trigonometric functions.*

(a) $\arcsin x + \arccos x = \dfrac{\pi}{2}.$ 22(198)

(b) $\arctan x + \operatorname{arccot} x = \dfrac{\pi}{2}.$ 22(198)

(c) $\arcsin x = \operatorname{sign} x \arccos \sqrt{1 - x^2}$

$$= \operatorname{sign} x \left(\frac{\pi}{2} - \arcsin \sqrt{1 - x^2} \right);$$ 22(201)

where this latter formula holds over the interval $\left(-\frac{1}{2} \sqrt{2}, \frac{1}{2} \sqrt{2} \right).$

(d) $\arcsin x = \arctan \dfrac{x}{\sqrt{1 - x^2}}$ $(|x| < 1).$ 22(200)

(e) $\arcsin x = \operatorname{arccot} \dfrac{\sqrt{1 - x^2}}{x} - \pi$ $(-1 \leqslant x < 0);$

$$= \operatorname{arccot} \frac{\sqrt{1 - x^2}}{x}$$ $(0 < x \leqslant 1).$ 22(203)

(f) $\arccos x = \pi - \arcsin \sqrt{1 - x^2}$ $(-1 \leqslant x \leqslant 0);$

$$= \arcsin \sqrt{1 - x^2}$$ $(0 \leqslant x \leqslant 1).$ 22(202)

(g) $\arccos x = \pi + \arctan \dfrac{\sqrt{1 - x^2}}{x}$ $(-1 \leqslant x < 0);$

$$= \arctan \frac{\sqrt{1 - x^2}}{x}$$ $(0 < x \leqslant 1).$ 22(202)

(h) $\arccos x = \operatorname{arccot} \dfrac{x}{\sqrt{1 - x^2}}$ $(-1 \leqslant x < 1).$ 22(200)

(i) $\arctan x = \arcsin \dfrac{x}{\sqrt{1 + x^2}}$ $(|x| < \infty).$ 22(200)

(j) $\arctan x = -\arccos \dfrac{1}{\sqrt{1+x^2}}$ $(x \leqslant 0)$;

$\qquad = \arccos \dfrac{1}{\sqrt{1+x^2}}$ $(x \geqslant 0)$.   22(202)

(k) $\arctan x = \operatorname{arc\,cot} \dfrac{1}{x} - \pi$ $(x < 0)$;

$\qquad = \operatorname{arc\,cot} \dfrac{1}{x}$ $(x > 0)$.   22(202)

(l) $\arctan x = \operatorname{sign} x \left(\dfrac{\pi}{2} - \arctan \dfrac{1}{|x|} \right)$

where this latter formula may be used for reduction of $\arctan x$ to the interval $(-1, 1)$.   18(110)

(m) $\operatorname{arc\,cot} x = \pi - \arcsin \dfrac{1}{\sqrt{1+x^2}}$ $(x < 0)$;

$\qquad = \arcsin \dfrac{1}{\sqrt{1+x^2}}$ $(x > 0)$.   22(203)

(n) $\operatorname{arc\,cot} x = \arccos \dfrac{x}{\sqrt{1+x^2}}$.   26(61)

(o) $\operatorname{arc\,cot} x = \pi + \arctan \dfrac{1}{x}$ $(x < 0)$;

$\qquad = \arctan \dfrac{1}{x}$ $(x > 0)$.   22(203)

(p) $\arctan x + \arctan \dfrac{1}{x} = -\dfrac{\pi}{2}$ $(x < 0)$;

$\qquad = \dfrac{\pi}{2}$ $(x > 0)$.   26(63); 9

(q) $\arctan x + \arctan \dfrac{1-x}{1+x} = -\dfrac{3}{4}\pi$ $(x < -1)$;

$\qquad = \dfrac{\pi}{4}$ $(x > -1)$;   26(63)

and since

$$\frac{|1-x|}{|1+x|} < 1$$

for $|x| > 1$, this latter formula leads to the interval $(-1, 1)$.

(r) There is an additional relation

$$\arcsin x = 3 \arcsin \overline{x},$$

where $\overline{x}$ is the root of the equation

$$4\overline{x}^3 - 3\overline{x} + x = 0, \qquad (*)$$

$$0{\cdot}966 \leqslant x \leqslant 1,$$

$$0{\cdot}4227 \leqslant \overline{x} \leqslant 0{\cdot}5.$$

This formula may be used for computing $\arcsin x$ when x is close to 1, solving the equation (*) by Newton's method (cf. [60], p. 92).

4°. *Trigonometric operations upon inverse trigonometric functions.*

$\sin(\arcsin x) = x$	$\cos(\arcsin x) = \sqrt{1-x^2}$
$\sin(\arccos x) = \sqrt{1-x^2}$	$\cos(\arccos x) = x$
$\sin(\arctan x) = \dfrac{x}{\sqrt{1+x^2}}$	$\cos(\arctan x) = \dfrac{1}{\sqrt{1+x^2}}$
$\sin(\arccot x) = \dfrac{1}{\sqrt{1+x^2}}$	$\cos(\arccot x) = \dfrac{x}{\sqrt{1+x^2}}$
$\tan(\arcsin x) = \dfrac{x}{\sqrt{1-x^2}}$	$\cot(\arcsin x) = \dfrac{\sqrt{1-x^2}}{x}$
$\tan(\arccos x) = \dfrac{\sqrt{1-x^2}}{x}$	$\cot(\arccos x) = \dfrac{x}{\sqrt{1-x^2}}$
$\tan(\arctan x) = x$	$\cot(\arctan x) = \dfrac{1}{x}$
$\tan(\arccot x) = \dfrac{1}{x}$	$\cot(\arccot x) = x$

22(195)

5°. *The principal values of the inverse trigonometric functions of the corresponding trigonometric functions.* These are:

(a) $\arcsin(\sin x) = x - 2n\pi \quad \left[2n\pi - \dfrac{\pi}{2} \leqslant x \leqslant 2n\pi + \dfrac{\pi}{2}\right];$

$\qquad = -x + (2n+1)\pi \left[(2n+1)\pi - \dfrac{\pi}{2} \leqslant x \leqslant (2n+1)\pi + \dfrac{\pi}{2}\right].$

(b) $\arccos(\cos x) = x - 2n\pi \quad [2n\pi \leqslant x \leqslant (2n+1)\pi];$

$\qquad = -x + 2(n+1)\pi \quad [(2n+1)\pi \leqslant x \leqslant 2(n+1)\pi].$

(c) $\arctan(\tan x) = x - n\pi \quad \left[n\pi - \dfrac{\pi}{2} < x < n\pi + \dfrac{\pi}{2}\right].$

(d) $\operatorname{arc cot}(\cot x) = x - n\pi \quad [n\pi < (n+1)\pi].$ $\qquad$ 26(60)

6°. *Connection between the inverse trigonometric functions, the inverse hyperbolic functions and the logarithmic function.*

(a) $\arcsin x = \dfrac{1}{i} \ln\left(ix + \sqrt{1 - x^2}\right) = \dfrac{1}{i} \operatorname{Arc sinh}(ix).$

(b) $\arccos x = \dfrac{1}{i} \ln\left(x + \sqrt{x^2 - 1}\right) = \dfrac{1}{i} \operatorname{Arc cosh} x.$

(c) $\arctan x = \dfrac{1}{2i} \ln \dfrac{1 + ix}{1 - ix} = \dfrac{1}{i} \operatorname{Arc tanh}(ix).$

(d) $\operatorname{arc ctg} x = \dfrac{1}{2i} \ln \dfrac{ix - 1}{ix + 1} = i \operatorname{Arc coth}(ix).$ $\qquad$ 26(60)

2.2. Power series expansions.

1°. $\arcsin x = \dfrac{\pi}{2} - \arccos x$

$\qquad = x + \dfrac{1}{2.3} x^3 + \dfrac{1.3}{2.4.5} x^5 + \dfrac{1.3.5}{2.4.6.7} x^7 + \ldots$

$\qquad = \displaystyle\sum_{k=0}^{\infty} \dfrac{(2k)!}{2^{2k}(k!)^2(2k+1)} x^{2k+1}$

$\qquad = xF\left(\dfrac{1}{2}, \dfrac{1}{2}; \dfrac{3}{2}; x^2\right) \ (|x| < 1).$ $\qquad$ 26(64); 32(479)

$2°.$ $\arccos x = \sqrt{\dfrac{1-x}{2}} \left[2 + \displaystyle\sum_{k=1}^{\infty} \dfrac{(2k-1)!!}{(2k)!!} \dfrac{(1-x)^k}{2^k \left(k + \dfrac{1}{2} \right)} \right].$

$3°.$ $\arctan x = \displaystyle\sum_{k=0}^{\infty} \dfrac{(-1)^k x^{2k+1}}{2k+1}$ $(|x| < 1).$ 26(64); 32(479)

$4°.$ $\arctan x = \dfrac{x}{1+x^2} \displaystyle\sum_{k=0}^{\infty} \dfrac{2^{2k}(k!)^2}{(2k+1)!} \left(\dfrac{x^2}{1+x^2} \right)^k$

$(|x| < \infty).$ 26(64); 39(122)

$5°.$ $\arctan x = \dfrac{\pi}{2} - \displaystyle\sum_{k=0}^{\infty} (-1)^k \dfrac{1}{(2k+1)x^{2k+1}}$

$(|x| \geqslant 1).$ 26(64); 39(122)

$6°.$ $\operatorname{arcsec} x = \dfrac{\pi}{2} - \dfrac{1}{x} - \dfrac{1}{2.3x^3} - \dfrac{1.3}{2.4.5x^5} - \cdots$

$= \dfrac{\pi}{2} - \displaystyle\sum_{k=0}^{\infty} \dfrac{(2k)! \, x^{-(2k+1)}}{(k!)^2 . 2^{2k} . (2k+1)}$

$= \dfrac{\pi}{2} - \dfrac{1}{x} F\left(\dfrac{1}{2}, \dfrac{1}{2}; \dfrac{3}{2}; \dfrac{1}{x^2} \right)$

$(|x| > 1).$ 26(64); 39(122)

$7°.$ $(\arcsin x)^2 = \displaystyle\sum_{k=0}^{\infty} \dfrac{2^{2k}(k!)^2 x^{2k+2}}{(2k+1)!(k+1)}$

$(|x| < 1).$ 26(64); 39(122)

$8°.$ $(\arcsin x)^3 = x^3 + \dfrac{3!}{5!} 3^2 \left(1 + \dfrac{1}{3^2} \right) x^5$

$+ \dfrac{3!}{7!} . 3^2 . 5^2 \left(1 + \dfrac{1}{3^2} + \dfrac{1}{5^2} \right) x^7 + \cdots$

$(|x| \leqslant 1).$ 26(65); 39(122); 43(188)

$9°.$ $e^{\arcsin x} = 1 + x + \dfrac{x^2}{2!} + \dfrac{2x^3}{3!} + \dfrac{5x^4}{4!} + \cdots$

26(37); 39(126)

$10°.$ $e^{\operatorname{arc} \tan x} = 1 + x + \dfrac{x^2}{2!} - \dfrac{x^3}{3!} + \dfrac{7x^4}{4!} - \cdots$

26(37); 39(126)

2.3. Expansions in polynomials, orthogonal and otherwise.

A. *Expansions in Chebyshev polynomials.*

$1°.$ $\arcsin x = \displaystyle\sum_{k=0}^{\infty} a_{2k+1} T_{2k+1}\left(\sqrt{2}x\right)$ $\left(|x| \leqslant \sin \dfrac{\pi}{4}\right).$

a_1	0·762 759 763 50	a_{13}	0·000 000 312 58
a_3	0·020 869 237 57	a_{15}	0·000 000 043 09
a_5	0·001 586 931 63	a_{17}	0·000 000 006 11
a_7	0·000 160 822 75	a_{19}	0·000 000 000 88
a_9	0·000 018 691 07	a_{21}	0·000 000 000 13
a_{11}	0·000 002 354 06	a_{23}	0·000 000 000 02

18(108)

$2°.$ $\arcsin x = \displaystyle\sum_{k=0}^{\infty} a_{2k+1} T_{2k+1}\left(x \operatorname{cosec} \dfrac{\pi}{8}\right)$ $\left(|x| \leqslant \sin \dfrac{\pi}{8}\right).$

a_1	0·390 105 751 22	a_9	0·000 000 028 59
a_3	0·002 547 040 01	a_{11}	0·000 000 000 83
a_5	0·000 045 198 32	a_{13}	0·000 000 000 03
a_7	0·000 001 062 70		

18(108)

$3°.$ $\arcsin x = x \displaystyle\sum_{k=0}^{\infty} a_k T_k (4x^2 - 1)$ $\left(|x| \leqslant \dfrac{\sqrt{2}}{2}\right),$

$\arccos x = \dfrac{\pi}{2} - x \displaystyle\sum_{k=0}^{\infty} a_k T_k (4x^2 - 1)$ $\left(0 \leqslant x \leqslant \dfrac{\sqrt{2}}{2}\right).$ 47(145)

a_0	1·051 231 959	a_5	0·000 005 881
a_1	0·054 946 487	a_6	0·000 000 777
a_2	0·004 080 631	a_7	0·000 000 107
a_3	0·000 407 890	a_8	0·000 000 015
a_4	0·000 046 985	a_9	0·000 000 002

4°. $\arctan x = 2 \sum\limits_{k=0}^{\infty} (-1)^k \dfrac{p^{2k+1}}{2k+1} \cdot T_{2k+1}(x)$

$$= \sum_{k=0}^{\infty} a_{2k+1}^{\S} T_{2k+1}(x) \quad (|x| \leqslant 1),$$

$$\frac{2p}{1-p^2} = 1, \quad p = \sqrt{2} - 1 \approx 0 \cdot 41 \dots , \qquad 19(14)$$

$$a_{2k+1} = (-1)^k \frac{2p^{2k+1}}{2k+1}.$$

a_1	0·828 427 124 75	a_{13}	0·000 001 625 56
a_3	−0·047 378 541 24	a_{15}	−0·000 000 241 71
a_5	0·004 877 323 53	a_{17}	0·000 000 036 59
a_7	−0·000 597 726 02	a_{19}	−0·000 000 005 61
a_9	0·000 079 763 89	a_{21}	0·000 000 000 84
a_{11}	−0·000 011 197 08	a_{23}	−0·000 000 000 12

18(111)

5°. $\arctan x = \sum\limits_{k=0}^{\infty} a_{2k+1} T_{2k+1}\left(x \cot \dfrac{\pi}{8} \right) \quad \left(|x| \leqslant \tan \dfrac{\pi}{8} \right).$

a_1	0·397 824 734 76	a_9	0·000 000 108 33
a_3	−0·005 246 795 04	a_{11}	−0·000 000 003 51
a_5	0·000 124 557 22	a_{13}	0·000 000 000 12
a_7	−0·000 003 520 18		

18(111)

6°. $\arctan x = x \sum\limits_{k=0}^{\infty} a_k T_k (2x^2 - 1) \quad (|x| \leqslant 1).$

When $|x| > 1$, the formula $\arctan x = \frac{1}{2}\pi - \arctan(1/x)$ should be used.

a_0	0·881 373 587	a_6	0·000 003 821
a_1	−0·105 892 925	a_7	−0·000 000 570
a_2	0·011 135 843	a_8	0·000 000 086
a_3	−0·001 381 195	a_9	−0·000 000 013
a_4	0·000 185 743	a_{10}	0·000 000 002
a_5	−0·000 026 215		

47(145)

$7°.\ \arctan x = \dfrac{\pi}{4} + 2 \displaystyle\sum_{k=0}^{\infty} \dfrac{(-1)^k \left(\sqrt{2}-1\right)^{2k+1}}{2k+1}\, T_{2k+1}\left(\dfrac{x-1}{x+1}\right)$

$$(0 \leqslant x < \infty). \qquad 63(16)$$

$8°.\ \arctan \dfrac{x}{a} = 2 \displaystyle\sum_{k=0}^{\infty} \dfrac{(-1)^k R^{2k+1}}{2k+1}\, T_{2k+1}(x),$

$$R = (a^2+1)^{\frac{1}{2}} \qquad (|x| < 1). \qquad 63(16)$$

This series converges for all values of a in the right half of the complex plane, except on the line connecting the points $a = \pm i$.

$$r_n \approx \dfrac{2|R^{2n+3}|}{(2n+3)|1-R^2|}\,.$$

$9°.\ \arctan(x\tan 2\theta) = 2 \displaystyle\sum_{k=0}^{\infty} \dfrac{(-1)^k \tan^{2k+1}\theta}{2k+1}\, T_{2k+1}(x)$

$$(|x| \leqslant 1), \quad 0 < \theta < \dfrac{\pi}{4}, \quad \varepsilon_{n-1} = \tan^{2n}\theta. \qquad 56(44)$$

Consult the reference [56], pp. 44 ff., for computations by these formulae.

Practical computational techniques, which are based on these formulae with $n = 9$ and $\tan\theta = \tan\dfrac{\pi}{48}$, are given in § 2.4, 10°.

B. *Expansion in Legendre polynomials.*

$10°.\ \arcsin \dfrac{\sqrt{2}}{2}\, x = \displaystyle\sum_{k=0}^{\infty} a_{2k+1} P_{2k+1}(x) \qquad (|x| < 1).$

a_1	0·750 000 000 000	a_{13}	0·000 000 933 713
a_3	0·031 941 517 568	a_{15}	0·000 000 137 799
a_5	0·003 042 677 300	a_{17}	0·000 000 020 740
a_7	0·000 359 433 936	a_{19}	0·000 000 003 169
a_9	0·000 046 941 925	a_{21}	0·000 000 000 492
a_{11}	0·000 006 496 677		

2.4. Approximations by means of polynomials (and square roots).

$1°.\ \arcsin x \approx \displaystyle\sum_{k=0}^{5} a_{2k+1} x^{2k+1} \qquad (|x| < 0·966),$

$$\text{if } |x| < \frac{1}{2}, \qquad r = 3 \times 10^{-8}.$$

a_1	0·999 999 971 1	a_7	0·045 938 779 8	
a_3	0·166 669 833 7	a_9	0·022 316 969 3	60(91)
a_5	0·074 901 474 4	a_{11}	0·044 856 984 6	

2°. $\arcsin x \approx \sum\limits_{k=0}^{9} a_{2k+1} x^{2k+1} \quad \left(|x| < \dfrac{\sqrt{2}}{2} \right).$

a_1	1	a_{11}	0·034 242 560 0
a_3	0·166 666 844	a_{13}	−0·033 161 216 0
a_5	0·074 992 448 0	a_{15}	0·143 654 912
a_7	0·044 792 576 0	a_{17}	−0·176 160 768
a_9	0·028 669 952 0	a_{19}	0·134 217 728

3°. $\arcsin x \approx \sum\limits_{k=0}^{10} a_{2k+1} x^{2k+1} \quad \left(|x| \leqslant \dfrac{\sqrt{2}}{2} \right).$

a_1	1·000 000 000 372	a_{13}	0·060 563 816 911
a_3	0·166 666 600 550	a_{15}	−0·124 609 821 872
a_5	0·075 003 446 490	a_{17}	0·289 558 388 282
a_7	0·044 560 473 601	a_{19}	−0·313 624 467 676
a_9	0·031 466 212 165	a_{21}	0·182 869 189 956
a_{11}	0·013 758 605 250		

4°. $\arcsin x \approx \dfrac{\pi}{2} - \sqrt{1-x} \sum\limits_{k=0}^{4} a_k (1-x)^k$

$$(0·966 \leqslant x \leqslant 1·0), \qquad r = 3 \times 10^{-9}.$$

a_0	1·414 213 562 5	a_3	0·007 848 558 3
a_1	0·117 851 094 8	a_4	0·003 044 958 4
a_2	0·026 518 600 7		

60 (91)

5°. Let us put

$$\arcsin x = \frac{1}{2} \pi - \sqrt{1-x}\, \psi(x).$$

We shall give a set of polynomials of best approximation (the formulae (a) to (e)) of degree k, where $3 \leqslant k \leqslant 7$, for $\psi(x)$ over the interval $(0, 1)$ (cf. [49], pp. 159–163).

(a) $\psi(x) \approx \displaystyle\sum_{k=0}^{3} a_k x^k$, $r < 7 \times 10^{-5}$.

a_0	1·570 728 8	a_2	0·074 261 0
a_1	−0·212 114 4	a_3	−0·018 729 3

(b) $\psi(x) \approx \displaystyle\sum_{k=0}^{4} a_k x^k$, $r < 8 \times 10^{-6}$.

a_0	1·570 787 86	a_3	−0·035 756 63
a_1	−0·214 124 53	a_4	0·008 648 84
a_2	0·084 666 49		

(c) $\psi(x) \approx \displaystyle\sum_{k=0}^{5} a_k x^k$, $r < 1\cdot2 \times 10^{-6}$.

a_0	1·570 795 207	a_3	−0·044 958 884
a_1	−0·214 512 362	a_4	0·019 349 939
a_2	0·087 876 311	a_5	−0·004 337 769

(d) $\psi(x) \approx \displaystyle\sum_{k=0}^{6} a_k x^k$, $r < 1\cdot5 \times 10^{-7}$.

a_0	1·570 796 172 8	a_4	0·026 899 948 2
a_1	−0·214 585 264 7	a_5	−0·011 146 229 4
a_2	0·088 755 628 6	a_6	0·002 295 964 8
a_3	−0·048 802 504 3		

(e) $\psi(x) \approx \displaystyle\sum_{k=0}^{7} a_k x^k$, $r < 2\cdot3 \times 10^{-8}$.

a_0	1·570 796 305 0	a_4	0·030 891 881 0
a_1	−0·214 598 801 6	a_5	−0·017 088 125 6
a_2	0·088 978 987 4	a_6	0·006 670 090 1
a_3	−0·050 174 304 6	a_7	−0·001 262 491 1

6°. We next give a set of polynomials of best approximation (the formulae (a)–(f)) for the function $y = \arctan x$ over the interval $|x| \leqslant 1$, where r is specified for the interval $0 \leqslant x \leqslant 1$.

We remark that each approximate equation

$$\arctan x \approx \sum_{k=0}^{m} a_{2k+1} x^{2k+1},$$

for $|x| \leqslant 1$, leads directly to an equation of the same accuracy for x in the range $0 < x < \infty$:

$$\arctan x \approx \frac{1}{4}\pi + \sum_{k=0}^{m} a_{2k+1}\left(\frac{x-1}{x+1}\right)^{2k+1}$$

(cf. [49], pp. 132–137).

(a) $\arctan x \approx \displaystyle\sum_{k=0}^{2} a_{2k+1} x^{2k+1}, \quad r = 7 \times 10^{-4}.$

a_0	0·995 354
a_3	−0·288 679
a_5	0·079 331

(b) $\arctan x \approx \displaystyle\sum_{k=0}^{3} a_{2k+1} x^{2k+1}, \quad r = 8 \times 10^{-5}.$

a_1	0·999 215 0	a_5	0·146 276 6
a_3	−0·321 181 9	a_7	−0·038 992 9

(c) $\arctan x \approx \displaystyle\sum_{k=0}^{4} a_{2k+1} x^{2k+1}, \quad r = 12 \times 10^{-6}.$

a_1	0·999 866 0	a_7	−0·085 133 0
a_3	−0·330 299 5	a_9	0·020 835 1
a_5	0·180 141 0		

(d) $\arctan x \approx \displaystyle\sum_{k=0}^{5} a_{2k+1} x^{2k+1}, \quad r = 18 \times 10^{-7}.$

a_1	0·999 977 26	a_7	−0·116 432 87
a_3	−0·332 623 47	a_9	0·052 653 32
a_5	0·193 543 46	a_{11}	−0·011 721 20

(e) $\arctan x \approx \sum\limits_{k=0}^{6} a_{2k+1} x^{2k+1}, \qquad r = 25 \times 10^{-8}.$

a_1	0·999 996 115	a_9	0·079 626 318
a_3	−0·333 173 758	a_{11}	−0·033 606 269
a_5	0·198 078 690	a_{13}	0·006 812 411
a_7	−0·132 335 096		

(f) $\arctan x \approx \sum\limits_{k=0}^{7} a_{2k+1} x^{2k+1}, \qquad r = 4 \times 10^{-8}.$

a_1	0·999 999 332 9	a_9	0·096 420 044 1
a_3	−0·333 298 560 5	a_{11}	−0·055 909 886 1
a_5	0·199 465 359 9	a_{13}	0·021 861 228 8
a_7	−0·139 085 335 1	a_{15}	−0·004 054 058 0

$7^\circ.$ $\arctan x \approx \sum\limits_{k=0}^{4} a_{2k+1} x^{2k+1} \qquad \left(|x| < \dfrac{\sqrt{3}-1}{\sqrt{3}+1} \approx 0·268 \right),$

$$r = 2^{-32}.$$

a_1	0·999 999 998 43	a_7	−0·141 734 606 13	
a_3	−0·333 332 893 64	a_9	0·094 919 549 52	7(12)
a_5	0·199 965 347 80			

$8^\circ.$ $\arctan x \approx \sum\limits_{k=0}^{8} a_{2k+1} x^{2k+1} \qquad (|x| \leqslant 1), \qquad r = 5 \times 10^{-8}.$

a_1	1·000 000 00	a_{11}	−0·074 869 25
a_3	−0·333 330 61	a_{13}	0·042 485 76
a_5	0·199 923 55	a_{15}	−0·015 941 63
a_7	−0·142 015 62	a_{17}	0·002 818 05
a_9	0·106 327 94		

11 (166)

$9^\circ.$ $\arctan x \approx \sum\limits_{k=0}^{10} a_{2k+1} x^{2k+1} \qquad (|x| \leqslant 1).$

a_1	$0{\cdot}999\ 999\ 995\ 3$	a_{13}	$0{\cdot}064\ 702\ 992\ 4$
a_3	$-0{\cdot}333\ 332\ 924\ 8$	a_{15}	$-0{\cdot}041\ 172\ 074\ 5$
a_5	$0{\cdot}199\ 989\ 259\ 0$	a_{17}	$0{\cdot}019\ 743\ 375\ 4$
a_7	$-0{\cdot}142\ 724\ 394\ 2$	a_{19}	$-0{\cdot}006\ 073\ 876\ 5$
a_9	$0{\cdot}110\ 179\ 121\ 7$	a_{21}	$0{\cdot}000\ 876\ 609\ 5$
a_{11}	$-0{\cdot}086\ 789\ 919\ 7$		

$10°.\quad \arctan x \approx \sum_{k=0}^{8} a_{2k+1} x^{2k+1} \left(0 \leqslant x < \tan\frac{\pi}{24}\right),\ r < 8 \times 10^{-22}.$

a_1	$1{\cdot}0$
a_3	$-0{\cdot}333\ 333\ 333\ 333\ 333\ 331\ 607$
a_5	$0{\cdot}199\ 999\ 999\ 999\ 998\ 244\ 448$
a_7	$-0{\cdot}142\ 857\ 142\ 856\ 331\ 306\ 529$
a_9	$0{\cdot}111\ 111\ 110\ 907\ 793\ 967\ 393$
a_{11}	$-0{\cdot}090\ 909\ 060\ 963\ 367\ 763\ 707\ 3$
a_{13}	$0{\cdot}076\ 920\ 407\ 324\ 915\ 408\ 132\ 0$
a_{15}	$-0{\cdot}066\ 524\ 822\ 941\ 310\ 827\ 790\ 5$
a_{17}	$0{\cdot}054\ 672\ 100\ 939\ 593\ 880\ 694\ 1$

69(271)

Rule for computing $\arctan x$ for any $x > 0$. The interval $(0, \infty)$ is to be subdivided into the seven intervals:

$0 \leqslant u < \tan\dfrac{\pi}{24},\ \tan\dfrac{(2j-3)\pi}{24} \leqslant u < \tan\dfrac{(2j-1)\pi}{24},\ \text{for } j = 2, 3,$

$4, 5, 6$ and $\tan\dfrac{11\pi}{24} \leqslant u < \infty$. The series of $10°$ should be used for $|x|$ with the first interval. When $|x|$ is within the $(j+1)$th interval $(j = 1, 2, 3, 4, 5)$ the formula

$$\arctan|x| = \frac{j\pi}{12} + \arctan t_j$$

should be used, where

$$t_j = \frac{|x| - \tan\dfrac{j\pi}{12}}{1 + |x| \tan\dfrac{j\pi}{12}}.$$

The series of $10°$ is to be used for computing $\arctan t_j$. When the value of $|x|$ lies in the seventh interval, then

$$\arctan|x| = \frac{\pi}{2} - \arctan\frac{1}{|x|} \quad \left(\frac{1}{|x|} \leqslant \tan\frac{\pi}{24}\right).$$

j	$\tan\dfrac{j\pi}{24}$
1	0·131 652 497 587 395 853 472
2	0·267 949 192 431 122 706 473
3	0·414 213 562 373 095 048 802
4	0·577 350 269 189 625 764 509
5	0·767 326 987 978 960 342 923
6	1·000 000 000 000 000 000 000
7	1·303 225 372 841 205 755 868
8	1·732 050 807 568 877 293 527
9	2·414 213 562 373 095 048 802
10	3·732 050 807 568 877 293 527
11	7·595 754 112 725 150 440 526

69(272)

$$\frac{\pi}{2} = 1\cdot570\ 796\ 326\ 794\ 896\ 619\ 231$$

2.5. Continued fraction expansions.

$1°.\quad e^{2v\operatorname{arccot}x} = 1 + \cfrac{2v}{x-v} + \cfrac{v^2+1}{3x} + \cfrac{v^2+4}{5x} + \ldots$

$$\ldots + \cfrac{v^2+n^2}{(2n+1)x} + \ldots \qquad 34(106)$$

$2°.\quad \arctan x = \cfrac{x}{1} + \cfrac{x^2}{3} + \cfrac{4x^2}{5} + \cfrac{9x^2}{7}$

$$\frac{0}{1} \quad \frac{x}{1} \quad \frac{3x}{3+x^2} \quad \frac{15x+4x^3}{15+9x^2} \quad \frac{105x+55x^3}{105+90x^2+9x^4}$$

$$+ \quad \cfrac{16x^2}{9} \qquad + \ldots + \cfrac{n^2x^2}{2n+1} + \ldots$$

$$\frac{945x+735x^3+64x^5}{945+1050x^2+225x^4} \qquad 34(114)$$

The fraction converges everywhere in the complex plane of the variable x, except on two semi-infinite intervals of the imaginary axis $(-i\infty,-i]$ and $[i,\ i\infty)$. The following chain of inequalities holds for real values of x:

$$\frac{3x}{3+x^2} \leqslant \frac{105x+55x^3}{105+90x^2+9x^4} \leqslant \ldots \leqslant \operatorname{arc\,tan} x \leqslant \ldots$$

$$\ldots \leqslant \frac{945x+735x^3+64x^5}{945+1050x^2+225x^4} \leqslant \frac{15x+4x^3}{15+9x^2} \leqslant x. \quad 34(115)$$

$3°.$ $\arctan x = x - \cfrac{x^3}{3} + \cfrac{9x^2}{5} + \cfrac{4x^2}{7}$

$$\cfrac{x}{1} \quad \cfrac{3x - x^3}{3} \quad \cfrac{15x + 4x^3}{15 + 9x^2} \quad \cfrac{105x + 40x^3 - 4x^5}{105 + 75x^2}$$

$$+ \cfrac{25x^2}{9} + \ldots + \cfrac{(2n+1)^2 x^2}{4n+1} + \cfrac{4n^2 x^2}{4n+3} + \ldots$$

The fraction converges everywhere on the complex plane of the variable x, except for the semi-infinite intervals of the imaginary axis $(-i\infty, -i]$ and $[i, i\infty)$.

$4°.$ $\cfrac{\arcsin x}{\sqrt{1-x^2}} = \cfrac{x}{1-x^2} + \cfrac{x^2}{3} + \cfrac{4x^2}{5(1-x^2)}$

$$\cfrac{0}{1} \quad \cfrac{x}{1-x^2} \quad \cfrac{3x}{3 - 2x^2} \quad \cfrac{15x - 11x^3}{15 - 21x^2 + 6x^4}$$

$$+ \cfrac{9x^2}{7} + \ldots + \cfrac{4n^2}{(4n+1)(1-x^2)}$$

$$\cfrac{105x - 50x^3}{105 - 120x^2 + 24x^4}$$

$$+ \cfrac{(2n+1)^2 x^2}{4n+3} + \ldots \qquad 34(116)$$

This fraction converges everywhere on the complex plane of the variable x, except for the semi-intervals on the real axis $(-\infty, -1]$ and $[1, \infty)$.

$5°.$ $\sqrt{1-x^2}\, \arcsin x = x - \cfrac{x^3}{3(1-x^2)} + \cfrac{9x^2}{5} + \cfrac{4x^2}{7(1-x^2)} + \ldots$

$$\ldots + \cfrac{(2n+1)^2 x^2}{4n+1} + \cfrac{4n^2 x^2}{(4n+3)(1-x^2)} + \ldots \qquad 34(117)$$

$6°.$ $\cfrac{\arccos x}{\sqrt{1-x^2}} = \cfrac{1}{x} + \cfrac{1-x^2}{3x} + \cfrac{4(1-x^2)}{5x} + \cfrac{9(1-x^2)}{7x} + \ldots$

$$\cfrac{0}{1} \quad \cfrac{1}{x} \quad \cfrac{3x}{1 + 2x^2} \quad \cfrac{4 + 11x^2}{9x + 6x^3} \quad \cfrac{55x + 50x^3}{9 + 72x^2 + 24x^4}$$

$$\ldots + \cfrac{n^2(1-x^2)}{(2n+1)x} + \ldots \qquad 34(117)$$

$7°.$
$$\frac{\arcsin x}{\sqrt{1-x^2}} = \frac{x}{1-} \frac{1.2x^2}{3-} \frac{1.2x^2}{5-} \dots$$

$$\dots - \frac{(2n-1)2nx^2}{4n-1-} \frac{(2n-1)2nx^2}{4n+1-} \dots \qquad 34(118)$$

$8°.$
$$\arctan x = \frac{x}{1+x^2-} \frac{1.2x^2}{3-} \frac{1.2x^2}{5(1+x^2)-} \dots$$

$$\dots - \frac{(2n-1)2nx^2}{4n-1-} \frac{(2n-1)2nx^2}{(4n+1)(1+x^2)-} \dots \qquad 34(119)$$

$9°.$
$$\frac{\arccos x}{\sqrt{1-x^2}} = \frac{x}{1-} \frac{1.2(1-x^2)}{3-} \frac{1.2(1-x^2)}{5-} \dots$$

$$\dots - \frac{(2n-1)2n(1-x^2)}{4n-1-} \frac{(2n-1)2n(1-x^2)}{4n+1-} \dots \qquad 34(119)$$

$10°.$ A series of rational approximations y_n for $y = \arctan x$ can be constructed for $n = 1, 2, 3, \dots$

$$y_{n-1} = \frac{x}{T_n\left(-\dfrac{2}{x^2}-1\right)} \sum_{k=1}^{n} (-1)^k \frac{c_n^k}{x^{2k}} S_{k-1}(x^2),$$

where $S_{k-1}(x^2) = 1 - \dfrac{x^2}{3} + \dfrac{(x^2)^2}{5} - \dots + (-1)^{k-1}\dfrac{(x^2)^{k-1}}{2k-1},$

$$17(482)$$

and where the c_n^k are the coefficients of the polynomials $T_n^*(x)$.

The sequence $\{y_n\}$ converges to y everywhere in the complex plane, except at points lying on the imaginary axis. In fact, the sequence also converges on that part of the imaginary axis lying between $-i$ and $+i$. The function $\arctan x$ has singularities at $x = \pm i$.

In particular, putting $n = 4$ we get

$$\arctan x = \frac{32x}{105} \frac{420 + 700x^2 + 329x^4 + 38x^6}{128 + 256x^2 + 160x^4 + 32x^6 + x^8}. \qquad 17(489)$$

2.6. Rational approximations.

1°. $\arctan x \approx \dfrac{\pi}{8} + \arctan y, \quad y = \dfrac{x - 0 \cdot 414\ 213\ 562\ 3}{1 + 0 \cdot 414\ 213\ 562\ 3x}$

$$(0 \leqslant x \leqslant 1),$$

$\arctan x \approx \dfrac{3\pi}{8} - \arctan \overline{y}, \quad \overline{y} = \dfrac{1 - 0 \cdot 414\ 213\ 562\ 3x}{x + 0 \cdot 414\ 213\ 562\ 3}$

$$(1 \leqslant x < +\infty),$$

$$\arctan y \approx \sum_{k=0}^{4} a_{2k+1} y^{2k+1}.$$

a_1	0·999 999 903 1	a_7	−0·137 516 498 4
a_3	−0·333 321 845 3	a_9	0·077 264 202 0
a_5	0·199 615 567 9		

$$r < 4 \times 10^{-9}$$

where

$$y = \frac{x - 0 \cdot 414\ 213\ 562\ 3}{1 + 0 \cdot 414\ 213\ 562\ 3x}, \quad \text{if } 0 \leqslant x \leqslant 1,$$

$$y = \frac{1 - 0 \cdot 414\ 213\ 562\ 3x}{x + 0 \cdot 414\ 213\ 562\ 3}, \quad \text{if } 1 \leqslant x < +\infty. \quad 60(89-90)$$

2°. $\dfrac{\arctan x}{x} \approx \dfrac{\displaystyle\sum_{k=0}^{3} a_{2k} x^{2k}}{\displaystyle\sum_{k=0} a_{2k+1} x^{2k}}.$

The upper bound for the absolute error is $\dfrac{|x|^9}{8}$ for small values of $|x|$, and is $1 \cdot 4 \times 10^{-5}$ for $|x| = 1$.

k	a_{2k}	a_{2k+1}	k	a_{2k}	a_{2k+1}
0	1	1	3	$\dfrac{19}{210}$	$\dfrac{1}{4}$
1	$\dfrac{5}{3}$	2	4		$\dfrac{1}{128}$
2	$\dfrac{47}{60}$	$\dfrac{5}{4}$			

Comment. This same expansion can be written in the form 3°.

3°.
$$\frac{\arctan x}{x} \approx \frac{\sum_{k=0}^{3} b_{2k}x^{2k}}{1 + \sum_{k=0}^{2} b_{2k+1}x^{2k+2}} \qquad (0 \leqslant x \leqslant 1), \quad r = 6 \times 10^{-10}.$$

k	b_{2k}	b_{2k+1}	
0	$1+19 \times 10^{-10}$	1·453 567 134 6	56(52)
1	1·120 234 014 3	0·565 030 979 6	
2	0·280 504 540 7	0·049 017 591 2	
3	0·008 561 188 9		

4°.
$$\arctan x = x \left\{ D_0 + \frac{A_1}{x^2 + D_1} - \frac{A_2}{x^2 + D_2} - \frac{A_3}{x^2 + D_3} \right\}$$

$$(0 \leqslant x \leqslant 1), \qquad 56(53)$$

$D_0 = 0·174\ 655\ 438\ 8; \qquad A_1 = 3·709\ 256\ 262;$

$D_1 = 6·762\ 139\ 240; \qquad A_2 = 7·106\ 760\ 045;$

$D_2 = 3·316\ 335\ 425; \qquad A_3 = 0·264\ 768\ 620\,2.$

$D_3 = 1·448\ 631\ 538$

5°.
$$\arctan x = \frac{\pi}{2} - \frac{1}{x} \left(D_0^* - \frac{A_1^*}{x^2 + D_1^*} - \frac{A_2^*}{x^2 + D_2^*} - \frac{A_3^*}{x^2 + D_3^*} \right)$$

$$(x \geqslant 1), \qquad 56(53)$$

where

$D_0^* = 0·999\ 999\ 998\ 1; \qquad A_1^* = 0·333\ 333\ 117\ 7;$

$D_1^* = 0·599\ 987\ 268\ 9; \qquad A_2^* = 0·068\ 475\ 358\ 2;$

$D_2^* = 0·505\ 974\ 018\ 4; \qquad A_3^* = 0·054\ 510\ 242\ 0.$

$D_3^* = 0·347\ 605\ 847\ 3.$

2.7. Iterative processes. 1°. We shall evaluate y by a "digit-by-digit" method, where

$$\frac{1}{2}\pi y = \arcsin x.$$

We seek the binary expansion

$$y = \alpha_0 \cdot \alpha_1 \alpha_2 \ldots \alpha_n \ldots = \sum_{k=0}^{\infty} \alpha_k 2^{-k} \qquad (\alpha_k = 0,\ 1).$$

We construct a sequence of pairs of numbers:

$$\{x_n,\ \alpha_n\} \qquad (n = 0, 1, 2, \ldots).$$

$x_0 = x \, (-1 \leqslant x \leqslant 1)$; if $x_0 > 0$, $\alpha_0 = 0$, then $x_1 = 2x_0^2 - 1$,

if $x_0 < 0$, $\alpha_0 = 1$, then $x_1 = 1 - 2x_0^2$.

Let the numbers $x_0, x_1, \ldots, x_k$ and the binary digits $\alpha_0, \alpha_1, \ldots, \alpha_{k-1}$ be already determined. Then if $x_k > 0$ and $\alpha_k = 0$ we have

$$x_{k+1} = 2x_k^2 - 1;$$

if $x_k < 0$ and $\alpha_k = 1$ then we have

$$x_{k+1} = 1 - 2x_k^2.$$

Having determined the binary number $\alpha_0 \cdot \alpha_1 \alpha_2 \ldots \alpha_k$, we then find

$$\arcsin x \approx \frac{\pi}{2} (\alpha_0 \cdot \alpha_1 \ldots \alpha_n) = \frac{\pi}{2} \sum_{k=0}^{n} \alpha_k 2^{-k}$$

18(105—107)

(within an accuracy of $2^{-(n+1)}\pi$).

2°. We shall now find y by a "digit-by-digit" method, where

$$\frac{1}{2} \pi y = \arctan x.$$

In fact, we shall find an expression for $\arctan x$ in a modified binary system, with digits $\tilde{\alpha}_n$ equal to 1 and -1 (cf. [20]):

$$\arctan x = \frac{\pi}{2} \operatorname{sign} x \times 0 \cdot \tilde{\alpha}_1 \tilde{\alpha}_2 \ldots \tilde{\alpha}_n \ldots = \frac{\pi}{2} \operatorname{sign} x \sum_{k=0}^{\infty} \tilde{\alpha}_k \times 2^{-k}.$$

We find the sequences x_k and $\tilde{\alpha}_{k+1}$ (where $k = 0, 1, 2, \ldots$):

$$x_0 = |x|, \qquad x_{i+1} = \frac{2x_i}{1 - x^2},$$

where $\tilde{\alpha}_1 = 1$, but if $i > 1$ then $\tilde{\alpha}_i = -\operatorname{sign} x_{i-1}$ $(i = 2, \ldots)$, and

$$\arctan x \approx \frac{\pi}{2} \operatorname{sign} x \sum_{k=1}^{n} \tilde{\alpha}_k 2^{-k}$$

$\left(\text{within an accuracy of } \dfrac{3\pi}{8} 2^{-n} \right).$ \hfill 18(108).

§ 3. Hyperbolic functions

3.1. General information. 1°. We shall use the following notation:

$$\sinh x, \ \cosh x, \ \tanh x = \frac{\sinh x}{\cosh x}, \ \coth x = \frac{\cosh x}{\sinh x}, \ \mathrm{sech}\, x = \frac{1}{\cosh x},$$

$$\mathrm{cosech}\, x = \frac{1}{\sinh x} :$$

(a) $\sinh x = \dfrac{e^x - e^{-x}}{2}$ *(the hyperbolic sine)*,

(b) $\cosh x = \dfrac{e^x + e^{-x}}{2}$ *(the hyperbolic cosine)*,

(c) $\tanh x = \dfrac{e^x - e^{-x}}{e^x + e^{-x}}$ *(the hyperbolic tangent)*,

(d) $\coth x = \dfrac{e^x + e^{-x}}{e^x - e^{-x}}$ *(the hyperbolic cotangent)*,

(e) $\mathrm{sech}\, x = \dfrac{2}{e^x + e^{-x}}$ *(the hyperbolic secant)*, and

(f) $\mathrm{cosech}\, x = \dfrac{2}{e^x - e^{-x}}$ *(the hyperbolic cosecant)*.

2°. *Domains of definition.* The domains of definition of the function $\sinh x$ and its range of values are each the interval $(-\infty, +\infty)$.

The domain of definition of the function $\cosh x$ is the interval $(-\infty, +\infty)$, and its range of values is the semi-infinite interval $[1, +\infty)$.

The domain of definition of the function $\tanh x$ is the interval $(-\infty, +\infty)$, and its range of values is the interval $(-1, 1)$, i.e. $|\tanh x| < 1$.

The domain of definition of the function $\coth x$ is the pair of open intervals $(-\infty, 0)$ and $(0, +\infty)$, and its range of values is the pair of open intervals $(-\infty, -1)$ and $(1, +\infty)$. Thus, $|\coth x| > 1$.

3°. The argument x of the hyperbolic functions $\sinh x$, $\cosh x$, etc., may be interpreted as twice the area of a sector of an hyperbola.

4°. The function $\cosh x$ is an even function, but $\sinh x$, $\tanh x$ and $\coth x$ are odd functions.

$\sinh x = \operatorname{sign} x \cdot \sinh |x|, \quad \cosh x = \cosh |x|,$

$\tanh x = \operatorname{sign} x \cdot \tanh |x|, \quad \coth x = \operatorname{sign} x \cdot \coth |x|.$

5°. *Expressions for an hyperbolic function in terms of another hyperbolic function.*

$\sinh x$		$\pm \sqrt{\cosh^2 x - 1}$	$\dfrac{\tanh x}{\sqrt{1 - \tanh^2 x}}$	$\pm \dfrac{1}{\sqrt{\coth^2 x - 1}}$
$\cosh x$	$\sqrt{\sinh^2 x + 1}$		$\dfrac{1}{\sqrt{1 - \tanh^2 x}}$	$\pm \dfrac{\coth x}{\sqrt{\coth^2 - 1}}$
$\tanh x$	$\dfrac{\sinh x}{\sqrt{\sinh^2 x + 1}}$	$\pm \dfrac{\sqrt{\cosh^2 x - 1}}{\cosh x}$		$\dfrac{1}{\coth x}$
$\coth x$	$\dfrac{\sqrt{\sinh^2 x + 1}}{\sinh x}$	$\pm \dfrac{\cosh x}{\sqrt{\cosh^2 x - 1}}$	$\dfrac{1}{\tanh x}$	

6°. *General formulae for multiple arguments.*

$$(\cosh x + \sinh x)^n = \cosh nx + \sinh nx \quad \text{(if } n \text{ is an integer).} \quad 26(39)$$

$$\sinh nx = \sinh x \sum_{k=1}^{E\left(\frac{n+1}{2}\right)} \binom{n}{2k-1} \sinh^{2k-1} x \cosh^{n-2k+1} x;$$

$$= \sinh x \sum_{k=0}^{E\left(\frac{n+1}{2}\right)} (-1)^k \binom{n-k-1}{k} 2^{n-2k-1} \cosh^{n-2k-1} x.$$

$$26(41)$$

$$\cosh nx = \sum_{k=0}^{E\left(\frac{n}{2}\right)} \binom{n}{2k} \sinh^{2k} x \cosh^{n-2k} x = 2^{n-1} \cosh^n x$$

$$+ n \sum_{k=1}^{E\left(\frac{n}{2}\right)} (-1)^k \frac{1}{k} \binom{n-2k-1}{k-1} 2^{n-2k-1} \cosh^{n-2k} x. \quad 26(41)$$

7°. *Relations between hyperbolic and trigonometric functions*

$$\cosh x = \cos ix \qquad\qquad 38(38)$$

$$\sinh x = -i \sin ix. \qquad\qquad 38(38)$$

$$\tanh x = -i \tan ix. \qquad\qquad 38(38)$$

$$\coth x = i \cot ix. \qquad\qquad 38(38)$$

3.2. Various formulae.

1°. $\dfrac{x^k \tanh x \sinh x}{\sinh 2x \pm 2x} = \dfrac{x^k \cosh x}{\sinh 2x \pm 2x} \pm \dfrac{x^{k-1} \sinh x}{\sinh 2x \pm 2x} \mp \dfrac{x^{k-1}}{2 \cosh x}.$

$$44(163)$$

2°. $\dfrac{x^k \coth x \cosh x}{\sinh 2x \pm 2x} = \dfrac{x^k \sinh x}{\sinh 2x \pm 2x} \mp \dfrac{x^{k-1} \cosh x}{\sinh 2x \pm 2x} \pm \dfrac{x^{k-1}}{2 \sinh x}.$

$$44(163)$$

3°. $\dfrac{x^k \tanh x}{\sinh 2x \pm 2x} = \dfrac{x^k}{\sinh 2x \pm 2x} \pm \dfrac{x^{k-1}(1 - e^{-2x})}{2(\sinh 2x \pm 2x)} \mp \dfrac{x^{k-1} e^{-x}}{2 \cosh x}.$

$$44(162)$$

4°. $\dfrac{x^k \coth x}{\sinh 2x \pm 2x} = \dfrac{x^k}{\sinh 2x \pm 2x} \mp \dfrac{x^{k-1}(1 - e^{-2x})}{2(\sinh 2x \pm 2x)} \pm \dfrac{x^{k-1} e^{-x}}{2 \sinh x}.$

$$44(162)$$

5°. $\sinh^2 x - \sinh^2 y = \sinh(x + y) \sinh(x - y)$

$$= \cosh^2 x - \cosh^2 y. \quad 26(39)$$

6°. $\sinh^2 x + \cosh^2 y = \cosh(x + y) \cosh(x - y)$

$$= \cosh^2 x + \sinh^2 y. \quad 26(39)$$

3.3. Power series expansions.

1°. $\sinh x = \displaystyle\sum_{k=1}^{\infty} \dfrac{x^{2k-1}}{(2k - 1)!}.$

$$26(48)$$

2°. $\cosh x = \displaystyle\sum_{k=0}^{\infty} \dfrac{x^{2k}}{(2k)!}.$

$$26(48)$$

3°. $\tanh x = x - \dfrac{x^3}{3} + \dfrac{2x^5}{15} - \dfrac{17x^7}{315} + \dots$

$$= \sum_{k=1}^{\infty} \dfrac{2^{2k}(2^{2k} - 1)}{(2k)!} B_{2k}{}^\dagger x^{2k-1} \quad \left(|x| < \dfrac{\pi}{2}\right). \quad 26(48)$$

---

† B_{2k} are the Bernoulli numbers (cf. [1], p. 348).

4°. $\coth x = \dfrac{1}{x} + \dfrac{x}{3} - \dfrac{x^3}{45} + \dfrac{2x^5}{945} - \cdots$

$$= \dfrac{1}{x} + \sum_{k=1}^{\infty} \dfrac{2^{2k}B_{2k}}{(2k)!}\, x^{2k-1} \quad (|x| < \pi).$$

26(49); 32(522)

5°. $\operatorname{sech} x = 1 - \dfrac{x^2}{2} + \dfrac{x^4}{24} - \dfrac{61x^6}{720} + \cdots$

$$= 1 + \sum_{k=1}^{\infty} (-1)^k\, \dfrac{E_{2k}^{\,\dagger}}{(2k)!}\, x^{2k} \quad \left(|x| < \dfrac{\pi}{2}\right). \qquad 26(49)$$

6°. $\operatorname{cosech} x = \dfrac{1}{x} - \dfrac{x}{6} + \dfrac{7x^3}{360} - \dfrac{31x^5}{15120} + \cdots$

$$= \dfrac{1}{x} - \sum_{k=1}^{\infty} \dfrac{2(2^{2k-1}-1)B_{2k}}{(2k)!}\, x^{2k-1} \quad (|x| < \pi). \qquad 26(49); 52(418)$$

7°. $\sinh x = \operatorname{cosec} x \displaystyle\sum_{k=1}^{\infty} (-1)^{k+1}\, \dfrac{2^{2k}x^{4k-2}}{(4k-2)!}. \qquad 26(49); 52$

8°. $\cosh x = \sec x + \sec x \displaystyle\sum_{k=1}^{\infty} (-1)^k\, \dfrac{2^{2k}x^{4k}}{(4k)!}. \qquad 26(49); 52$

9°. $\sinh x = x\sec x - \sec x \displaystyle\sum_{k=1}^{\infty} \dfrac{2^k x^{2k+1}}{(2k+1)!}$

$$= \sec x \sum_{k=1}^{\infty} (-1)^{E\left(\frac{k}{2}\right)}\, \dfrac{2^{k-1}x^{2k-1}}{(2k-1)!}. \qquad 26(49); 52$$

10°. $\cosh x = x\operatorname{cosec} x + \operatorname{cosec} x \displaystyle\sum_{k=1}^{\infty} (-1)^{k+1}\, \dfrac{2^k x^{2k+1}}{(2k+1)!}$

$$= \operatorname{cosec} x \sum_{k=1}^{\infty} (-1)^{E\left(\frac{k-1}{2}\right)}\, \dfrac{2^{k-1}x^{2k-1}}{(2k-1)!}. \qquad 26(49); 52$$

11°. $\tanh x = \dfrac{1}{\sinh 2x} \cdot \displaystyle\sum_{k=1}^{\infty} \dfrac{(2x)^{2k}}{(2k)!}. \qquad 44(164)$

---

† E_{2k} are the Euler numbers (cf. [1], p. 359).

3.4. Infinite products.

$1°.$ $\quad \sinh x = x \prod_{k=1}^{\infty} \left(1 + \dfrac{x^2}{k^2 \pi^2} \right).$ $\qquad$ 26(51); 36(148)

$2°.$ $\quad \cosh x = \prod_{k=0}^{\infty} \left(1 + \dfrac{4x^2}{(2k+1)^2 \pi^2} \right).$ $\qquad$ 26(51); 36(149)

$3°.$ $\quad \dfrac{\cosh x - \cos a}{1 - \cos a} = \prod_{k=-\infty}^{\infty} \left[1 + \left(\dfrac{x}{2k\pi + a} \right)^2 \right]$ 26(51); 66(216)

3.5. Series of exponential functions.

$1°.$ $\quad \tanh x = 1 + 2 \sum_{k=1}^{\infty} (-1)^k e^{-2kx}$ $\qquad (x > 0).$ $\qquad$ 26(37)

$2°.$ $\quad \operatorname{sech} x = 2 \sum_{k=0}^{\infty} (-1)^k e^{-(2k+1)x}$ $\qquad (x > 0).$ $\qquad$ 26(37)

$3°.$ $\quad \operatorname{cosech} x = 2 \sum_{k=0}^{\infty} e^{-(2k+1)x}$ $\qquad (x > 0).$ $\qquad$ 26(37)

3.6. Expansions in elementary rational functions.

$1°.$ $\quad \tanh \dfrac{\pi}{2} x = \dfrac{4x}{\pi} \sum_{k=1}^{\infty} \dfrac{1}{(2k-1)^2 + x^2}.$ $\qquad$ 25(50)

$2°.$ $\quad \coth \pi x = \dfrac{1}{\pi x} + \dfrac{2x}{\pi} \sum_{k=1}^{\infty} \dfrac{1}{x^2 + k^2}.$ $\qquad$ 26(50)

3.7. Expansions in polynomials, orthogonal and otherwise.
A. *Expansions in Legendre polynomials.*

$1°.$ $\quad \sinh x = \sum_{k=1}^{\infty} a_{2k-1} P_{2k-1}(x)$ $\qquad (|x| < 1).$

a_1	1·103 638 323 514	a_7	0·000 007 620 547 335
a_3	0·070 455 633 668	a_9	0·000 000 029 718 090
a_5	0·001 099 586 127	a_{11}	0·000 000 000 072 731

$2°.\quad \cosh x = \sum_{k=1}^{\infty} a_{2k} P_{2k}(x) \quad (|x| < 1).$

a_0	1·175 201 193 644	a_6	0·000 099 454 339 113
a_2	0·357 814 350 647	a_8	0·000 000 506 471 975
a_4	0·009 965 128 149	a_{10}	0·000 000 001 560 966

B. *Expansions in Hermite polynomials.*

$3°.\quad \dfrac{1}{e}\sinh 2x = \sum_{k=0}^{\infty} \dfrac{1}{(2k+1)!} H_{2k+1}(x).$ 26(412)

$4°.\quad \dfrac{1}{e}\cosh 2x = \sum_{k=0}^{\infty} \dfrac{1}{(2k)!} H_{2k}(x).$ 26(412)

3.8. Polynomial approximations.

$1°.\quad \sinh x = \sum_{k=0}^{\infty} a_{2k+1} x^{2k+1} \quad (|x| < 1), \quad r = 10^{-10}.$

a_1	0·999 999 999 988	a_7	0·000 198 411 962
a_3	0·166 666 666 713	a_9	0·000 002 756 445
a_5	0·008 333 333 485	a_{11}	0·000 000 025 052

$2°.\quad \cosh x = \sum_{k=1}^{\infty} a_{2k} x^{2k} \quad (|x| < 1), \quad r = 10^{-9}.$

a_0	0·999 999 999 999	a_6	0·001 388 892 118
a_2	0·500 000 000 058	a_8	0·000 024 795 048
a_4	0·041 666 665 951	a_{10}	0·000 000 281 639

3.9. Continued fraction expansions.

$1°.\quad \sinh x \approx x + \quad \dfrac{x^3}{6} \quad - \quad \dfrac{3x^2}{10} \quad + \quad \dfrac{11x^2}{42}$

$$\dfrac{x}{1} \quad \dfrac{6x + x^3}{6} \quad \dfrac{60x + 7x^3}{60 - 3x^2} \quad \dfrac{2520x + 360x^3 + 11x^5}{2520 - 60x^2}$$

$$- \dfrac{25x^2}{66} + \ldots \qquad 34(164)$$

$2°.$ $\sinh x = \dfrac{x(1+F)}{(1+F)^2 - \dfrac{x^2}{4}}$,   65(264)

where F is defined in Ch. II, § 1.5, 7°.

This expression converges more rapidly than any other expansion which is known for $\sinh x$.

$3°.$ $\cosh x = \dfrac{1}{1} \ \ - \ \ \dfrac{\dfrac{x^2}{2}}{ } \ \ + \ \ \dfrac{\dfrac{5x^2}{6}}{ } \ \ - \ \ \dfrac{\dfrac{3x^2}{50}}{ }$

$$\dfrac{0}{1} \quad \dfrac{1}{1} \quad \dfrac{2}{2-x^2} \quad \dfrac{12+5x^2}{12-x^2} \quad \dfrac{600+244x^2}{600-56x^2+3x^4}$$

$+ \ \ \dfrac{\dfrac{313x^2}{126}}{ } \ \ - \ \ ...$ 34(166)

$$\dfrac{75\,600 + 34\,500x^2 + 5.313x^4}{75\,600 - 3300x^2 + 65x^4}$$

$$\dfrac{15\,120 + 6900x^2 + 313x^4}{15\,120 - 660x^2 + 13x^4}$$

$4°.$ $\cosh x \approx 1 + \dfrac{\dfrac{x^2}{2}}{ } \ \ - \ \ \dfrac{\dfrac{x^2}{6}}{ } \ \ + \ \ \dfrac{\dfrac{3x^2}{10}}{ }$

$$\dfrac{1}{1} \quad \dfrac{2+x^2}{2} \quad \dfrac{12+5x^2}{12-x^2} \quad \dfrac{120+56x^2+3x^4}{120-4x^2}$$

$- \ \ \dfrac{\dfrac{13x^2}{126}}{ } \ \ + \ \ ...$ 34(167)

$$\dfrac{15\,120 + 6900x^2 + 313x^4}{15\,120 - 660x^2 + 13x^4}$$

$5°.$ $\cosh x = 1 + \dfrac{\dfrac{x^2}{2}}{(1+F)^2 - \dfrac{x^2}{4}}$,

where F is defined in Ch. II, § 1.5, 7°.

This expression converges more rapidly than any other expansion which is known for $\cosh x$.

6°. $\tanh x = \dfrac{x}{1} + \dfrac{x^2}{3} + \dfrac{x^2}{5} + \ldots + \dfrac{x^2}{2n+1} + \ldots$

$$34(121);\ 20(133)$$

This fraction converges everywhere in the complex plane, except at points of inessential divergence. The following chain of inequalities holds for real x:

$$\frac{3x}{3+x^2} \leqslant \frac{105x+x^3}{105+45x^2+x^4} \leqslant \ldots \leqslant \tanh x \leqslant \ldots$$

$$\ldots \leqslant \frac{945x+105x^3+x^5}{945+420x^2+15x^4} \leqslant \frac{15x+x^3}{15+6x^2} \leqslant x. \qquad 34(121)$$

7°. $\tanh x = x - \dfrac{5x^3}{15+7x^2} - \dfrac{x^2}{1} - \dfrac{9x^2}{315+28x^2}$

$$\dfrac{x}{1} \quad \dfrac{15x+2x^3}{15+7x^2} \quad \dfrac{15x+x^3}{15+6x^2} \quad \dfrac{4725x+600x^3+10x^5}{4725+2175x^2+105x^4}$$

$$\dfrac{945+120x^3+2x^5}{945+435x^2+21x^4}$$

$$- \quad \dfrac{5x^2}{1} \quad - \dfrac{13x^2}{1287-44x^2} - \ldots$$

$$\dfrac{4725x+525x^3+5x^5}{4725+2100x^2+75x^4}$$

$$\dfrac{945+105x^3+x^5}{945x+420x^2+15x^4}$$

$$\ldots - \dfrac{(4n+1)x^2}{(4n-3)(4n-1)(4n+1)+4(4n-1)x^2} - \dfrac{(4n-3)x^2}{1} - \ldots$$

$$34(122)$$

8°. $\tanh x = \dfrac{x}{1} + \dfrac{\dfrac{x^2}{3}}{1} + \dfrac{\dfrac{x^2}{15}}{1} + \dfrac{\dfrac{x^2}{35}}{1} + \ldots,$

where

$$a_1 = x, \qquad a_{n+1} = \frac{x^2}{4n^2-1} \quad \text{for} \quad n \geqslant 1,$$

$$|r_{n-1}(x)| \leqslant \frac{|x^{2n-1}|}{D_{n-1}D_n \prod\limits_{i=1}^{n}(4i^2-1)}. \qquad 65(264)$$

The following table gives the number of terms which are needed in order to get 12 significant decimal digits correct:

x	tanh x in the form of 8°
0·1	4
1	8
10	19

9°. $\tanh x = \dfrac{\dfrac{x}{2}}{\dfrac{1}{2}} + \dfrac{\dfrac{x^2}{4.2}}{\dfrac{3}{4}} + \dfrac{\dfrac{x^2}{4.8}}{\dfrac{5}{8}} + \dfrac{\dfrac{x^2}{8.8}}{\dfrac{7}{8}} + \cdots$ $\qquad$ 65(264)

10°. $\tanh x \approx \dfrac{C_k^1(2k-1)(2k-2)\ldots}{k(2k-1)\ldots}$

$\dfrac{\ldots(k+1)x - C_k^3(2k-3)(2k-4)\ldots(k+1)4x^3+\ldots}{\ldots(k+1) + C_k^2(2k-2)(2k-3)\ldots(k+1)2x^2+\ldots}$ $\qquad$ 34(152)

This is a general expression for all of the convergents of the expansion in § 3.6.

§ 4. Inverse hyperbolic functions

4.1. General information. 1°. *Definitions.*

If $x = \sinh y$, then $y = \text{Arc} \sinh x$.

If $x = \cosh y$, then $y = \text{Arc} \cosh x$.

If $x = \tanh y$, then $y = \text{Arc} \tanh x$.

If $x = \coth y$, then $y = \text{Arc} \coth x$.

2°. The domain of definition of the function Arc sinh x and its range of values are each the interval $(-\infty, +\infty)$.

The function Arc cosh x is two-valued and consists of two branches having a common domain of definition $[1, +\infty)$. The range of values on one branch of the function is $[0, +\infty)$, and the range of values for the other branch is $(-\infty, 0]$.

The domain of definition of the function Arc tanh x is the interval $(-1, +1)$, and its range of values is $(-\infty, +\infty)$.

The domain of definition of the function Arc coth x is the pair of open intervals $(-\infty, -1)$ and $(1, +\infty)$. The corresponding ranges of values are the open intervals $(-\infty, 0)$ and $(0, +\infty)$.

3°. The function $\operatorname{Arc\,cosh} x$ is even, but $\operatorname{Arc\,sinh} x$, $\operatorname{Arc\,tanh} x$ and $\operatorname{Arc\,coth} x$ are all odd functions.

$$\operatorname{Arc\,sinh} x = \operatorname{sign} x .\ \operatorname{Arc\,sinh} |x| ,$$
$$\operatorname{Arc\,tanh} x = \operatorname{sign} x .\ \operatorname{Arc\,tanh} |x| ,$$
$$\operatorname{Arc\,coth} x = \operatorname{sign} x .\ \operatorname{Arc\,coth} |x| .$$

4°. *Functional relations.* (a) Expressions for one inverse hyperbolic function in terms of another.

$\operatorname{Arc\,sinh} x =$		$\pm \operatorname{Arc\,cosh}\sqrt{x^2+1}$	$\operatorname{Arc\,tanh} \dfrac{x}{\sqrt{x^2+1}}$	$\operatorname{Arc\,coth} \dfrac{\sqrt{x^2+1}}{x}$
$\operatorname{Arc\,cosh} x =$	$\pm \operatorname{Arc\,sinh}\sqrt{x^2-1}$		$\pm \operatorname{Arc\,tanh}\dfrac{\sqrt{x^2-1}}{x}$	$\pm \operatorname{Arc\,coth}\dfrac{x}{\sqrt{x^2-1}}$
$\operatorname{Arc\,tanh} x =$	$\operatorname{Arc\,sinh} \dfrac{x}{\sqrt{1-x^2}}$	$\pm \operatorname{Arc\,cosh}\dfrac{1}{\sqrt{1-x^2}}$		$\operatorname{Arc\,coth} \dfrac{1}{x}$
$\operatorname{Arc\,coth} x =$	$\operatorname{Arc\,sinh} \dfrac{1}{\sqrt{x^2-1}}$	$\pm \operatorname{Arc\,cosh}\dfrac{x}{\sqrt{x^2-1}}$	$\operatorname{Arc\,tanh} \dfrac{1}{x}$	

38 (27); 37 (68

In the expressions containing $\operatorname{Arc\,cosh} x$, the plus sign should be taken if $x > 0$, and the minus sign should be taken if $x < 0$.

However, both signs must be taken in the expressions for $\operatorname{Arc\,cosh} x$ itself.

(b) Relations between inverse hyperbolic functions, inverse trigonometric functions and logarithms.

$$\operatorname{Arc\,sinh} x = \ln\!\left(x + \sqrt{x^2 + 1}\right) = \frac{1}{i}\,\arcsin(ix). \qquad 38(28)$$

$$\operatorname{Arc\,cosh} x = \ln\!\left(x + \sqrt{x^2 - 1}\right) = i\arccos x. \qquad 38(28)$$

$$\operatorname{Arc\,tanh} x = \frac{1}{2}\ln\frac{1+x}{1-x} = \frac{1}{i}\,\arctan(ix). \qquad 38(28)$$

$$\operatorname{Arc\,coth} x = \frac{1}{2}\ln\frac{x+1}{x-1} = \frac{1}{i}\,\operatorname{arc\,cot}(-ix). \qquad 38(28)$$

4.2. Power series expansions.

1°. $\quad \operatorname{Arc\,sinh} x = x - \dfrac{1}{2.3}\,x^3 + \dfrac{1.3}{2.4.5}\,x^5 - \ldots$

$$= \sum_{k=0}^{\infty} (-1)^k \frac{(2k)!}{2^{2k}(k!)^2(2k+1)} x^{2k+1}$$

$$= xF\left(\frac{1}{2},\ \frac{1}{2},\ \frac{3}{2}\ ;\ -x^2\right) \qquad (|x| < 1). \qquad 26(64);\ 32(480)$$

$2°.$ $\mathrm{Arc\,sinh}\,x = \ln 2x + \dfrac{1}{2} \cdot \dfrac{1}{2x^2} - \dfrac{1.3}{2.4} \cdot \dfrac{1}{4x^4} + \ldots$

$$= \ln 2x + \sum_{k=1}^{\infty} (-1)^{k+1} \frac{(2k)!\, x^{-2k}}{2^{2k}(k!)^2 2k} \qquad (|x| > 1). \qquad 26(64);\ 39$$

$3°.$ $\mathrm{Arc\,cosh}\,x = \ln 2x - \displaystyle\sum_{k=1}^{\infty} \dfrac{(2k)!}{2^{2k}(k!)^2 2k}\, x^{-2k}$

$$(|x| > 1). \qquad 26(64);\ 39$$

$4°.$ $\mathrm{Arc\,tanh}\,x = x + \dfrac{x^3}{3} + \dfrac{x^5}{5} + \ldots = \displaystyle\sum_{k=0}^{\infty} \dfrac{x^{2k+1}}{2k+1}$

$$(|x| < 1). \qquad 26(64);\ 39$$

$5°.$ $\mathrm{Arc\,sinh}\,\dfrac{1}{x} = \mathrm{Arc\,cosech}\,x = \displaystyle\sum_{k=0}^{\infty} \dfrac{(-1)^k (2k)!}{2^{2k}(k!)^2(2k+1)}\, x^{-2k-1}$

$$(|\,x\,| > 1). \qquad 26(64);\ 39$$

$6°.$ $\mathrm{Arc\,cosh}\,\dfrac{1}{x} = \mathrm{Arc\,sech}\,x = \ln \dfrac{2}{x} - \displaystyle\sum_{k=1}^{\infty} \dfrac{(2k)!}{2^{2k}(k!)^2 2k}\, x^{2k}$

$$(0 < x < 1). \qquad 26(65);\ 39$$

$7°.$ $\mathrm{Arc\,sinh}\,\dfrac{1}{x} = \mathrm{Arc\,cosech}\,x = \ln \dfrac{2}{x} + \displaystyle\sum_{k=1}^{\infty} \dfrac{(-1)^{k+1}(2k)!}{2^{2k}(k!)^2 2k}\, x^{2k}$

$$(0 < x < 1). \qquad 26(65);\ 39$$

$8°.$ $\mathrm{Arc\,tanh}\,\dfrac{1}{x} = \mathrm{Arc\,coth}\,x = \displaystyle\sum_{k=0}^{\infty} \dfrac{x^{-(2k+1)}}{2k+1} \qquad (|x| > 1).$

$$26(65);\ 39$$

4.3. Continued fraction expansions.

$1°.$ $\operatorname{Arctanh} x = \dfrac{x}{1} - \dfrac{x^2}{3} - \dfrac{4x^2}{5} - \ldots - \dfrac{n^2x^2}{2n+1} - \ldots$

$$34(115)$$

This fraction converges everywhere in the plane of the complex variable x, except for the two semi-intervals on the real axis $(-\infty, -1]$ and $[1, +\infty)$.

$2°.$ $\operatorname{Arctanh} x = x + \dfrac{x^3}{3} - \dfrac{9x^2}{5} - \dfrac{4x^2}{7} - \dfrac{25x^2}{9} - \ldots$

$$\ldots - \frac{(2n+1)^2x^2}{4n+1} - \frac{4n^2x^2}{4n+3} - \ldots \qquad 34(115)$$

This fraction converges everywhere in the plane of the complex variable x, except for the two semi-intervals on the real axis $(-\infty, -1]$ and $[1, +\infty)$.

$3°.$ $\dfrac{\operatorname{Arcsinh} x}{\sqrt{1+x^2}} = \dfrac{x}{1+x^2} - \dfrac{x^2}{3} - \dfrac{4x^2}{5(1+x^2)} - \dfrac{9x^2}{7} - \ldots$

$$\ldots - \frac{4n^2x^2}{(4n+1)(1+x^2)} - \frac{(2n+1)^2x^2}{4n+3} - \ldots \qquad 34(116)$$

$4°.$ $\sqrt{1+x^2}\,\operatorname{Arcsinh} x = x + \dfrac{x^3}{3(1+x^2)} - \dfrac{9x^2}{5} - \dfrac{4x^2}{7(1+x^2)} - \ldots$

$$\ldots - \frac{(2n+1)^2x^2}{4n+1} - \frac{4n^2x^2}{(4n+3)(1+x^2)} - \ldots \qquad 34(117)$$

$5°.$ $\dfrac{\operatorname{Arc\,cosh} x}{\sqrt{x^2-1}} = \dfrac{1}{x} - \dfrac{x^2-1}{3x} - \ldots - \dfrac{n^2(x^2-1)}{(2n+1)x} - \ldots \qquad 34(118)$

$6°.$ $\dfrac{\operatorname{Arcsinh} x}{\sqrt{1+x^2}} = \dfrac{x}{1} + \dfrac{1.2x^2}{3} + \dfrac{1.2x^2}{5} + \ldots$

$$\ldots + \frac{(2n-1)2nx^2}{4n-1} + \frac{(2n-1)2nx^2}{4n+1} + \ldots \qquad 34(119)$$

$7°.$ $\operatorname{Arc tanh} x = \dfrac{x}{1-x^2} + \dfrac{1.2x^2}{3} + \dfrac{1.2x^2}{5(1-x^2)} + \ldots$

$$\ldots + \dfrac{(2n-1)2nx^2}{4n-1} + \dfrac{(2n-1)2nx^2}{(4n+1)(1-x^2)} + \ldots \qquad 34(119)$$

$8°.$ $\dfrac{\operatorname{Arc cosh} x}{\sqrt{x^2-1}} = \dfrac{x}{1+} \dfrac{1.2(x^2-1)}{3} + \dfrac{1.2(x^2-1)}{5} + \ldots$

$$\ldots + \dfrac{(2n-1)2n(x^2-1)}{4n-1} + \dfrac{(2n-1)2n(x^2-1)}{4n+1} + \ldots \qquad 34(119)$$

4.4. Rational approximations. $1°.$ We shall now give a set of rational approximations (or Padè approximations) for $\operatorname{Arcsinh} x/2$, of the form

$$\operatorname{Arc sinh} \frac{x}{2} \approx \frac{x}{2} \frac{N_p\left[\left(\dfrac{x}{4}\right)^2\right]}{D_q\left[\left(\dfrac{x}{4}\right)^2\right]},$$

with $p = 0(1)4$, $q = 0(1)4$ (cf. [58], p. 43), where p and q are the degrees of N_p and D_q respectively, as polynomials in $(x/4)^2$.

(a) $p = 0$

$q = 0$	1
$q = 1$	$\dfrac{1}{1 + \dfrac{2}{3}\left(\dfrac{x}{4}\right)^2}$
$q = 2$	$\dfrac{1}{1 + \dfrac{2}{3}\left(\dfrac{x}{4}\right)^2 - \dfrac{34}{45}\left(\dfrac{x}{4}\right)^4}$
$q = 3$	$\dfrac{1}{1 + \dfrac{2}{3}\left(\dfrac{x}{4}\right)^2 - \dfrac{34}{45}\left(\dfrac{x}{4}\right)^4 + \dfrac{1468}{945}\left(\dfrac{x}{4}\right)^6}$
$q = 4$	$\dfrac{1}{1 + \dfrac{2}{3}\left(\dfrac{x}{4}\right)^2 - \dfrac{34}{45}\left(\dfrac{x}{4}\right)^4 + \dfrac{1468}{945}\left(\dfrac{x}{4}\right)^6 - \dfrac{27\,859}{14\,175}\left(\dfrac{x}{4}\right)^8}$

(b) $p = 1$

$q = 0$	$1 - \dfrac{2}{3}\left(\dfrac{x}{4}\right)^2$
$q = 1$	$\dfrac{1 + \dfrac{17}{15}\left(\dfrac{x}{4}\right)^2}{1 + \dfrac{9}{5}\left(\dfrac{x}{4}\right)^2}$
$q = 2$	$\dfrac{1 + \dfrac{734}{357}\left(\dfrac{x}{4}\right)^2}{1 + \dfrac{324}{119}\left(\dfrac{x}{4}\right)^2 + \dfrac{366}{595}\left(\dfrac{x}{4}\right)^4}$
$q = 3$	$\dfrac{1 + \dfrac{27\,859}{11\,010}\left(\dfrac{x}{4}\right)^2}{1 + \dfrac{11\,733}{3670}\left(\dfrac{x}{4}\right)^2 + \dfrac{1709}{1835}\left(\dfrac{x}{4}\right)^4 - \dfrac{69\,049}{192\,675}\left(\dfrac{x}{4}\right)^6}$

(c) $p = 2$

$q = 0$	$1 - \dfrac{2}{3}\left(\dfrac{x}{4}\right)^2 + \dfrac{6}{5}\left(\dfrac{x}{4}\right)^4$
$q = 1$	$\dfrac{1 + \dfrac{12}{7}\left(\dfrac{x}{4}\right)^2 - \dfrac{122}{315}\left(\dfrac{x}{4}\right)^4}{1 + \dfrac{50}{21}\left(\dfrac{x}{4}\right)^2}$
$q = 2$	$\dfrac{1 + \dfrac{1709}{549}\left(\dfrac{x}{4}\right)^2 + \dfrac{69\,049}{57\,645}\left(\dfrac{x}{4}\right)^4}{1 + \dfrac{2075}{549}\left(\dfrac{x}{4}\right)^2 + \dfrac{1075}{427}\left(\dfrac{x}{4}\right)^4}$
$q = 3$	$\dfrac{1 + \dfrac{9\,274\,172}{2\,278\,617}\left(\dfrac{x}{4}\right)^2 + \dfrac{12\,022\,609}{3\,797\,695}\left(\dfrac{x}{4}\right)^4}{1 + \dfrac{3\,597\,750}{759\,539}\left(\dfrac{x}{4}\right)^2 + \dfrac{3\,891\,575}{759\,539}\left(\dfrac{x}{4}\right)^4 + \dfrac{9\,391\,090}{15\,950\,319}\left(\dfrac{x}{4}\right)^6}$

(d) $p = 3$

$q = 0$	$1 - \dfrac{2}{3}\left(\dfrac{x}{4}\right)^2 + \dfrac{6}{5}\left(\dfrac{x}{4}\right)^4 - \dfrac{20}{7}\left(\dfrac{x}{4}\right)^6$
$q = 1$	$\dfrac{1 + \dfrac{37}{18}\left(\dfrac{x}{4}\right)^2 - \dfrac{83}{135}\left(\dfrac{x}{4}\right)^4 + \dfrac{43}{105}\left(\dfrac{x}{4}\right)^6}{1 + \dfrac{49}{18}\left(\dfrac{x}{4}\right)^2}$
$q = 2$	$\dfrac{1 + \dfrac{27\,218}{7095}\left(\dfrac{x}{4}\right)^2 + \dfrac{73\,628\,599}{30\,203\,415}\left(\dfrac{x}{4}\right)^4 - \dfrac{888\,397\,114}{3\,171\,358\,575}\left(\dfrac{x}{4}\right)^6}{1 + \dfrac{31\,948}{7\,095}\left(\dfrac{x}{4}\right)^2 + \dfrac{54\,145}{12\,771}\left(\dfrac{x}{4}\right)^4}$
$q = 3$	$\dfrac{1 + \dfrac{186\,989\,305}{36\,625\,251}\left(\dfrac{x}{4}\right)^2 + \dfrac{4\,289\,878\,962}{671\,462\,935}\left(\dfrac{x}{4}\right)^4 + \dfrac{17\,487\,984\,593}{1\,410\,072\,635}\left(\dfrac{x}{4}\right)^6}{1 + \dfrac{70\,468\,713}{12\,208\,391}\left(\dfrac{x}{4}\right)^2 + \dfrac{1\,213\,595\,250}{134\,292\,587}\left(\dfrac{x}{4}\right)^4 + \dfrac{1\,287\,365\,485}{402\,877\,761}\left(\dfrac{x}{4}\right)^6}$

(e) $p = 4$

$q = 0$	$1 - \dfrac{2}{3}\left(\dfrac{x}{4}\right)^2 + \dfrac{6}{5}\left(\dfrac{x}{4}\right)^4 - \dfrac{20}{7}\left(\dfrac{x}{4}\right)^6 + \dfrac{70}{9}\left(\dfrac{x}{4}\right)^8$

CHAPTER IV

ALGORITHMS USED FOR COMPUTING ELEMENTARY FUNCTIONS ON SOME SOVIET COMPUTERS

Introductory remarks

In program-controlled machines, the values of elementary functions are computed by means of "standard programs" based on some one or other algorithm for computing these functions. Standard programs for the following functions are usually included: $\frac{1}{x}$ (in machines without automatic division), $\sqrt{x}$ (in machines without automatic extraction of the square root), 2^x, $\ln x$, trigonometric functions, inverse trigonometric functions.

Heron's iterative method is usually employed for finding $y = \sqrt{x}$ (cf. Ch. I, § 3.6, 1°), but the algorithms differ in their choice of the initial approximation y_0. If

$$x = 2^p z$$

where

$$\tfrac{1}{4} \leqslant z < 1,$$

then

$$\sqrt{x} = 2^{p/2} \sqrt{z},$$

so that the evaluation of $\sqrt{x}$ reduces to the evaluation of $\sqrt{z}$. (In machines without automatic division, this is replaced by the iterative processes of 2° in Ch. I, § 3.6.)

When trigonometric functions are being computed, the argument is first reduced to the first quadrant or octant.

When 2^x is computed, the exponent x is represented in the form $x = p + z$ (where $p = E(x)$, $z = \{x\}$), thereby reducing the computation of 2^x to that of computing 2^z (where $0 \leqslant z < 1$), and then $2^x = 2^p \cdot 2^z$.

Similarly, if $x = 2^p z$, where $\frac{1}{2} \leqslant z < 1$, then $\ln x = p \ln 2 + \ln z$, and the computation of $\ln x$ reduces to computing $\ln z$.

§ 1. "Strela"[†]

1.1. Computation of 2^x $(0 \leqslant x \leqslant 1)$.

$1°$. $\displaystyle 2^x \approx \sum_{k=0}^{8} a_k x^k$.

The coefficients a_k are given in Ch. II, § 1.4, $2°$(b).

$2°$. $2^x = (2^{\frac{x}{8}})^8 = \{[(2^{\frac{x}{8}})^2]^2\}^2$,

$$2^{\frac{x}{8}} \approx \sum_{k=0}^{4} a_k x^k.$$

The coefficients a_k are given in Ch. II, § 1.4, $2°$(c).

The error of the computation of $2^{x/8}$ does not exceed 0.88×10^{-10}. The relative error in the computation of 2^x may be as large as 5×10^{-10}, when $|x|$ is close to 0.5.

1.2. Computation of $\ln x$ $(\frac{1}{2} \leqslant x < 1)$.

$$\ln x = -\mu_i \ln 2 + (((((a_6 z + a_5) z + a_4) z + a_3) z + a_2) z + a_1) z,$$

$$z = \lambda x,$$

$$\lambda = \lambda_i, \text{ if } x_i \leqslant x < x_{i+1} \quad (i = 1, 2, 3, 4),$$

$$\lambda_i = (\sqrt[4]{2})^i, \quad x_i = \frac{1}{2} (\sqrt[4]{2})^i.$$

μ_1	3·659 646 860 780	μ_3	4·159 646 860 780
μ_2	3·909 646 860 780	μ_4	4·409 646 860 780

a_1	5·500 472 922 511	a_4	−2·638 754 306 465
a_2	−6·299 229 808 534	a_5	0·772 171 339 086
a_3	5·126 738 196 584	a_6	−0·098 011 234 843

[†] Cf. [10].

1.3. Computation of sines. Computation of $\sin \dfrac{\pi}{2} x$.

(a) $\sin \dfrac{\pi}{2}\, x \approx \displaystyle\sum_{k=0}^{5} a_{2k+1} x^{2k+1}$ $(|x| \leqslant 1)$.

The coefficients a_{2k+1} are given in Ch. III, § 1.6, 2° (d). The relative error may be as large as $0{\cdot}5 \times 10^{-9}$, when x is close to 1.

(b) $\sin x \approx \displaystyle\sum_{k=0}^{5} a_{2k+1} x^{2k+1}$ $\left(|x| < \dfrac{\pi}{2}\right)$.

The coefficients a_{2k+1} are given in Ch. III, § 1.6, 3°(c).

1.4. Computation of tangents.

$$\tan \frac{\pi}{4}\, x \approx \sum_{k=0}^{8} a_{2k+1} x^{2k+1}   (|x| < 1).$$

The coefficients a_{2k+1} are given in Ch. III, § 1.6, 10°(a). The error is $0{\cdot}2 \times 10^{-9}$.

1.5. Computation of cotangents.

$$\cot \frac{\pi}{4}\, x \approx \frac{a_{-1}}{x} + \sum_{k=0}^{4} a_{2k+1} x^{2k+1}.$$

The coefficients a_{2k+1} are given in Ch. III § 1.6, 11°. The error is $0{\cdot}2 \times 10^{-9}$.

1.6. Computation of $\arcsin x$. If $x^2 < 0{\cdot}5$, then

$$\arcsin x \approx \sum_{k=0}^{9} a_{2k+1} x^{2k+1};$$

but if $x^2 > 0{\cdot}5$, then

$$\arcsin x = \frac{\pi}{2} - \arcsin \sqrt{1 - x^2}.$$

The coefficients a_{2k+1} are given in Ch. III, § 2·4, 2°.

§ 2. BESM

2.1. Computation of $y = \sqrt{x}\left(\dfrac{1}{2} \leqslant x < 1\right)$. The initial approximation is taken as

$$y_0 = k(x + b - \varDelta) \text{ if } \frac{1}{2} \leqslant x < k,$$

or as

$$y_0 = k(x + b) \text{ if } k \leqslant x < 1; \text{ where}$$

$$k = 0 \cdot 57155, \quad b = 0 \cdot 75787, \quad \varDelta = 0 \cdot 013857.$$

Two iterations of Heron's formula are then performed (cf. Ch. I, § 3.6, 1°): these are combined into the single formula

$$y = \frac{1}{4}\left(y_0 + \frac{x}{y_0}\right) + \frac{x}{y_0 + \dfrac{x}{y_0}} ; \qquad 7(9, 10)$$

which produces an error of 2^{-33}.

2.2. Computation of 2^x $(0 \leqslant x < 1)$.

$1°.\ 2^x \approx \displaystyle\sum_{k=0}^{7} a_k x^k.$

The coefficients a_k are given in Ch. II, § 1.4, 2°(a).

$2°$. The following formula is used for computing the resulting polynomial, in order to reduce the number of multiplications to be performed:

$$2^x = a_0 + \overline{x}\{c_1 + \overline{x}[c_2 + \overline{x}\{[(\overline{x}+B)^2 + C + \overline{x}][(\overline{x}+B)^2 + D] - E\}]\},$$

where $\overline{x} = \lambda x$.

λ	0·215 596 346 446	B	0·105 963 619 947
c_1	3·215 022 885 576	C	−1·277 917 410 482
c_2	5·168 182 735 768	D	3·881 751 544 667
		E	−10·469 925 626 182

Spot checks made by computing 2^x, using these coefficients, give 11 correct significant figures. 7(6, 7).

2.3. Computation of $\ln x \left(\dfrac{1}{2} \leqslant x < 1 \right)$

$$\ln x = -\frac{1}{2} \ln 2 + \sum_{k=0}^{3} a_{2k+1} u^{2k+1},$$

$$u = \frac{x - \dfrac{\sqrt{2}}{2}}{x + \dfrac{\sqrt{2}}{2}}.$$

The coefficients a_{2k+1} are given in Ch. II, § 2.6, 3°.

2.4. Computation of $\sin x$ **and** $\cos x \left(0 \leqslant x \leqslant \dfrac{\pi}{4} \right)$. The functions $\sin x$ and $\cos x$ are found in terms of the tangent of half the argument.

$$2 \tan \frac{x}{2} = \frac{z}{\sum\limits_{k=0}^{4} a_k z^{2k}}, \qquad z = \frac{x}{\pi}. \qquad 7(7)$$

The coefficients a_k are given in Ch. III, § 1.8, 9°.

In order to reduce the number of multiplications required, the following formula is used for evaluating the expression above:

$$2 \tan \frac{x}{2} \approx \frac{\overline{x}}{E - [(\overline{x}^2 + B)^2 + C + \overline{x}^2][(\overline{x}^2 + B)^2 + D]},$$

where $x = \lambda z$.

λ	0·106 785 251 669	D	0·705 279 988 224
B	−0·072 162 649 192	E	0·111 522 419 569
C	−0·039 607 473 057		

Spot checks, in which $\sin x$ and $\cos x$ have been computed by means of the above coefficients, give 11 correct decimal places.

2.5. Computation of $\arcsin x$.

$$\arcsin x = \begin{cases} \arctan \dfrac{x}{\sqrt{1 - x^2}} & \left(|x| \leqslant \dfrac{\sqrt{2}}{2} \right), \\[3mm] \text{arc cot} \dfrac{\sqrt{1 - x^2}}{x} & \left(x \geqslant \dfrac{\sqrt{2}}{2} \right). \end{cases} \qquad 7(3)$$

2.6. Computation of $\arctan x$ $(0 \leqslant x \leqslant 1)$.

$$\arctan x = \arctan z + c \begin{cases} x < x_0, & z = x, \quad c = 0 \\ \\ x \geqslant x_0, & z = \dfrac{x - \dfrac{1}{\sqrt{3}}}{1 + \dfrac{x}{\sqrt{3}}}, \end{cases}$$

$$c = \arctan \frac{1}{\sqrt{3}} = \frac{\pi}{6},$$

$$x_0 = \frac{\sqrt{3}-1}{\sqrt{3}+1}, \quad |z| \leqslant x_0 = \frac{\sqrt{3}-1}{\sqrt{3}+1} \approx 0\cdot268, \qquad 7(11)$$

$$\arctan z \approx \sum_{k=0}^{4} a_{2k+1} z^{2k+1}.$$

The coefficients a_{2k+1} are given in Ch. III, § 2.4, 7°.

In order to reduce the time involved in computing the polynomial approximating to $\arctan z$, we may use the following economical scheme:

$$\arctan z = z\{[(Az^2 + B)^2 + C + z^2][(Az^2 + B)^2 + D] - E\};$$

A	$0\cdot555\,058\,703\,74$	D	$0\cdot175\,045\,006\,22$
B	$-0\cdot657\,607\,298\,52$	E	$-0\cdot586\,132\,618\,27$
C	$0\cdot248\,824\,379\,98$		

$$7(13)$$

Spot checks, in which values of $\arctan x$ is computed in the above manner, give ten correct decimal places.

§ 3. M-2

3.1. Computation of $\sqrt{x}$ $(\frac{1}{2} \leqslant x < 1)$ (floating point). Heron's iterative process (cf. Ch. I, § 3.6, 1°) is used for computing $y = \sqrt{x}$, with the initial approximation

$$y_0 = \frac{1}{2} + \frac{1}{2}x. \qquad 11(163)$$

On the average, two iterations are required to compute $\sqrt{x}$ within an error of 10^{-8}.

3.2. Computation of e^x.   1°. *Computation of* e^x *in floating point arithmetic.*

$$e^x = 2^{\left[\frac{x}{\ln 2}\right]}(e^z)^2, \quad z = \left\{\frac{x}{\ln 2}\right\} \cdot \frac{\ln 2}{2}, \quad |z| \leqslant \frac{\ln 2}{2}, \quad \text{11(159)}$$

$$e^z \approx \frac{12(z^2+10)+z(z^2+60)}{12(z^2+10)-z(z^2+60)}, \quad r = 0 \cdot 9 \times 10^{-8}. \quad \text{11(160)}$$

2°. *Computation of* e^x *in fixed point arithmetic.*

$$e^x = 2^p \cdot (e^z)^2,$$

$$\text{if} \left\{\frac{x}{\ln 2}\right\} < 0 \quad z = \frac{\ln 2}{2}\left\{\frac{x}{\ln 2}\right\}, \quad p = \left[\frac{x}{\ln 2}\right],$$

$$\text{if} \left\{\frac{x}{\ln 2}\right\} \geqslant 0 \quad z = \frac{\ln 2}{2}\left(\left\{\frac{x}{\ln 2}\right\} - 1\right), \quad p = \left[\frac{x}{\ln 2}\right] + 1.$$

$$\text{11(192)}$$

If the power series

$$e^z = \sum_{k=0}^{\infty} \frac{z^k}{k!}$$

is truncated at that term for which

$$\left|\frac{z^k}{k!}\right| \leqslant 2^{-28},$$

then the error of the computation is less than 2^{-32}.   11(193)

3.3. Computation of $\ln x$ $(\frac{1}{2} \leqslant x < 1)$.   1°. *Computation in floating point arithmetic.*

$$\ln x \approx -\frac{1}{2}\ln 2 + \sum_{k=0}^{2} a_{2k+1} u^{2k+1}, \quad u = \frac{x - \frac{\sqrt{2}}{2}}{x + \frac{\sqrt{2}}{2}}.$$

The coefficients a_{2k+1} are given in Ch. II, § 2·6, 2°. The error is less than $0 \cdot 3 \times 10^{-7}$.

2°. *Computation of* $\ln x$ *in fixed point arithmetic.*

$$\ln x = -\frac{1}{2}\ln 2 + \ln(\sqrt{2} \cdot x).$$

The computation proceeds according to the formula

$$\ln(\sqrt{2}x) \approx \sum_{k=0}^{3} a_{2k+1} u^{2k+1}, \quad u = 2\,\frac{x - \sqrt{\dfrac{1}{2}}}{x + \sqrt{\dfrac{1}{2}}},$$

$$a_{2k+1} = \frac{1}{(2k+1)\,2^{2k}}. \qquad\qquad 11(189)$$

3.4. Computation of $\sin x$ **and** $\cos x$. The problem is reduced to the computation of the cosine of an angle lying in the first quadrant:

$$\cos\frac{\pi}{2}x \approx \sum_{k=0}^{4} a_{2k} x^{2k}.$$

The coefficients a_{2k} are given in Ch. III, § 1.6, 8°(b). The error is less than 5×10^{-8}, for $0 \leqslant x \leqslant 1$.

3.5. Computation of arc tan x **(floating point).** For $|x| \leqslant 1$,

$$\arctan x \approx \sum_{k=0}^{8} a_{2k+1} x^{2k+1}. \qquad\qquad 11(166)$$

The coefficients a_{2k+1} are given in Ch. III, § 2.4, 8°. The error is less than 5×10^{-8}.
If $|x| > 1$, then

$$\arctan x = \frac{\pi}{2} - \arctan\left(\frac{1}{x}\right).$$

COMMENT. The following formulae were formerly used for computing the trigonometric functions:

$$\tan\frac{x}{2} = \frac{x}{2} - \frac{x^2}{6} - \frac{x^2}{10} - \frac{x^2}{14},$$

$$\sin x = \frac{2\tan\dfrac{x}{2}}{1 + \tan^2\dfrac{x}{2}}, \quad \cos x = \frac{1 - \tan^2\dfrac{x}{2}}{1 + \tan^2\dfrac{x}{2}},$$

together with the formulae for double angles:

$$\cos 2x = 2\cos^2 x - 1, \quad \sin 2x = 2\sin x . \cos x.$$

The following formulae were used for computing e^x and e^{-x}:

$$e^x = \cosh x + \sinh x, \quad e^{-x} = \frac{1}{e^x}.$$

Here, $\cosh x$ and $\sinh x$ were computed by formulae analogous to those used for $\cos x$ and $\sin x$.

§ 4. M-3

4.1. Computation of $\sqrt{x}$. Heron's iterative process (cf. Ch. I, § 3.6, 1°) is used for computing $\sqrt{x}$, with the initial approximation

$$y_0 = 0 \cdot 5903 x + 0 \cdot 4173.$$

Two iterations are required for computing $\sqrt{x}$ within an error of 2^{-32}.

4.2. Computation of e^x.

$$e^x = 2^{\left[\frac{x}{\ln 2}\right]} (e^z)^4, \quad z = \left\{\frac{x}{\ln 2}\right\} \frac{\ln 2}{4}, \quad |z| \leqslant \frac{\ln 2}{4},$$

$$e^z = \frac{12(z^2 + 10) + z(z^2 + 60)}{12(z^2 + 10) - z(z^2 + 60)}, \quad r = 10^{-10}.$$

4.3. Computation of $\ln x$ ($\frac{1}{2} \leqslant x < 1$).

$$\ln x = \ln 2\left[-\frac{1}{2} + P(t)\right], \quad P(t) = \sum_{k=0}^{3} a_{2k+1} u^{2k+1}, \quad u = \frac{x - \frac{\sqrt{2}}{2}}{x + \frac{\sqrt{2}}{2}}.$$

The coefficients a_{2k+1} are given in Ch. II, § 2·6, 4°. The error is less than 2^{-32}.

4.4. Computation of tangent and cotangent.

$$1°. \quad \tan \frac{\pi}{4} x = \frac{z}{z \cot \frac{\pi}{4} z} \quad (|x| < 1), \quad \text{if } uv \geqslant 0,$$

$$u = \left\{\frac{x}{\pi} - \frac{1}{4}\right\}, \quad v = |u| - \frac{1}{2},$$

$$z = 4|v| - 1 = \left|4 \cdot \left|\left\{\frac{x}{\pi} - \frac{1}{4}\right\}\right| - 2\right| - 1.$$

$2°.$ $\tan\dfrac{\pi}{4}x = \dfrac{z \cdot \cot\dfrac{\pi}{4}z}{z}$ $(|x| < 1)$ if $uv < 0$.

$$z\cot\frac{\pi}{4}z \approx \sum_{k=0}^{5} a_{2k}z^{2k}.$$

The coefficients a_{2k} may be taken from Ch. III, § 1.6, 11°.

4.5. Computation of arc tan x $(0 < x \leqslant 1)$.

$$\arctan x = \arctan z + c \begin{cases} \text{if } |x| < 2 - \sqrt{3}, \quad \text{then } z = x, \quad c = 0, \\[2mm] \text{if } |x| \geqslant 2 - \sqrt{3}, \quad \text{then } z = \dfrac{x - \dfrac{1}{\sqrt{3}}}{1 + \dfrac{x}{\sqrt{3}}}, \\[6mm] \qquad\qquad\qquad c = \arctan\dfrac{1}{\sqrt{3}} = \dfrac{\pi}{6}, \end{cases}$$

$$\arctan z = \sum_{k=0}^{4} a_{2k+1}z^{2k+1}.$$

The coefficients a_{2k+1} may be taken from Ch. III, § 2.4, 7°. The error is less than 2^{-32}.

§ 5. "Ural"

5.1. Computation of $\sqrt{x}$ $(\tfrac{1}{2} \leqslant x < 1)$ (fixed point). Heron's iterative formula (cf. Ch. I, § 3.6, 1°) is used, with the initial approximation

$$y_0 = 0\cdot 57422x + 0\cdot 42578.\qquad\qquad 3(282)$$

5.2. Computation of $\tfrac{1}{4}e^x$ $(|x| < 1)$ (fixed point). The computation is based on the polynomial

$$\frac{1}{4}e^x \approx \sum_{k=0}^{10} a_k x^k.$$

The coefficients a_k are given in Ch. II, § 1.4, 1°(d).

5.3. Computation of $\dfrac{1}{25}\ln x\,(2^{-35} < x < 1)$ (fixed point).

$$\ln x \approx x \sum_{x=0}^{5} a_{2k} u^{2k}, \qquad u = 3\frac{x-1}{x+1}.$$

The coefficients a_{2k} are given in Ch. II, § 2.6, 5°.

5.4. Computation of $\sin x\left(|x| < \dfrac{\pi}{2}\right)$ (fixed point).

$$\sin x \approx 2 \sum_{x=0}^{5} a_{2k+1} x^{2k+1}.$$

The coefficients a_{2k+1} are half the values of the corresponding coefficients given in Ch. III, § 1.6, 3°(c).

5.5. Computation of $\cos x\left(|x| < \dfrac{\pi}{2}\right)$ (fixed point).

$$\cos x \approx 2 \sum_{k=0}^{5} a_{2k} x^{2k}. \tag{3(289)}$$

The error is less than 5×10^{-10}.

The coefficients a_{2k} are half the values of the corresponding coefficients of the expansion given in Ch. III, § 1.6, 9°(b).

5.6. Computation of $\sin x$ **and** $\cos x\left(|x| < \dfrac{\pi}{2}\right)$ (fixed point).

The computation of $\sin x$ and of $\cos x$ is reduced to the computation of $\sin\dfrac{\pi}{2}y$, where $|y| < 1$:

$$\sin\frac{\pi}{2}y \approx y + \sum_{k=0}^{5} a_{2k+1} y^{2k+1}.$$

The values of the coefficients a_{2k+1} are as given in Ch. III, § 1.6, 2°(d), except for the coefficient a_1 $(k = 0)$, which is to be reduced by 1 from the value given there.

5.7. Computation of $\tan x\left(0 \leqslant x < \dfrac{\pi}{4}\right)$.   1°. *Computation of* $\tan x$ *in fixed point arithmetic:*

$$\tan x \approx x \, \frac{a_0 + (a_1 + a_2 x^2) x^2}{a_0 + [a_3 + (a_4 + a_5 x^2) x^2] x^2}.$$

The coefficients a_k are given in Ch. III, § 1.8, 10°.

2°. *Computation of* tan x *in floating point arithmetic.* If

$$|x| < \frac{\pi}{4}, \qquad \tan x = \tan \pi y, \qquad y \leqslant \frac{1}{4}$$

then

$$\tan \pi y \approx y \, \frac{\sum\limits_{k=0}^{2} a_k y^{2k}}{\sum\limits_{k=0}^{3} b_k y^{2k}}. \qquad\qquad 3(337)$$

The coefficients a_k and b_k are given in Ch. III, § 1.8, 8°.

5.8.   Computation of $\frac{1}{2}$ arc sin $x \left(|x| \leqslant \frac{\sqrt{2}}{2} \right)$ (fixed point).

$$\frac{1}{2} \arcsin x \approx \sum_{k=0}^{10} a_{2k+1} x^{2k+1}. \qquad\qquad 3(295)$$

The coefficients a_{2k+1} are half the values of the corresponding coefficients of the expansion given in Ch. III, § 2.4, 3°.

If $\dfrac{\sqrt{2}}{2} < x < 1$, then

$$\frac{1}{2} \arcsin x = \frac{\pi}{4} - \frac{1}{2} \arcsin \sqrt{1 - x^2}.$$

If $-1 < x < -\dfrac{\sqrt{2}}{2}$, then

$$\frac{1}{2} \arcsin x = -\left(\frac{\pi}{4} - \frac{1}{2} \arcsin \sqrt{1 - x^2} \right)$$

where $\frac{1}{2}$ arcsin $\sqrt{1 - x^2}$ is computed by the series given above.

5.9.   Computation of $\frac{1}{4}$ arc cos x (fixed point).

$$\frac{1}{4} \arccos x = \frac{\pi}{8} - \frac{1}{4} \arcsin x \qquad\qquad 3(299)$$

where $\frac{1}{4}$ arcsin x is computed by using the subroutine for $\frac{1}{2}$ arcsin x.

I. SPECIAL POLYNOMIALS
AND OTHER FUNCTIONS

§ 1. Gudermannian (or Hyperbolic Amplitude)

1.1. It is possible to establish relations between the hyperbolic and the trigonometric functions without employing any functions of imaginary argument, by means of a special angle γ called the *Gudermannian* or the *hyperbolic amplitude,* such that $\sinh x = \tan \gamma$. This leads to the following relations between the hyperbolic functions of argument x and the corresponding trigonometric functions of argument γ.

$1°$. $\sinh x = \tan \gamma$.
$2°$. $\cosh x = \sec \gamma$.
$3°$. $\tanh x = \sin \gamma$.
$4°$. $\coth x = \operatorname{cosec} \gamma$.
$5°$. $\operatorname{sech} x = \cos \gamma$.
$6°$. $\operatorname{cosech} x = \cot \gamma$.

The following relation holds between functions of half the arguments:

$7°$. $\tanh \tfrac{1}{2}x = \tan \tfrac{1}{2}\gamma$.

The following notation is used for the Gudermannian γ corresponding to the argument x of a hyperbolic function:

$8°$. $\gamma = \operatorname{gd} x = \operatorname{amh} x$.

Using the Gudermannian notation, the formulae above may be written as:

$9°$. $\sinh x = \tan(\operatorname{gd} x)$.
$10°$. $\cosh x = \sec(\operatorname{gd} x)$.
$11°$. $\tanh x = \sin(\operatorname{gd} x)$.
$12°$. $\coth x = \operatorname{cosec}(\operatorname{gd} x)$.
$13°$. $\operatorname{sech} x = \cos(\operatorname{gd} x)$.
$14°$. $\operatorname{cosech} x = \cot(\operatorname{gd} x)$.
$15°$. $\tanh \tfrac{1}{2}x = \tan(\tfrac{1}{2}\operatorname{gd} x)$.

In view of the formula

$$e^x = \cosh x + \sinh x,$$

we get the following relations:

$16°$. $e^x = \sec\gamma + \tan\gamma = \tan\left(\dfrac{\pi}{4} + \dfrac{\gamma}{2}\right) = \dfrac{1+\sin\gamma}{\cos\gamma} = \dfrac{1+\tan\frac{1}{2}\gamma}{1-\tan\frac{1}{2}\gamma}\,.$

4(57)

We may introduce the function which is inverse to the Gudermannian. If $\gamma = \mathrm{gd}\, x$, then the inverse function (inverse Gudermannian) of x is denoted by the symbol

17°. $x = \arg \mathrm{gd}\, \gamma$.

If the argument x is known, then the Gudermannian can be found and conversely, by means of the formulae:

18°. $\gamma = \mathrm{gd}\, x = 2 \arctan e^x - \dfrac{\pi}{2} = 2 \arctan \left(\tanh \dfrac{x}{2} \right) = \displaystyle\int\limits_0^x \dfrac{dt}{\cosh t}\,.$

12(73)

19°. $x = \arg \mathrm{gd}\, \gamma = \ln \tan \left(\dfrac{\pi}{4} + \dfrac{\gamma}{2} \right) = \displaystyle\int\limits_0^\gamma \dfrac{d\varphi}{\cos \varphi}\,.$ 12(73)

The concept of the Gudermannian may be generalized to the case of imaginary argument. Proceeding from the equation $\gamma = \mathrm{gd}\, x$, we get the relation:

20°. $ix = \mathrm{gd}\, i\gamma.$ 12(74)

If $\gamma = \gamma_1 + i\gamma_2$, $x = x_1 + ix_2$, we get:

$$\tan \gamma_1 = \frac{\sinh x_1}{\cos x_2}\,, \quad \tanh x_1 = \frac{\sin \gamma_1}{\cosh \gamma_2}\,, \quad \tanh \gamma_2 = \frac{\sin x_2}{\cosh x_1}\,, \quad \tan x_2 = \frac{\sinh \gamma_2}{\cosh \gamma_1}\,.$$

12(74)

1.2. Representation in series form.

1°. $\gamma = \dfrac{\pi}{2} - \left(\dfrac{1}{\cosh x} + \dfrac{1}{2\cdot3\cosh^3 x} + \dfrac{1\cdot3}{2\cdot4\cdot5\cosh^5 x} \right.$

$$\left. + \dfrac{1\cdot3\cdot5}{2\cdot4\cdot6\cdot7\cosh^7 x} + \ldots \right).$$ 11(37)

2°. $\gamma = 2 \displaystyle\sum_{k=0}^{\infty} \dfrac{(-1)^k}{2k+1} \tanh^{2k+1} \dfrac{x}{2} = 2 \displaystyle\sum_{k=0}^{\infty} \dfrac{(-1)^k}{2k+1} \tan^{2k+1} \dfrac{\gamma}{2}\,.$ 4(57)

3°. $\gamma = x - \dfrac{x^3}{6} + \dfrac{x^5}{24} - \dfrac{61 x^7}{5040} + \ldots + \dfrac{(-1)^k E_k}{(2k+1)!} x^{2k+1} + \ldots$†

$$\left(|x| < \dfrac{\pi}{2} \right).$$ 12(74)

4°. $\gamma = x - \dfrac{4}{3} \tanh^3 \dfrac{x}{2} - \dfrac{4}{7} \tanh^7 \dfrac{x}{2} - \ldots \left(\left| \tanh \dfrac{x}{2} \right| < 1 \right).$ 11(37)

---

† The E_k are the Euler numbers (cf. [I], p. 359).

$5°.$ $x = 2 \sum\limits_{k=0}^{\infty} \dfrac{1}{2k+1} \tan^{2k+1} \dfrac{\gamma}{2} = 2 \sum\limits_{k=0}^{\infty} \dfrac{1}{2k+1} \tanh^{2k+1} \dfrac{x}{2}.$ \hfill 4(57)

$6°.$ $x = \gamma + \dfrac{\gamma^3}{6} + \dfrac{\gamma^5}{24} + \dfrac{61\gamma^7}{5040} + \ldots$

$$\ldots + \frac{E_k}{(2k+1)!}\, \gamma^{2k+1} + \ldots \quad \left(|\gamma| < \frac{\pi}{2}\right). \qquad 12(74)$$

$7°.$ $x = \gamma + \dfrac{4}{3} \tan^3 \dfrac{\gamma}{2} + \dfrac{4}{7} \tan^7 \dfrac{\gamma}{2} + \ldots \quad \left(\left|\tan\dfrac{\gamma}{2}\right| < 1\right).$ \hfill 11(37)

For small x and γ, we have the following expressions:

$8°.$ $\gamma \approx x - \dfrac{x^3}{6\sqrt{\cosh x}}.$ \hfill 11(39)

$9°.$ $x \approx \gamma + \dfrac{\gamma^3}{6\sqrt{\cos \gamma}}.$ \hfill 11(39)

The following expressions hold for large x and γ:

$10°.$ $\gamma = \operatorname{gd} x \approx \begin{cases} 1\cdot5706 & \text{if} \quad 9\cdot00 < x \leqslant 9\cdot52, \\ 1\cdot5707 & \text{if} \quad 9\cdot52 < x \leqslant 10\cdot67, \\ 1\cdot5708 & \text{if} \quad 10\cdot67 < x < +\infty. \end{cases}$ \hfill 3(207)

$11°.$ $x = \arg\operatorname{gd}\gamma \approx 5\cdot298 - \ln 100 \left(\dfrac{\pi}{2} - \gamma\right)$

$$\approx 5\cdot298 - \ln 100(1\cdot570796 - \gamma) \quad \text{if} \quad x > 1\cdot554. \qquad 3(208)$$

1.3. Derivatives and integrals.

$1°.$ $\dfrac{d\gamma}{dx} = \dfrac{d}{dx}(\operatorname{gd} x) = \operatorname{sech} x,$

$2°.$ $\dfrac{dx}{d\gamma} = \dfrac{d}{d\gamma}(\arg\operatorname{gd}\gamma) = \sec\gamma.$

$3°.$ $\displaystyle\int \dfrac{dx}{\cosh x} = \operatorname{gd} x + C = 2\arctan e^x + C_1 = \arctan(\sinh x) + C$

$$= \arcsin(\tanh x) + C. \qquad 4(104)$$

$4°.$ $\displaystyle\int \dfrac{d\gamma}{\cos\gamma} = \arg\operatorname{gd}\gamma + C = \ln\tan\left(\dfrac{\gamma}{2} + \dfrac{\pi}{4}\right) + C.$

1.4. Values of the function $\dfrac{2}{\pi}\,\mathrm{gd}\left(\dfrac{\pi}{2}\,x\right)$ 12 (74)

x	0·1	0·2	0·3	0·4	0·5	0·6	0·7
$\dfrac{2}{\pi}\,\mathrm{gd}\left(\dfrac{\pi}{2}\,x\right)$	0·09959	0·19679	0·2895	0·3760	0·4553	0·5269	0·5907

x	0·8	0·9	1·0	1·1	1·2	1·3	1·4
$\dfrac{2}{\pi}\,\mathrm{gd}\left(\dfrac{\pi}{2}\,x\right)$	0·6470	0·6898	0·7390	0·7761	0·8081	0·8357	0·8594

x	1·5	1·6	1·7	1·8	1·9	2·0
$\dfrac{2}{\pi}\,\mathrm{gd}\left(\dfrac{\pi}{2}\,x\right)$	0·8797	0·8971	0·9120	0·9248	0·9357	0·9450

§ 2. Harmonic polynomials

2.1. Functions which satisfy Laplace's equation†

$$\frac{\partial^2 u}{\partial x^2} + \frac{\partial^2 u}{\partial y^2} = 0$$

are said to be *harmonic*. Polynomials which are harmonic functions are called *harmonic polynomials*. Any harmonic polynomial is a linear combination of the homogeneous harmonic polynomials $H_n^{(0)}(x, y)$ and $H_n^{(1)}(x, y)$, which are defined as the real and imaginary parts of the function z^n, where $z = x + iy$.

1°. $H_n^{(0)}(x, y) = \mathrm{Re}[(x+iy)^n] = \displaystyle\sum_{k=0}^{\left[\frac{n}{2}\right]} (-1)^k \binom{n}{2k} x^{n-2k} y^{2k}$

$$= x^n - C_n^2 x^{n-2} y^2 + C_n^4 x^{n-4} y^4 - C_n^6 x^{n-6} y^6 + C_n^8 x^{n-8} y^8 - \ldots$$

---

† Thus the functions are taken as having continuous partial derivatives of the first and second orders.

$2°.\ H_n^{(1)}(x,y) = \mathrm{Im}[(x+iy)^n] = \sum_{k=0}^{\left[\frac{n-1}{2}\right]} (-1)^k \binom{n}{2k+1} x^{n-2k-1} y^{2k+1}$

$$= nx^{n-1}y - C_n^3 x^{n-3}y^3 + C_n^5 x^{n-5}y^5 - C_n^7 x^{n-7}y^7 + \cdots$$

2.2. Some harmonic polynomials.

$1°.\ H_0^{(0)}(x,y) = 1.$

$2°.\ H_1^{(0)}(x,y) = x.$

$3°.\ H_2^{(0)}(x,y) = x^2 - y^2.$

$4°.\ H_3^{(0)}(x,y) = x(x^2 - 3y^2).$

$5°.\ H_4^{(0)}(x,y) = x^4 - 6x^2y^2 + y^4.$

$6°.\ H_5^{(0)}(x,y) = x^5 - 10x^3y^2 + 5xy^4.$

$7°.\ H_6^{(0)}(x,y) = x^6 - 15x^4y^2 + 15x^2y^4 - y^6.$

$8°.\ H_7^{(0)}(x,y) = x^7 - 21x^5y^2 + 35x^3y^4 - 7xy^6.$

$9°.\ H_1^{(1)}(x,y) = y.$

$10°.\ H_2^{(1)}(x,y) = 2xy.$

$11°.\ H_3^{(1)}(x,y) = y(3x^2 - y^2).$

$12°.\ H_4^{(1)}(x,y) = 4xy(x^2 - y^2).$

$13°.\ H_5^{(1)}(x,y) = 5x^4y - 10x^2y^3 + y^5.$

$14°.\ H_6^{(1)}(x,y) = 6x^5y - 20x^3y^3 + 6xy^5.$

$15°.\ H_7^{(1)}(x,y) = 7x^6y - 35x^4y^3 + 21x^2y^5 - y^7.$

2.3. After transformation to the polar coordinates

$$x = r\cos\varphi, \quad y = r\sin\varphi,$$

we get:

$1°.\ H_n^{(0)}(x,y) = H_n^{(0)}(r\cos\varphi, r\sin\varphi) = r^n \cos n\varphi.$

$2°.\ H_n^{(1)}(x,y) = H_n^{(1)}(r\cos\varphi, r\sin\varphi) = r^n \sin n\varphi.$

Then if $r = 1$ we have:

$3°.\ \cos n\varphi = H_n^{(0)}(\cos\varphi, \sin\varphi) = \sum_{k=0}^{\left[\frac{n}{2}\right]} (-1)^k C_n^{2k} \cos^{n-2k}\varphi \sin^{2k}\varphi.$

$4°.\ \sin n\varphi = H_n^{(1)}(\cos\varphi, \sin\varphi)$

$$= \sum_{k=0}^{\left[\frac{n-1}{2}\right]} (-1)^k C_n^{2k+1} \cos^{n-2k-1}\varphi \sin^{2k+1}\varphi.$$

$5°.\ \tan n\varphi = \dfrac{H_n^{(1)}(1,\tan\varphi)}{H_n^{(0)}(1,\tan\varphi)} = \dfrac{\displaystyle\sum_{k=0}^{\left[\frac{n-1}{2}\right]}(-1)^k C_n^{2k+1}\tan^{2k+1}\varphi}{\displaystyle\sum_{k=0}^{\left[\frac{n}{2}\right]}(-1)^k C_n^{2k}\tan^{2k}\varphi}.$

$6°.\ \cot n\varphi = \dfrac{H_n^{(0)}(\cot\varphi,1)}{H_n^{(1)}(\cot\varphi,1)} = \dfrac{\displaystyle\sum_{k=0}^{\left[\frac{n}{2}\right]}(-1)^k C_n^{2k}\cot^{n-2k}\varphi}{\displaystyle\sum_{k=0}^{\left[\frac{n-1}{2}\right]}(-1)^k C_n^{2k+1}\cot^{n-2k-1}\varphi}.$

In particular,

$7°.\ \cos 2\varphi = 2\cos^2\varphi - 1.$

$8°.\ \cos 3\varphi = 4\cos^3\varphi - 3\cos\varphi.$

$9°.\ \cos 4\varphi = 8\cos^4\varphi - 8\cos^2\varphi + 1.$

$10°.\ \cos 5\varphi = 16\cos^5\varphi - 20\cos^3\varphi + 5\cos\varphi.$

$11°.\ \cos 6\varphi = 32\cos^6\varphi - 48\cos^4\varphi + 18\cos^2\varphi - 1.$

$12°.\ \cos 7\varphi = 64\cos^7\varphi - 112\cos^5\varphi + 56\cos^3\varphi - 7\cos\varphi.$

$13°.\ \sin 2\varphi = 2\sin\varphi\cos\varphi.$

$14°.\ \sin 3\varphi = 3\sin\varphi - 4\sin^3\varphi.$

$15°.\ \sin 4\varphi = \cos\varphi(4\sin\varphi - 8\sin^3\varphi).$

$16°.\ \sin 5\varphi = 5\sin\varphi - 20\sin^3\varphi + 16\sin^5\varphi.$

$17°.\ \sin 6\varphi = \cos\varphi(6\sin\varphi - 32\sin^3\varphi + 32\sin^5\varphi).$

$18°.\ \sin 7\varphi = 7\sin\varphi - 56\sin^3\varphi + 112\sin^5\varphi - 64\sin^7\varphi.$

$19°.\ \tan 2\varphi = \dfrac{2\tan\varphi}{1 - \tan^2\varphi}.$

$20°.\ \tan 3\varphi = \dfrac{3\tan\varphi - \tan^3\varphi}{1 - 3\tan^2\varphi}.$

$21°.\ \tan 4\varphi = \dfrac{4\tan\varphi - 4\tan^3\varphi}{1 - 6\tan^2\varphi + \tan^4\varphi}.$

$22°.\ \cot 2\varphi = \dfrac{\cot^2\varphi - 1}{2\cot\varphi}.$

$23°.\ \cot 3\varphi = \dfrac{\cot^3\varphi - 3\cot\varphi}{3\cot^2\varphi - 1}.$

$24°.\ \cot 4\varphi = \dfrac{\cot^4\varphi - 6\cot^2\varphi + 1}{4\cot^3\varphi - 4\cot\varphi}.$

§ 3. The hypergeometric function

3.1. The *hypergeometric series* (or *hypergeometric function*) is defined by the power series:

$$F(\alpha, \beta, \gamma; x) = 1 + \frac{\alpha\beta}{\gamma}\frac{x}{1!} + \frac{\alpha(\alpha+1)\beta(\beta+1)}{\gamma(\gamma+1)}\frac{x^2}{2!}$$
$$+ \frac{\alpha(\alpha+1)(\alpha+2)\beta(\beta+1)(\beta+2)}{\gamma(\gamma+1)(\gamma+2)}\frac{x^3}{3!} + \cdots$$

The origin of the name is due to the fact that, in the particular case $\alpha = 1$, $\beta = \gamma$, this series reduces to the geometric series

$$1 + x + x^2 + x^3 + \cdots + x^n + \cdots$$

The hypergeometric series converges absolutely if $|x| < 1$, and diverges if $|x| > 1$. If $x = \pm 1$, the convergence of the hypergeometric series depends upon the number $\gamma - \alpha - \beta$, in the following manner: for $x = 1$ the series converges absolutely if $\gamma - \alpha - \beta > 0$, but diverges if $\gamma - \alpha - \beta \leqslant 0$; for $x = -1$ the series converges absolutely if $\gamma - \alpha - \beta > 0$, converges conditionally if $-1 < \gamma - \alpha - \beta < 0$ and diverges if $\gamma - \alpha - \beta \leqslant -1$.

If either α or β equals a negative integer or zero, then the hypergeometric series terminates at some term and it becomes a finite series, i.e. a polynomial. If γ is a negative integer or zero ($\gamma = -n$), then the hypergeometric series is undefined unless either $\alpha = -m$ or $\beta = -m$, where m is a positive integer with $m < n$.

3.2. The general solution of the hypergeometric differential equation

$$x(1-x)\frac{d^2y}{dx^2} + [\gamma - (\alpha + \beta + 1)x]\frac{dy}{dx} - \alpha\beta y = 0,$$

(where γ is not an integer) is given in terms of hypergeometric functions:

$$y = C_1 F(\alpha, \beta, \gamma; x) + C_2 x^{1-\gamma} F(\alpha - \gamma + 1, \beta - \gamma + 1, 2 - \gamma; x). \quad 4(421)$$

3.3. Some particular values of the hypergeometric function and their notation.

1°. $F\left(1, 1, \frac{3}{2}; \frac{1}{2}\right) = \frac{\pi}{2},$ \hfill 4(418)

2°. $F(\alpha, \beta, \gamma; 1) = \dfrac{\Gamma(\gamma)\Gamma(\gamma - \alpha - \beta)}{\Gamma(\gamma - \alpha)\Gamma(\gamma - \beta)} = A$ \hfill 6(57)

(for $\gamma - \alpha - \beta > 0$, where γ is neither zero nor a negative integer).

3°. $F(\gamma - \alpha, \gamma - \beta, \gamma; 1) = \dfrac{\Gamma(\gamma)\Gamma(\alpha + \beta - \gamma)}{\Gamma(\alpha)\Gamma(\beta)} = B.$ \hfill 6(57)

4°. $F(\alpha, \gamma - \beta, \gamma; 1) = \dfrac{\Gamma(\gamma)\Gamma(\beta - \alpha)}{\Gamma(\beta)\Gamma(\gamma - \alpha)} = C.$ \hfill 6(59)

$5°.$ $F(\gamma - \alpha, \beta, \gamma; 1) = \dfrac{\Gamma(\gamma)\Gamma(\alpha - \beta)}{\Gamma(\alpha)\Gamma(\gamma - \beta)} = D.$ 6(59)

3.4. Bolza's formulae.

$$F(\alpha, \beta, \gamma; x) = A.F(\alpha, \beta, \alpha + \beta - \gamma + 1; 1 - x)$$
$$+ B.(1 - x)^{\gamma - \alpha - \beta} F(\gamma - \alpha, \gamma - \beta, \gamma - \alpha - \beta + 1; 1 - x);   6(59)$$

$$= (1 - x)^{-\alpha} F\left(\alpha, \gamma - \beta, \gamma; \frac{x}{x - 1}\right)$$

$$= (1 - x)^{-\beta} F\left(\gamma - \alpha, \beta, \gamma; \frac{x}{x - 1}\right);   6(59)$$

$$= C(1 - x)^{-\alpha} F\left(\alpha, \gamma - \beta, \alpha - \beta + 1; \frac{1}{1 - x}\right)$$

$$+ D(1 - x)^{-\beta} F\left(\gamma - \alpha, \beta, \beta - \alpha + 1; \frac{1}{1 - x}\right);   6(59)$$

$$= Ax^{-\alpha} F\left(\alpha, \alpha - \gamma + 1, \alpha + \beta - \gamma + 1; \frac{x - 1}{x}\right)$$

$$+ B.x^{\alpha - \gamma}(1 - x)^{\gamma - \alpha - \beta} \times$$
$$\times F\left(\gamma - \alpha, 1 - \alpha, \gamma - \alpha - \beta + 1; \frac{x - 1}{x}\right);   6(59)$$

$$= C(-x)^{-\alpha} F\left(\alpha, \alpha - \gamma + 1, \alpha - \beta + 1; \frac{1}{x}\right)$$

$$+ D(-x)^{-\beta} F\left(\beta - \gamma + 1, \beta, \beta - \alpha + 1; \frac{1}{x}\right).   6(59)$$

3.5. Some relations.

$1°.$ $F(\alpha, \beta, \gamma; 1) = F(-\alpha, -\beta, \gamma - \alpha - \beta; 1)   (\gamma > 0).$ 4(418)

$2°.$ $F(\alpha, \beta, \gamma; 1) = \dfrac{1}{F(-\alpha, \beta, \gamma - \alpha; 1)}   (\gamma - \beta > 0).$ 4(418)

$3°.$ $F(\alpha, \beta, \gamma; 1) = \dfrac{1}{F(\alpha, -\beta, \gamma - \beta; 1)}   (\gamma - \alpha > 0).$ 4(418)

3.6. Recurrence relations.

$1°.$ $(\alpha - \beta)F(\alpha, \beta, \gamma; x) - \alpha F(\alpha + 1, \beta, \gamma; x) + \beta F(\alpha, \beta + 1, \gamma; x)$
$$= 0.   6(53)$$

$2°.$ $(1 - \gamma)F(\alpha, \beta, \gamma - 1; x) - (\alpha - \gamma + 1)F(\alpha, \beta, \gamma; x)$
$$+ \alpha F(\alpha + 1, \beta, \gamma; x) = 0.   6(53)$$

$3°.$ $(\beta - \alpha)(1 - x)F(\alpha, \beta, \gamma; x) + (\alpha - \gamma)F(\alpha - 1, \beta, \gamma; x)$
$$+ (\gamma - \beta)F(\alpha, \beta - 1, \gamma; x) = 0. \quad 6(53)$$

$4°.$ $(\gamma - \alpha)F(\alpha - 1, \beta, \gamma; x) + [2\alpha - \gamma - (\alpha - \beta)x]F(\alpha, \beta, \gamma; x)$
$$+ \alpha(x - 1)F(\alpha + 1, \beta, \gamma; x) = 0. \quad 6(53)$$

$5°.$ $\gamma(\gamma - 1)(x - 1)F(\alpha, \beta, \gamma - 1; x) + \gamma[\gamma - 1 - (2\gamma - \alpha - \beta - 1)x] \times$
$$\times F(\alpha, \beta, \gamma; x) + (\gamma - \alpha)(\gamma - \beta)x \cdot F(\alpha, \beta, \gamma + 1; x) = 0. \quad 6(53)$$

3.7. Integral representations.

$1°.$ $\quad F(\alpha, \beta, \gamma; x) = \dfrac{\Gamma(\gamma)}{\Gamma(\alpha)\Gamma(\gamma - \alpha)} \displaystyle\int_0^1 t^{\alpha-1}(1 - t)^{\gamma-\alpha-1}(1 - xt)^{-\beta}dt$
$$(0 < \alpha < \gamma). \quad 6(53)$$

$2°.$ $\quad F(\alpha, \beta, \gamma; x) = \dfrac{\Gamma(\gamma)}{\Gamma(\alpha)\Gamma(\gamma - \alpha)} \displaystyle\int_1^\infty t^{\beta-\gamma}(t - 1)^{\gamma-\alpha-1}(t - x)^{-\beta}dt.$
$$6(55)$$

3.8. Representation of elementary functions in terms of hypergeometric functions.

$1°.$ $\quad \displaystyle\sum_{k=0}^n x^k = F(-n, 1, -n; x).$ $\qquad\qquad\qquad$ $2(615)$

$2°.$ $\quad \displaystyle\sum_{k=0}^n \frac{\alpha(\alpha + 1)\dots(\alpha + k - 1)}{k!} x^k = F(\alpha, -n, -n; x)$
$$= F(-n, \alpha, -n; x). \quad 2(614)$$

$3°.$ $\quad (1 + x)^n = F(-n, \beta, \beta; -x) = F(-n, 1, 1; -x).$ $\quad 2(614)$

$4°.$ $\quad (1 - x)^{-n} = F(n, \beta, \beta; x).$ $\qquad\qquad\qquad$ $6(61)$

$5°.$ $\quad (1 - x)^{-1} = F(1, 1, 1; x) = F(1, \beta, \beta; x) = F(\alpha, 1, \alpha; x).$
$$2(614)$$

$6°.$ $\quad \dfrac{1 - (1 - x)^n}{nx} = F(1 - n, 1, 2; x).$ $\qquad\qquad$ $2(614)$

$7°.$ $\quad \dfrac{(1 + x)^n + (1 - x)^n}{2} = F\left(-\dfrac{n}{2}, -\dfrac{n - 1}{2}, \dfrac{1}{2}; x^2\right).$ $\quad 2(615)$

$8°.$ $\quad \dfrac{(1 + x)^n - (1 - x)^n}{2nx} = F\left(-\dfrac{n - 1}{2}, -\dfrac{n}{2} + 1, \dfrac{3}{2}; x^2\right).$ $\quad 2(615)$

$9°.$ $\quad \dfrac{\ln(1 + x)}{x} = F(1, 1, 2; -x).$ $\qquad\qquad\qquad$ $2(615)$

$10°. \quad \dfrac{\ln(1-x)}{x} = -F(1, 1, 2; x).$ 6(61)

$11°. \quad \dfrac{1}{2x} \ln \dfrac{1+x}{1-x} = F\left(\dfrac{1}{2}, 1, \dfrac{3}{2}; x^2\right).$ 2(615)

$12°. \quad \dfrac{x}{\sin x} = F\left(\dfrac{1}{2}, \dfrac{1}{2}, \dfrac{3}{2}; \sin^2 x\right).$ 4(417)

$13°. \quad \dfrac{2x}{\sin 2x} = F\left(1, 1, \dfrac{3}{2}; \sin^2 x\right).$ 4(417)

$14°. \quad \dfrac{x}{\tan x} = F\left(\dfrac{1}{2}, 1, \dfrac{3}{2}; -\tan^2 x\right).$ 4(417)

$15°. \quad \dfrac{\arcsin x}{x} = F\left(\dfrac{1}{2}, \dfrac{1}{2}, \dfrac{3}{2}; x^2\right).$ 2(615)

$16°. \quad \dfrac{\arctan x}{x} = F\left(\dfrac{1}{2}, 1, \dfrac{3}{2}; -x^2\right).$ 2(615)

$17°. \quad \dfrac{\operatorname{Arc\,sinh} x}{x} = F\left(\dfrac{1}{2}, \dfrac{1}{2}, \dfrac{3}{2}; -x^2\right).$ 4(417)

$18°. \quad \dfrac{\sin nx}{n \sin x} = F\left(\dfrac{n+1}{2}, -\dfrac{n-1}{2}, \dfrac{3}{2}; \sin^2 x\right).$ 14(8)

$19°. \quad \dfrac{2\sin nx}{n \sin 2x} = F\left(\dfrac{n+2}{2}, -\dfrac{n-2}{2}, \dfrac{3}{2}, \sin^2 x\right).$ 4(417)

$20°. \quad \cos nx = F\left(\dfrac{n}{2}, -\dfrac{n}{2}, \dfrac{1}{2}; \sin^2 x\right).$ 14(8)

$21°. \quad \cos nx \cos^n x = F\left(\dfrac{n+1}{2}, \dfrac{n}{2}, \dfrac{1}{2}; -\tan^2 x\right).$ 4(417)

$22°. \quad \dfrac{1}{\cos x} = F\left(\dfrac{1}{2}, 1, 1; \sin^2 x\right).$ 4(417)

$23°. \quad \dfrac{\cos nx}{\cos x} = F\left(\dfrac{n+1}{2}, -\dfrac{n-1}{2}, \dfrac{1}{2}; \sin^2 x\right).$ 14(8)

$24°. \quad \dfrac{\cos nx}{\cos^n x} = F\left(-\dfrac{n}{2}, -\dfrac{n-1}{2}, \dfrac{1}{2}; -\tan^2 x\right).$ 14(8)

$25°. \quad \dfrac{\sin nx}{n \sin x \cos^{n-1} x} = F\left(-\dfrac{n-2}{2}, -\dfrac{n-1}{2}, \dfrac{3}{2}; -\tan^2 x\right).$ 4(417)

$26°. \quad \dfrac{\sin(n \arcsin x)}{nx} = F\left(\dfrac{n+1}{2}, -\dfrac{n-1}{2}, \dfrac{3}{2}; x^2\right).$ 14(8)

27°. $\dfrac{\sin(n\arcsin x)}{nx\sqrt{1-x^2}} = F\left(1+\dfrac{n}{2},\ 1-\dfrac{n}{2},\ \dfrac{3}{2};\ x^2\right).$ 14(8)

28°. $\cos(n\arcsin x) = F\left(\dfrac{n}{2},\ -\dfrac{n}{2},\ \dfrac{1}{2};\ x^2\right).$ 14(8)

29°. $\dfrac{\cos(n\arcsin x)}{\sqrt{1-x^2}} = F\left(\dfrac{n+1}{2},\ -\dfrac{n-1}{2},\ \dfrac{1}{2};\ x^2\right).$ 14(8)

3.9. Elementary functions as limits of hypergeometric functions.

1°. $e^x = \lim\limits_{k\to\infty} F\left(1,\ k.\ 1;\ \dfrac{x}{k}\right) = 1 + x\lim\limits_{k\to\infty} F\left(1,\ k,\ 2;\ \dfrac{x}{k}\right)$

$$= 1 + x + \dfrac{x^2}{2}\lim\limits_{k\to\infty} F\left(1,\ k,\ 3,\ \dfrac{x}{k}\right). \qquad 4(417)$$

2°. $\cos x = \lim\limits_{\substack{k\to\infty \\ k'\to\infty}} F\left(k,\ k',\ \dfrac{1}{2};\ -\dfrac{x^2}{4kk'}\right).$ 4(417)

3°. $\cosh x = \lim\limits_{\substack{k\to\infty \\ k'\to\infty}} \left(k,\ k',\ \dfrac{1}{2};\ \dfrac{x^2}{4kk'}\right).$ 4(417)

4°. $\dfrac{\sin x}{x} = \lim\limits_{\substack{k\to\infty \\ k'\to\infty}} F\left(k,\ k',\ \dfrac{3}{2};\ -\dfrac{x^2}{4kk'}\right).$ 4(417)

5°. $\dfrac{\sinh x}{x} = \lim\limits_{\substack{k\to\infty \\ k'\to\infty}} F\left(k,\ k',\ \dfrac{3}{2};\ \dfrac{x^2}{4kk'}\right).$ 4(417)

3.10. Derivatives of the hypergeometric function.

1°. $\dfrac{d}{dx} F(\alpha,\ \beta,\ \gamma;\ x) = \dfrac{\alpha\beta}{\gamma} F(\alpha+1,\ \beta+1,\ \gamma+1;\ x)$ 6(52)

unless γ is a non-positive integer.

2°. $\dfrac{d^2}{dx^2} F(\alpha,\ \beta,\ \gamma;\ x) = \dfrac{\alpha(\alpha+1)\beta(\beta+1)}{\gamma(\gamma+1)} F(\alpha+2,\ \beta+2,\ \gamma+2;\ x).$

14(8)

3°. $\dfrac{d}{dx} [x^\alpha F(\alpha,\ \beta,\ \gamma;\ x)] = \alpha x^{\alpha-1} F(\alpha+1,\ \beta,\ \gamma;\ x).$ 6(52)

4°. $\dfrac{d}{dx} [x^\beta F(\alpha,\ \beta,\ \gamma;\ x)] = \beta x^{\beta-1} F(\alpha,\ \beta+1,\ \gamma;\ x).$ 6(52)

5°. $\dfrac{d}{dx} [x^{\gamma-1} F(\alpha,\ \beta,\ \gamma;\ x)] = (\gamma-1)x^{\gamma-2} F(\alpha,\ \beta,\ \gamma-1;\ x).$ 6(52)

6°. $\dfrac{d}{dx} [x^{\gamma-\alpha}(1-x)^{\alpha+\beta-\gamma} F(\alpha,\ \beta,\ \gamma;\ x)]$

$$= (\gamma-a)x^{\gamma-\alpha-1}(1-x)^{\alpha+\beta-\gamma-1} F(\alpha-1,\ \beta,\ \gamma;\ x). \qquad 6(52)$$

§ 4. Orthogonal polynomials

We give below the formulae for some of the polynomials of Legendre, Chebyshev, Laguerre and Hermite, expressed in terms of powers of the argument x, together with the zeros of these polynomials. To start with, we cite briefly some facts about them. For more detailed properties of these polynomials, consult [I], pp. 239-262.

4.1. Definitions. $1°$. *Legendre polynomials* $P_n(x)$:

$$P_n(x) = \frac{1}{2^n n!} \frac{d^n}{dx^n} (x^2 - 1)^n = \frac{1}{2^n} \sum_{k=0}^{\left[\frac{n}{2}\right]^\dagger} (-1)^k \frac{(2n - 2k)!}{k!(n-k)!(n-2k)} x^{n-2k}$$

$$= \frac{(2n)!}{2^n (n!)^2} \left[x^n - \frac{n(n-1)}{2(2n-1)} x^{n-2} + \frac{n(n-1)(n-2)(n-3)}{2 \cdot 4(2n-1)(2n-3)} x^{n-4} - \dots \right].$$

In particular,

$$P_n(1) = 1, \quad P_n(-1) = (-1)^n, \quad P_{2n}(0) = (-1)^n \frac{(2n)!}{2^{2n}(n!)^2},$$

$$P_{2n+1}(0) = 0.$$

The relation between $P_n(-x)$ and $P_n(x)$ is:

$$P_n(-x) = (-1)^n P_n(x).$$

The Legendre polynomials are connected with the hypergeometric function by the relation

$$P_n(x) = (-1)^{n-1} F\left(-n, \ n+1, \ 1; \ \frac{1-x}{2} \right).$$

$2°$. *The modified Legendre polynomials* $P_n^*(x)$:

$$P_n^*(x) = (-1)^{n-1} P_n(2x - 1).$$

As the argument of the polynomial P_n varies from -1 to $+1$, the argument of the modified polynomial P_n^* varies from 0 to $+1$.

The modified Legendre polynomials $P_n^*(x)$ are connected with the hypergeometric function by the relation

$$P_n^*(x) = (-1)^{n-1} F(-n, \ n+1, \ 1; \ 1-x).$$

$3°$. *Chebyshev polynomials of the first type* $T_n(x)$:

$$T_n(x) = \cos(n \arccos x) = x^n - \binom{n}{2} x^{n-2}(1 - x^2)$$

$$+ \binom{n}{4} x^{n-4}(1 - x^2)^2 - \binom{n}{6} x^{n-6}(1 - x^2)^3 - \dots$$

$\dagger$ The sum is taken over integers k from 0 to $\dfrac{n-1}{2}$ for odd n, and from 0 to $\dfrac{n}{2}$ for even n.

In particular,

$$T_n(1) = 1, \quad T_n(-1) = (-1)^n, \quad T_{2n}(0) = (-1)^n, \quad T_{2n+1}(0) = 0.$$

The Chebyshev polynomials of the first type are connected with the hypergeometric function by the relation

$$T_n(x) = F\left(n, \ -n, \ \frac{1}{2}; \ \frac{1-x}{2}\right).$$

4°. *The modified Chebyshev polynomials of the first type* $T_n^*(x)$:

$$T_n^*(x) = T_n(2x - 1).$$

5°. *The polynomials* $C_n(x)$:

$$C_n(x) = 2\cos\left(n \operatorname{arc} \cos \frac{x}{2}\right).$$

6°. *Chebyshev polynomials of the second type* $U_n(x)$:

$$U_n(x) = \frac{\sin[(n+1)\operatorname{arc}\cos x]}{\sqrt{1-x^2}} = \binom{n+1}{1}x^n - \binom{n+1}{3}x^{n-2}(1-x^2)$$

$$+ \binom{n+1}{5}x^{n-4}(1-x^2)^2 - \dots = \frac{1}{n+1}\frac{d}{dx}T_{n+1}(x).$$

In particular,

$$U_{2n}(0) = (-1)^n, \quad U_{2n+1}(0) = 0.$$

The Chebyshev polynomials of the second type are connected with the hypergeometric function by the relation

$$U_n(x) = (n+1)F\left(-n, \ n+2, \ \frac{3}{2}; \ \frac{1-x}{2}\right).$$

7°. *Modified Chebyshev polynomials of the second type* $U_n^*(x)$:

$$U_n^*(x) = U_n(2x - 1).$$

8°. *The polynomials* $S_n(x)$:

$$S_n(x) = \frac{2\sin\left[(n+1)\operatorname{arc}\cos\dfrac{x}{2}\right]}{\sqrt{4-x^2}}.$$

9°. *Relations between the Chebyshev polynomials*:

$$C_n(x) = 2T_n\left(\frac{x}{2}\right) = 2T_n^*\left(\frac{2+x}{4}\right), \quad T_n^*(x) = \frac{1}{2}C_n(4x - 2),$$

$$S_n(x) = U_n\left(\frac{x}{2}\right) = U_n^*\left(\frac{2+x}{4}\right), \quad U_n(x) = S_n(2x) = U_n^*\left(\frac{1+x}{2}\right),$$

$$T_n(x) = \frac{1}{2}C_n(2x) = T_n^*\left(\frac{1+x}{2}\right), \quad U_n^*(x) = S_n(4x - 2).$$

10°. *Laguerre polynomials $L_n(x)$:*

$$L_n(x) = e^x \frac{d^n}{dx^n}(x^n e^{-x}) = \sum_{k=0}^{n} (-1)^k \binom{n}{n-k} \frac{n!}{k!} x^k$$

$$= n! \left[1 - nx + \frac{n(n-1)}{(2!)^2} x^2 - \frac{n(n-1)(n-2)}{(3!)^2} x^3 + \cdots + (-1)^n \frac{x^n}{n!} \right].$$

In particular $L_n(0) = n!$

11°. *Hermite polynomials $H_n(x)$:*

$$H_n(x) = (-1)^n e^{x^2} \frac{d^n}{dx^n}(e^{-x^2}) = \sum_{k=0}^{\left[\frac{n}{2}\right]^\dagger} (-1)^k \frac{2^{n-2k} n!}{k!(n-2k)!} x^{n-2k}$$

$$= 2^n x^n - 2^{n-1} \binom{n}{2} x^{n-2} + 2^{n-2} \cdot 1 \cdot 3 \binom{n}{4} x^{n-4} - \cdots$$

$$= (2x)^n - \frac{n(n-1)}{1!}(2x)^{n-2} + \frac{n(n-1)(n-2)(n-3)}{2!}(2x)^{n-4} - \cdots,$$

where the last term is

$$(-1)^{\frac{n}{2}} \cdot \frac{n!}{\left(\frac{n}{2}\right)!}$$

for even n, and

$$(-1)^{\frac{n-1}{2}} \frac{n!}{\left(\frac{n-1}{2}\right)!} 2x$$

for odd n.

In particular,

$$H_{2n}(0) = (-1)^n \frac{(2n)!}{n!},$$

$$H_{2n+1}(0) = 0$$

12°. *Hermite polynomials $h_n(x)$:*

$$h_n(x) = (-1)^n e^{\frac{x^2}{2}} \frac{d^n}{dx^n}(e^{-\frac{x^2}{2}})$$

$$= x^n - \binom{n}{2} x^{n-2} + 1 \cdot 3 \binom{n}{4} x^{n-4} - 1 \cdot 3 \cdot 5 \binom{n}{6} x^{n-6} + \cdots,$$

---

† The sum is taken over integer k from 0 to $\frac{n-1}{2}$ if n is odd and from 0 to $\frac{n}{2}$ if n is even.

where the last term is

$$(-1)^{\frac{n}{2}} \frac{n!}{2^{\frac{n}{2}} \left(\frac{n}{2}\right)!}$$

for even n, and

$$(-1)^{\frac{n-1}{2}} \frac{n!}{2^{\frac{n-1}{2}} \left(\frac{n-1}{2}\right)!} x$$

for odd n.

13°. *Relations between the functions* $H_n(x)$ *and* $h_n(x)$:

$$h_n(x) = \frac{1}{2^{\frac{n}{2}}} H_n\left(\frac{x}{\sqrt{2}}\right).$$

$$H_n(x) = 2^{\frac{n}{2}} h_n(x\sqrt{2}).$$

4.2. Generating functions.

1°. $\dfrac{1}{\sqrt{1 - 2xt + t^2}} = \displaystyle\sum_{n=0}^{\infty} t^n P_n(x) \qquad (|t| < 1).$

2°. $\dfrac{1 - xt}{1 - 2xt + t^2} = \displaystyle\sum_{n=0}^{\infty} t^n T_n(x) \qquad (|t| < 1).$

3°. $\dfrac{1}{1 - 2xt + t^2} = \displaystyle\sum_{n=0}^{\infty} t^n U_n(x) \qquad (|t| < 1).$

4°. $\dfrac{e^{-\frac{xt}{1-t}}}{1 - t} = \displaystyle\sum_{n=0}^{\infty} \frac{t^n}{n!} L_n(x) \qquad (|t| < 1).$

5°. $e^{-t^2 + 2xt} = \displaystyle\sum_{n=0}^{\infty} \frac{t^n}{n!} H_n(x) \qquad (|t| < \infty).$

6°. $e^{-\frac{t^2}{2} + xt} = \displaystyle\sum_{n=0}^{\infty} \frac{t^n}{n!} h_n(x) \qquad (|t| < \infty).$

4.3. Recurrence relations.

1°. $P_{n+1}(x) = [(2n + 1)xP_n(x) - nP_{n-1}(x)] \dfrac{1}{n + 1}.$

2°. $T_{n+1}(x) = 2xT_n(x) - T_{n-1}(x).$

3°. $U_{n+1}(x) = 2xU_n(x) - U_{n-1}(x)$.

4°. $L_{n+1}(x) = (2n + 1 - x)L_n(x) - n^2L_{n-1}(x)$.

5°. $H_{n+1}(x) = 2xH_n(x) - 2nH_{n-1}(x)$.

6°. $h_{n+1}(x) = xh_n(x) - nh_{n-1}(x)$.

7°. $C_{n+1}(x) = xC_n(x) - C_{n-1}(x)$.

8°. $S_{n+1}(x) = xS_n(x) - S_{n-1}(x)$.

4.4. Differential equations, satisfied by the polynomials.

1°. $(x^2 - 1)P_n''(x) + 2xP_n'(x) - n(n + 1)P_n(x) = 0$.

2°. $(1 - x^2)T_n''(x) - xT_n'(x) + n^2T_n(x) = 0$.

3°. $(1 - x^2)U_n''(x) - xU_n'(x) + n^2U_n(x) = 0$.

4°. $xL_n''(x) + (1 - x)L_n'(x) + nL_n(x) = 0$.

5°. $H_n''(x) - 2xH_n'(x) + 2nH_n(x) = 0$.

6°. $h_n''(x) - xh_n'(x) + nh_n(x) = 0$.

4.5. Certain polynomials, expanded in powers of x.

1°. *Legendre polynomials $P_n(x)$.*

$P_0(x) = 1$.

$P_1(x) = x$.

$P_2(x) = \dfrac{1}{2}(3x^2 - 1)$.

$P_3(x) = \dfrac{1}{2}(5x^3 - 3x)$.

$P_4(x) = \dfrac{1}{8}(35x^4 - 30x^2 + 3)$.

$P_5(x) = \dfrac{1}{8}(63x^5 - 70x^3 + 15x)$.

$P_6(x) = \dfrac{1}{16}(231x^6 - 315x^4 + 105x^2 - 5)$.

$P_7(x) = \dfrac{1}{16}(429x^7 - 693x^5 + 315x^3 - 35x)$.

$P_8(x) = \dfrac{1}{128}(6435x^8 - 12\,012x^6 + 6930x^4 - 1260x^2 + 35)$.

$P_9(x) = \dfrac{1}{128}(12\,155x^9 - 25\,740x^7 + 18\,018x^5 - 4620x^3 + 315x)$.

$P_{10}(x) = \dfrac{1}{256}(46\,189x^{10} - 109\,395x^8 + 90\,090x^6 - 30\,030x^4 + 3465x^2 - 63)$.

$$P_{11}(x) = \frac{1}{256}\,(88\ 179x^{11} - 230\ 945x^9 + 218\ 790x^7 - 90\ 090x^5 + 15\ 015x^3$$
$$- 693x).$$

$$P_{12}(x) = \frac{1}{1024}\,(676\ 039x^{12} - 1\ 939\ 938x^{10} + 2\ 078\ 505x^8 - 1\ 021\ 020x^6$$
$$+ 225\ 225x^4 - 18\ 018x^2 + 231).$$

$$P_{13}(x) = \frac{1}{1024}\,(1\ 300\ 075x^{13} - 4\ 056\ 234x^{11} + 4\ 849\ 845x^9 - 2\ 771\ 340x^7$$
$$+ 765\ 765x^5 - 90\ 090x^3 + 3003x).$$

$$P_{14}(x) = \frac{1}{2048}\,(5\ 014\ 575x^{14} - 16\ 900\ 975x^{12} + 22\ 309\ 287x^{10}$$
$$- 14\ 549\ 535x^8 + 4\ 849\ 845x^6 - 765\ 765x^4 + 45\ 045x^2 - 429).$$

$$P_{15}(x) = \frac{1}{2048}\,(9\ 694\ 845x^{15} - 35\ 102\ 025x^{13} + 50\ 702\ 925x^{11}$$
$$- 37\ 182\ 145x^9 + 14\ 549\ 535x^7 - 2\ 909\ 907x^5 + 255\ 255x^3 - 6435x).$$

$$P_{16}(x) = \frac{1}{32\ 768}\,(300\ 540\ 195x^{16} - 1\ 163\ 381\ 400x^{14} + 1\ 825\ 305\ 300x^{12}$$
$$- 1\ 487\ 285\ 800x^{10} + 669\ 278\ 610x^8 - 162\ 954\ 792x^6 + 19\ 399\ 380x^4$$
$$- 875\ 160x^2 + 6435).$$

$$P_{17}(x) = \frac{1}{32\ 768}\,(583\ 401\ 555x^{17} - 2\ 404\ 321\ 560x^{15} + 4\ 071\ 834\ 900x^{13}$$
$$- 3\ 650\ 610\ 600x^{11} + 1\ 859\ 107\ 250x^9 - 535\ 422\ 888x^7$$
$$+ 81\ 477\ 396x^5 - 5\ 542\ 680x^3 + 109\ 395x).$$

$$P_{18}(x) = \frac{1}{65\ 536}\,(2\ 268\ 783\ 825x^{18} - 9\ 917\ 826\ 435x^{16} + 18\ 032\ 411\ 700x^{14}$$
$$- 17\ 644\ 617\ 900x^{12} + 10\ 039\ 179\ 150x^{10} - 3\ 346\ 393\ 050x^8 + 624\ 660\ 036x^6$$
$$- 58\ 198\ 140x^4 + 2\ 078\ 505x^2 - 12\ 155).$$

$$P_{19}(x) = \frac{1}{65\ 536}\,(4\ 418\ 157\ 975x^{19} - 20\ 419\ 055\ 425x^{17} + 39\ 671\ 305\ 740x^{15}$$
$$- 42\ 075\ 627\ 300x^{13} + 26\ 466\ 926\ 850x^{11} - 10\ 039\ 179\ 150x^9$$
$$+ 2\ 230\ 928\ 700x^7 - 267\ 711\ 444x^5 + 14\ 549\ 535x^3 - 230\ 945x).$$

$$P_{20}(x) = \frac{1}{262\ 144}\,(34\ 461\ 632\ 205x^{20} - 167\ 890\ 003\ 050x^{18}$$
$$+ 347\ 123\ 905\ 225x^{16} - 3\ 967\ 130\ 574\ 007\ 400x^{14} + 273\ 491\ 577\ 450x^{12}$$
$$- 116\ 454\ 478\ 140x^{10} + 30\ 117\ 537\ 450x^8 - 4\ 461\ 857\ 400x^6$$
$$+ 334\ 639\ 305x^4 - 9\ 699\ 690x^2 + 46\ 189).$$

2°. *Modified Legendre polynomials* $P_n^*(x)$.

$P_0^*(x) = 1.$

$P_1^*(x) = 2x - 1.$

$P_2^*(x) = -6x^2 + 6x - 1.$

$P_3^*(x) = 20x^3 - 30x^2 + 12x - 1.$

$P_4^*(x) = -70x^4 + 140x^3 - 90x^2 + 20x - 1.$

$P_5^*(x) = 252x^5 - 630x^4 + 560x^3 - 210x^2 + 30x - 1.$

$P_6^*(x) = -924x^6 + 2772x^5 - 3150x^4 + 1680x^3 - 420x^2 + 42x - 1.$

$P_7^*(x) = 3432x^7 - 12\ 012x^6 + 16\ 632x^5 - 11\ 550x^4 + 4200x^3$
$$- 756x^2 + 56x - 1.$$

$P_8^*(x) = -12\ 870x^8 + 51\ 480x^7 - 84\ 084x^6 + 72\ 072x^5 - 34\ 650x^4$
$$+ 9240x^3 - 1260x^2 + 72x - 1.$$

$P_9^*(x) = 48\ 620x^9 - 218\ 790x^8 + 411\ 840x^7 - 420\ 420x^6 + 252\ 252x^5$
$$- 90\ 090x^4 + 18\ 480x^3 - 1980x^2 + 90x - 1.$$

$P_{10}^*(x) = -184\ 756x^{10} + 923\ 780x^9 - 1\ 969\ 110x^8 + 2\ 333\ 760x^7$
$$- 1\ 681\ 680x^6 + 756\ 756x^5 - 210\ 210x^4 + 34\ 320x^3 - 2970x^2 + 110x - 1.$$

$P_{11}^*(x) = 705\ 432x^{11} - 3\ 879\ 876x^{10} + 9\ 237\ 800x^9 - 12\ 471\ 030x^8$
$$+ 10\ 501\ 920x^7 - 5\ 717\ 712x^6 + 2\ 018\ 016x^5 - 450\ 450x^4$$
$$+ 60\ 060x^3 - 4290x^2 + 132x - 1.$$

$P_{12}^*(x) = -2\ 704\ 156x^{12} + 16\ 224\ 936x^{11} - 42\ 678\ 636x^{10} + 64\ 664\ 600x^9$
$$- 62\ 355\ 150x^8 + 39\ 907\ 296x^7 - 17\ 153\ 136x^6 + 4\ 900\ 896x^5$$
$$- 900\ 900x^4 + 100\ 100x^3 - 6006x^2 + 156x - 1.$$

$P_{13}^*(x) = 10\ 400\ 600x^{13} - 97\ 603\ 900x^{12} + 194\ 699\ 232x^{11} - 327\ 202\ 876x^{10}$
$$+ 355\ 655\ 300x^9 - 261\ 891\ 630x^8 + 133\ 024\ 320x^7 - 46\ 558\ 512x^6$$
$$+ 11\ 027\ 016x^5 - 1\ 701\ 700x^4 + 160\ 160x^3 - 8190x^2 + 182x - 1.$$

$P_{14}^*(x) = -40\ 116\ 600x^{14} + 280\ 816\ 200x^{13} - 878\ 850\ 700x^{12}$
$$+ 1\ 622\ 493\ 600x^{11} - 1\ 963\ 217\ 256x^{10} + 1\ 636\ 014\ 380x^9$$
$$- 960\ 269\ 310x^8 + 399\ 072\ 960x^7 - 116\ 396\ 280x^6 + 23\ 279\ 256x^5$$
$$- 3\ 063\ 060x^4 + 247\ 520x^3 - 10\ 920x^2 + 210x - 1.$$

$P_{15}^*(x) = 155\ 117\ 520x^{15} - 1\ 163\ 381\ 400x^{14} + 3\ 931\ 426\ 800x^{13}$
$$- 7\ 909\ 656\ 300x^{12} + 10\ 546\ 208\ 400x^{11} - 9\ 816\ 086\ 280x^{10}$$
$$+ 6\ 544\ 057\ 520x^9 - 3\ 155\ 170\ 590x^8 + 1\ 097\ 450\ 640x^7 - 271\ 591\ 320x^6$$
$$+ 46\ 558\ 512x^5 - 5\ 290\ 740x^4 + 371\ 280x^3 - 14\ 280x^2 + 240x - 1.$$

$3°$. *Chebyshev polynomials of the first type* $T_n(x)$.

$T_0(x) = 1$ (however, we take $T_0 = \frac{1}{2}$).

$T_1(x) = x.$

$T_2(x) = 2x^2 - 1.$

$T_3(x) = 4x^3 - 3x.$

$T_4(x) = 8x^4 - 8x^2 + 1.$

$T_5(x) = 16x^5 - 20x^3 + 5x.$

$T_6(x) = 32x^6 - 48x^4 + 18x^2 - 1.$

$T_7 (x) = 64x^7 - 112x^5 + 56x^3 - 7x.$

$T_8 (x) = 128x^8 - 256x^6 + 160x^4 - 32x^2 + 1.$

$T_9 (x) = 256x^9 - 576x^7 + 432x^5 - 120x^3 + 9x.$

$T_{10}(x) = 512x^{10} - 1280x^8 + 1120x^6 - 400x^4 + 50x^2 - 1.$

$T_{11}(x) = 1024x^{11} - 2816x^9 + 2816x^7 - 1232x^5 + 220x^3 - 11x.$

$T_{12}(x) = 2048x^{12} - 6144x^{10} + 6912x^8 - 3584x^6 + 840x^4 - 72x^2 + 1.$

$T_{13}(x) = 4096x^{13} - 13\,312x^{11} + 16\,640x^9 - 9984x^7 + 2912x^5 - 364x^3 + 13x.$

$T_{14}(x) = 8292x^{14} - 28\,672x^{12} + 39\,424x^{10} - 26\,880x^8 + 9408x^6$
$$- 1568x^4 + 98x^2 - 1.$$

$T_{15}(x) = 16\,384x^{15} - 61\,440x^{13} + 92\,160x^{11} - 70\,400x^9 + 28\,800x^7$
$$- 6048x^5 + 560x^3 - 15x.$$

$T_{16}(x) = 32\,768x^{16} - 131\,072x^{14} + 212\,992x^{12} - 180\,224x^{10} + 84\,480x^8$
$$- 21\,504x^6 + 2688x^4 - 128x^2 + 1.$$

$T_{17}(x) = 65\,536x^{17} - 278\,528x^{15} + 487\,424x^{13} - 452\,608x^{11} + 239\,360x^9$
$$- 71\,808x^7 + 11\,424x^5 - 816x^3 + 17x.$$

$T_{18}(x) = 131\,072x^{18} - 589\,824x^{16} + 1\,105\,920x^{14} - 1\,118\,208x^{12}$
$$+ 658\,944x^{10} - 228\,096x^8 + 44\,352x^6 - 4320x^4 + 162x^2 - 1.$$

$T_{19}(x) = 262\,144x^{19} - 1\,245\,184x^{17} + 2\,490\,368x^{15} - 2\,723\,840x^{13}$
$$+ 1\,770\,496x^{11} - 695\,552x^9 + 160\,512x^7 - 20\,064x^5 + 1140x^3 - 19x.$$

$T_{20}(x) = 524\,288x^{20} - 2\,621\,440x^{18} + 5\,570\,560x^{16} - 6\,553\,600x^{14}$
$$+ 4\,659\,200x^{12} - 2\,050\,048x^{10} + 549\,120x^3 - 84\,480x^6$$
$$+ 6600x^4 - 200x^2 + 1.$$

$T_{21}(x) = 1\,048\,576x^{21} - 550\,502x^{19} + 12\,386\,304x^{17} - 15\,597\,568x^{15}$
$$+ 12\,042\,240x^{13} - 5\,870\,592x^{11} + 1\,793\,792x^9 - 329\,472x^7$$
$$+ 33\,264x^5 - 1540x^3 + 21x.$$

$T_{22}(x) = 2\,097\,152x^{22} - 11\,534\,336x^{20} + 27\,394\,048x^{18} - 36\,765\,696x^{16}$
$$+ 30\,638\,080x^{14} - 16\,400\,384x^{12} + 5\,637\,632x^{10} - 1\,208\,064x^8$$
$$+ 151\,008x^6 - 9680x^4 + 242x^2 - 1.$$

4°. *Modified Chebyshev polynomials of the first type* $T_n^*(x)$.

$T_0^* (x) = 1 \left(\text{however, we take } T_0^* = \dfrac{1}{2} \right).$

$T_1^* (x) = 2x - 1.$

$T_2^* (x) = 8x^2 - 8x + 1.$

$T_3^* (x) = 32x^3 - 48x^2 + 18x - 1.$

$T_4^* (x) = 128x^4 - 256x^3 + 160x^2 - 32x + 1.$

$T_5^* (x) = 512x^5 - 1280x^4 + 1120x^3 - 400x^2 + 50x - 1.$

$T_6^* (x) = 2048x^6 - 6144x^5 + 6912x^4 - 3584x^3 + 840x^2 - 72x + 1.$

$$T_7^*(x) = 8192x^7 - 28\ 672x^6 + 39\ 424x^5 - 26\ 880x^4 + 9408x^3 - 1568x^2$$
$$+ 98x - 1.$$

$$T_8^*(x) = 32\ 768x^8 - 131\ 072x^7 + 212\ 992x^6 - 180\ 244x^5 + 84\ 480x^4$$
$$- 21\ 504x^3 + 2688x^2 - 128x + 1.$$

$$T_9^*(x) = 131\ 072x^9 - 589\ 824x^8 + 1\ 105\ 920x^7 - 1\ 118\ 208x^6 + 658\ 944x^5$$
$$- 228\ 096x^4 + 44\ 352x^3 - 4320x^2 + 162x - 1.$$

$$T_{10}^*(x) = 524\ 288x^{10} - 2\ 621\ 440x^9 + 5\ 570\ 560x^8 - 6\ 553\ 600x^7$$
$$+ 4\ 659\ 200x^6 - 2\ 050\ 048x^5 + 549\ 120x^4 - 84\ 480x^3 + 6600x^2$$
$$- 200x + 1.$$

$$T_{11}^*(x) = 2\ 097\ 152x^{11} - 11\ 534\ 336x^{10} + 27\ 394\ 048x^9 - 36\ 765\ 696x^8$$
$$+ 30\ 638\ 080x^7 - 16\ 400\ 384x^6 + 5\ 637\ 632x^5 - 1\ 208\ 064x^4$$
$$+ 151\ 008x^3 - 9680x^2 + 242x - 1.$$

$$T_{12}^*(x) = 8\ 388\ 608x^{12} - 50\ 331\ 648x^{11} + 132\ 120\ 576x^{10} - 199\ 229\ 440x^9$$
$$+ 190\ 513\ 152x^8 - 120\ 324\ 096x^7 + 50\ 692\ 096x^6 - 14\ 057\ 472x^5$$
$$+ 2\ 471\ 040x^4 - 256\ 256x^3 + 13\ 728x^2 - 288x + 1.$$

$$T_{13}^*(x) = 33\ 554\ 432x^{13} - 218\ 103\ 808x^{12} + 627\ 048\ 448x^{11}$$
$$- 1\ 049\ 624\ 576x^{10} + 1\ 133\ 117\ 440x^9 - 825\ 556\ 992x^8$$
$$+ 412\ 778\ 496x^7 - 141\ 213\ 696x^6 + 32\ 361\ 472x^5 - 4\ 759\ 040x^4$$
$$+ 416\ 416x^3 - 18\ 928x^2 + 338x - 1.$$

$$T_{14}^*(x) = 134\ 217\ 728x^{14} - 939\ 524\ 096x^{13} + 2\ 936\ 012\ 800x^{12}$$
$$- 5\ 402\ 263\ 552x^{11} + 6\ 499\ 598\ 336x^{10} - 5\ 369\ 233\ 408x^9$$
$$+ 3\ 111\ 714\ 816x^8 - 1\ 270\ 087\ 680x^7 + 361\ 181\ 184x^6$$
$$- 69\ 701\ 632x^5 + 8\ 712\ 704x^4 - 652\ 288x^3 + 25\ 480x^2 - 392x + 1.$$

$$T_{15}^*(x) = 536\ 870\ 912x^{15} - 4\ 026\ 531\ 840x^{14} + 13\ 589\ 544\ 960x^{13}$$
$$- 27\ 262\ 976\ 000x^{12} + 36\ 175\ 872\ 000x^{11} - 33\ 426\ 505\ 728x^{10}$$
$$+ 22\ 052\ 208\ 640x^9 - 10\ 478\ 223\ 360x^8 + 3\ 572\ 121\ 600x^7 - 859\ 955\ 200x^6$$
$$+ 141\ 892\ 608x^5 - 15\ 275\ 520x^4 + 990\ 080x^3 - 33\ 600x^2 + 450x - 1.$$

$$T_{16}^*(x) = 2\ 147\ 483\ 648x^{16} - 17\ 179\ 869\ 184x^{15} + 62\ 277\ 025\ 792x^{14}$$
$$- 135\ 291\ 469\ 824x^{13} + 196\ 293\ 427\ 200x^{12} - 200\ 655\ 503\ 360x^{11}$$
$$+ 148\ 562\ 247\ 680x^{10} - 80\ 648\ 077\ 312x^9 + 32\ 133\ 218\ 304x^8$$
$$- 9\ 313\ 976\ 320x^7 + 1\ 926\ 299\ 648x^6 - 275\ 185\ 664x^5$$
$$+ 25\ 798\ 656x^4 - 1\ 462\ 272x^3 + 43\ 520x^2 - 512x + 1.$$

$$T_{17}^*(x) = 8\ 589\ 934\ 592x^{17} - 73\ 014\ 444\ 032x^{16} + 282\ 930\ 970\ 624x^{15}$$
$$- 661\ 693\ 399\ 040x^{15} + 1\ 042\ 167\ 103\ 488x^{13} - 1\ 167\ 945\ 891\ 840x^{12}$$
$$+ 959\ 384\ 125\ 440x^{11} - 586\ 290\ 298\ 880x^{10} + 267\ 776\ 819\ 200x^9$$
$$- 91\ 044\ 118\ 528x^8 + 22\ 761\ 029\ 632x^7 - 4\ 093\ 386\ 752x^6$$
$$+ 511\ 673\ 344x^5 - 42\ 170\ 880x^4 + 2\ 108\ 544x^3 - 55\ 488x^2 + 578x - 1.$$

$T_{18}^*(x) = 34\,359\,738\,368x^{18} - 309\,237\,645\,312x^{17} + 1\,275\,605\,286\,912x^{16}$

$\qquad - 3\,195\,455\,668\,224x^{15} + 5\,429\,778\,186\,240x^{14} - 6\,620\,826\,304\,512x^{13}$

$\qquad + 5\,977\,134\,858\,240x^{12} - 4\,063\,273\,943\,040x^{11} + 2\,095\,125\,626\,880x^{10}$

$\qquad - 819\,082\,035\,200x^9 + 240\,999\,137\,280x^8 - 52\,581\,629\,952x^7$

$\qquad + 8\,307\,167\,232x^6 - 916\,844\,544x^5 + 66\,977\,280x^4 - 2\,976\,768x^3$

$\qquad\qquad\qquad\qquad\qquad\qquad + 69\,768x^2 - 648x + 1.$

$T_{19}^*(x) = 137\,438\,953\,472x^{19} - 1\,305\,670\,057\,984x^{18} + 5\,712\,306\,503\,680x^{17}$

$\qquad - 15\,260\,018\,802\,688x^{16} + 27\,827\,093\,110\,784x^{15} - 36\,681\,168\,191\,488x^{14}$

$\qquad + 36\,108\,024\,938\,496x^{13} - 27\,039\,419\,596\,800x^{12} + 15\,547\,666\,268\,060x^{11}$

$\qquad - 6\,880\,289\,095\,680x^{10} + 2\,334\,383\,800\,320x^9 - 601\,280\,675\,840x^8$

$\qquad + 115\,630\,899\,200x^7 - 16\,188\,325\,888x^6 + 1\,589\,924\,864x^5$

$\qquad\qquad - 103\,690\,752x^4 + 4\,124\,064x^3 - 86\,640x^2 + 722x - 1.$

$T_{20}^*(x) = 549\,755\,813\,888x^{20} - 5\,497\,558\,138\,880x^{19} + 25\,426\,206\,392\,320x^{18}$

$\qquad - 72\,155\,450\,572\,800x^{17} + 140\,552\,804\,761\,600x^{16} - 199\,183\,403\,319\,296x^{15}$

$\qquad + 212\,364\,657\,950\,720x^{14} - 173\,752\,901\,959\,680x^{13} + 110\,292\,369\,408\,000x^{12}$

$\qquad - 54\,553\,214\,976\,000x^{11} + 21\,002\,987\,765\,760x^{10} - 6\,254\,808\,268\,800x^9$

$\qquad + 1\,424\,085\,811\,200x^8 - 243\,433\,472\,000x^7 + 30\,429\,184\,000x^6$

$\qquad - 2\,677\,768\,192x^5 + 156\,900\,480x^4 - 5\,617\,920x^3 + 106\,400x^2 - 800x + 1.$

5°. *The polynomials* $C_n(x)$.

$C_0(x) = 2.$

$C_1(x) = x.$

$C_2(x) = x^2 - 2.$

$C_3(x) = x^3 - 3x.$

$C_4(x) = x^4 - 4x^2 + 2.$

$C_5(x) = x^5 - 5x^3 + 5x.$

$C_6(x) = x^6 - 6x^4 + 9x^2 - 2.$

$C_7(x) = x^7 - 7x^5 + 14x^3 - 7x.$

$C_8(x) = x^8 - 8x^6 + 20x^4 - 16x^2 + 2.$

$C_9(x) = x^9 - 9x^7 + 27x^5 - 30x^3 + 9x.$

$C_{10}(x) = x^{10} - 10x^8 + 35x^6 - 50x^4 + 25x^2 - 2.$

$C_{11}(x) = x^{11} - 11x^9 + 44x^7 - 77x^5 + 55x^3 - 11x.$

$C_{12}(x) = x^{12} - 12x^{10} + 54x^8 - 112x^6 + 105x^4 - 36x^2 + 2.$

6°. *Chebyshev polynomials of the second type* $U_n(x)$.

$U_0(x) = 1.$

$U_1(x) = 2x.$

$U_2(x) = 4x^2 - 1.$

$U_3(x) = 8x^3 - 4x.$

$U_4(x) = 16x^4 - 12x^2 + 1.$

$U_5(x) = 32x^5 - 32x^3 + 6x.$

$U_6(x) = 64x^6 - 80x^4 + 24x^2 - 1.$

$U_7(x) = 128x^7 - 192x^5 + 80x^3 - 8x.$

$U_8(x) = 256x^8 - 448x^6 + 240x^4 - 40x^2 + 1.$

$U_9(x) = 512x^9 - 1024x^7 + 672x^5 - 160x^3 + 10x.$

$U_{10}(x) = 1024x^{10} - 2304x^8 + 1792x^6 - 560x^4 + 60x^2 - 1.$

$U_{11}(x) = 2048x^{11} - 512x^9 + 4608x^7 - 1792x^5 + 280x^3 - 12x.$

$U_{12}(x) = 4096x^{12} - 11\,264^{10} + 11\,520x^8 - 5376x^6 + 1120x^4 - 84x^2 + 1.$

7°. *Modified Chebyshev polynomials of the second type* $U_n^*(x)$.

$U_0^*(x) = 1.$

$U_1^*(x) = 4x - 2.$

$U_2^*(x) = 16x^2 - 16x + 3.$

$U_3^*(x) = 64x^3 - 96x^2 + 40x - 4.$

$U_4^*(x) = 256x^4 - 512x^3 + 336x^2 - 80x + 5.$

$U_5^*(x) = 1024x^5 - 2560x^4 + 2304x^3 - 896x^2 + 140x - 6.$

$U_6^*(x) = 4096x^6 - 12\,288x^5 + 14\,080x^4 - 7680x^3 + 2016x^2 - 224x + 7.$

$U_7^*(x) = 16\,384x^7 - 57\,344x^6 + 79\,872x^5 - 56\,320x^4 + 21\,120x^3 - 4032x^2$
$$+ 336x - 8.$$

$U_8^*(x) = 65\,536x^8 - 262\,144x^7 + 430\,080x^6 - 372\,736x^5 + 183\,040x^4$
$$- 50\,688x^3 + 7392x^2 - 480x + 9.$$

$U_9^*(x) = 262\,144x^9 - 1\,179\,648x^8 + 2\,228\,224x^7 - 2\,293\,760x^6$
$$+ 1\,397\,760x^5 - 512\,512x^4 + 109\,824x^3 - 12\,672x^2 + 660x - 10.$$

$U_{10}^*(x) = 1\,048\,576x^{10} - 5\,242\,880x^9 + 11\,206\,656x^8 - 13\,369\,344x^7$
$$+ 9\,748\,480x^6 - 4\,472\,832x^5 + 1\,281\,280x^4 - 219\,648x^3$$
$$+ 20\,592x^2 - 880x + 11.$$

$U_{11}^*(x) = 4\,194\,304x^{11} - 23\,068\,672x^{10} + 55\,050\,240x^9 - 74\,711\,040x^8$
$$+ 63\,504\,384x^7 - 35\,094\,528x^6 + 12\,673\,024x^5 - 2\,928\,640x^4$$
$$+ 411\,840x^3 - 32\,032x^2 + 1144x - 12.$$

$U_{12}^*(x) = 16\,777\,216x^{12} - 100\,663\,296x^{11} + 265\,289\,728x^{10} - 403\,701\,760x^9$
$$+ 392\,232\,960x^8 - 254\,017\,536x^7 + 111\,132\,672x^6 - 32\,587\,776x^5$$
$$+ 6\,223\,360x^4 - 732\,160x^3 + 48\,048x^2 - 1456x + 13.$$

$U_{13}^*(x) = 67\,108\,864x^{13} - 436\,207\,616x^{12} + 1\,258\,291\,200x^{11}$
$$- 2\,122\,317\,824x^{10} + 2\,321\,285\,120x^9 - 1\,725\,825\,024x^8$$
$$+ 889\,061\,376x^7 - 317\,521\,920x^6 + 77\,395\,968x^5 - 12\,446\,720x^4$$
$$+ 1\,244\,672x^3 - 69\,888x^2 + 1820x - 14.$$

8°. *The polynomials* $S_n(x)$.

$S_0(x) = 1.$

$S_1(x) = x.$

$S_2(x) = x^2 - 1.$

$S_3(x) = x^3 - 2x.$

$S_4(x) = x^4 - 3x^2 + 1.$

$S_5(x) = x^5 - 4x^3 + 3x.$

$S_6(x) = x^6 - 5x^4 + 6x^2 - 1.$

$S_7(x) = x^7 - 6x^5 + 10x^3 - 4x.$

$S_8(x) = x^8 - 7x^6 + 15x^4 - 10x^2 + 1.$

$S_9(x) = x^9 - 8x^7 + 21x^5 - 20x^3 + 5x.$

$S_{10}(x) = x^{10} - 9x^8 + 28x^6 - 35x^4 + 15x^2 - 1.$

$S_{11}(x) = x^{11} - 10x^9 + 36x^7 - 56x^5 + 35x^3 - 6x.$

$S_{12}(x) = x^{12} - 11x^{10} + 45x^8 - 84x^6 + 70x^4 - 21x^2 + 1.$

9°. *Laguerre polynomials* $L_n(x)$.

$L_0(x) = 1.$

$L_1(x) = -x + 1.$

$L_2(x) = x^2 - 4x + 2.$

$L_3(x) = -x^3 + 9x^2 - 18x + 6.$

$L_4(x) = x^4 - 16x^3 + 72x^2 - 96x + 24.$

$L_5(x) = -x^5 + 25x^4 - 200x^3 + 600x^2 - 600x + 120.$

$L_6(x) = x^6 - 36x^5 + 450x^4 - 2400x^3 + 5400x^2 - 4320x + 720.$

$L_7(x) = -x^7 + 49x^6 - 882x^5 + 7350x^4 - 29\,400x^3 + 52\,920x^2 - 35\,280x$
$$+ 5040.$$

$L_8(x) = x^8 - 64x^7 + 1568x^6 - 18\,816x^5 + 117\,600x^4 - 376\,320x^3$
$$+ 564\,480x^2 - 322\,560x + 40\,320.$$

$L_9(x) = -x^9 + 81x^8 - 2592x^7 + 42\,336x^6 - 381\,024x^5 + 1\,905\,120x^4$
$$- 5\,080\,320x^3 + 6\,531\,840x^2 - 3\,265\,920x + 362\,880.$$

$L_{10}(x) = x^{10} - 100x^9 + 4050x^8 - 86\,400x^7 + 1\,058\,400x^6 - 7\,620\,480x^5$
$$+ 31\,752\,000x^4 - 72\,576\,000x^3 + 81\,648\,000x^2 - 36\,288\,000x + 3\,628\,800.$$

$L_{11}(x) = -x^{11} + 121x^{10} - 6050x^9 + 163\,350x^8 - 2\,613\,600x^7$
$$+ 25\,613\,280x^6 - 153\,679\,680x^5 + 548\,856\,000x^4 - 1\,097\,712\,000x^3$$
$$+ 1\,097\,712\,000x^2 - 439\,084\,800x + 39\,916\,800.$$

10°. *Hermite polynomials* $H_n(x)$.

$H_0(x) = 1.$

$H_1(x) = 2x.$

$H_2(x) = 4x^2 - 2.$

$H_3(x) = 8x^3 - 12x.$

$H_4(x) = 16x^4 - 48x^2 + 12.$

$H_5(x) = 32x^5 - 160x^3 + 120x.$

$H_6 (x) = 64x^6 - 480x^4 + 720x^2 - 120.$

$H_7 (x) = 128x^7 - 1344x^5 + 3360x^3 - 1680x.$

$H_8 (x) = 256x^8 - 3584x^6 + 13\,440x^4 - 13\,440x^2 + 1680.$

$H_9 (x) = 512x^9 - 9216x^7 + 48\,384x^5 - 80\,640x^3 + 30\,240x.$

$H_{10}(x) = 1024x^{10} - 23\,040x^8 + 161\,280x^6 - 403\,200x^4 + 302\,400x^2 - 30\,240.$

[For § 4.5, 11°, *see page* 76.]

4.6. Zeros of polynomials. 1°. *Zeros of Chebyshev polynomials.* It follows from the definition of Chebyshev polynomials of the first type $T_n(x)$ that their zeros are given by the formula

$$x_k^{(n)} = \cos \frac{2k - 1}{2n} \pi \quad (k = 1, 2, ..., n).$$

Similarly, the zeros of the Chebyshev polynomials of the second type $U_n(x)$ are given by the formula

$$x_k^{(n)} = \cos \frac{k}{n + 1} \pi \quad (k = 1, 2, ..., n).$$

2°. *Zeros of the Legendre polynomials* $P_n(x)$.

$n = 1$	$n = 2$	$n = 3$	$n = 4$	$n = 5$
0·000000	0·577350	0·000000	0·339981	0·000000
		0·774597	0·861136	0·538469
				0·906180

$n = 6$	$n = 7$	$n = 8$	$n = 9$	$n = 10$
0·238619	0·000000	0·183435	0·000000	0·148874
0·661209	0·405845	0·525533	0·324253	0·433395
0·932470	0·741531	0·796666	0·613371	0·679410
	0·949108	0·960290	0·836031	0·865063
			0·968160	0·973907

$n = 11$	$n = 12$	$n = 13$	$n = 14$	$n = 15$
0·000000	0·125233	0·000000	0·108055	0·000000
0·269543	0·367832	0·230458	0·319112	0·201194
0·519095	0·587318	0·448493	0·515249	0·394151
0·730152	0·769903	0·642349	0·697293	0·570972
0·887063	0·904117	0·801578	0·827202	0·724418
0·978229	0·981561	0·917598	0·928435	0·848207
		0·984183	0·986284	0·937273
				0·987993

$n = 16$	$n = 17$	$n = 18$	$n = 19$	$n = 20$
0·095012	0·000000	0·084775	0·000000	0·076527
0·281605	0·178484	0·251886	0·160359	0·227786
0·458017	0·351232	0·411751	0·316564	0·373706
0·617876	0·512691	0·559771	0·464571	0·510867
0·755404	0·657671	0·691687	0·600545	0·636054
0·865631	0·781514	0·803705	0·720966	0·746332
0·944575	0·880239	0·892603	0·822715	0·839117
0·989401	0·950676	0·955824	0·903156	0·912235
	0·990575	0·991565	0·960208	0·963972
			0·992407	0·993129

$n = 21$	$n = 22$	$n = 23$	$n = 24$	$n = 25$
0·000000	0·069739	0·000000	0·064057	0·000000
0·145562	0·207860	0·133257	0·191119	0·122865
0·288021	0·341936	0·264136	0·315043	0·243867
0·424342	0·469356	0·390301	0·433794	0·361172
0·551619	0·587640	0·509502	0·545421	0·473003
0·667139	0·694487	0·619610	0·648094	0·577663
0·768440	0·787817	0·718661	0·740124	0·673566
0·853363	0·865812	0·804888	0·820002	0·759259
0·920100	0·926957	0·876752	0·886415	0·833443
0·967227	0·970061	0·932971	0·938275	0·894992
0·993752	0·994295	0·972542	0·974729	0·942975
		0·994769	0·995187	0·976664
				0·995557

$n = 26$	$n = 27$	$n = 28$	$n = 29$	$n = 30$
0·059230	0·000000	0·055079	0·000000	0·051472
0·176859	0·113973	0·164569	0·106278	0·153870
0·292005	0·226459	0·272062	0·211352	0·254637
0·403052	0·335994	0·376252	0·314032	0·352705
0·508441	0·441148	0·475874	0·413153	0·447034
0·606692	0·540552	0·569720	0·507593	0·536624
0·696427	0·632908	0·656651	0·596282	0·620526
0·776386	0·717013	0·735611	0·678215	0·697850
0·845446	0·791772	0·805641	0·752463	0·767777
0·902638	0·856208	0·865892	0·818185	0·829566
0·947159	0·909482	0·915633	0·874638	0·882560
0·978385	0·950901	0·954259	0·921180	0·926200
0·995886	0·979923	0·981303	0·957286	0·960022
	0·996179	0·996442	0·982545	0·983668
			0·996679	0·996893

$n = 31$	$n = 32$	$n = 33$	$n = 34$	$n = 35$
0·000000	0·048308	0·000000	0·045510	0·000000
0·099555	0·144472	0·093631	0·136152	0·088371
0·198121	0·239287	0·186439	0·225667	0·176051
0·294718	0·331869	0·277609	0·313311	0·262353
0·388386	0·421351	0·366339	0·398359	0·346602
0·478194	0·506900	0·451850	0·480106	0·428138
0·563249	0·587716	0·533390	0·557876	0·506323
0·642707	0·663044	0·610242	0·631022	0·580545
0·715777	0·732182	0·681732	0·698939	0·650224
0·781733	0·794484	0·747231	0·761065	0·714814
0·839920	0·849368	0·806162	0·816884	0·773810
0·889760	0·896321	0·858010	0·865935	0·826750
0·930757	0·934906	0·902317	0·907810	0·873219
0·962504	0·964762	0·938694	0·942162	0·912854
0·984686	0·985612	0·966823	0·968708	0·945345
0·997087	0·997264	0·986456	0·987228	0·970438
		0·997425	0·997572	0·987936
				0·997707

$n = 36$	$n = 37$	$n = 38$	$n = 39$	$n = 40$
0·043018	0·000000	0·040785	0·000000	0·038772
0·128736	0·083670	0·122084	0·079444	0·116084
0·213501	0·166754	0·202570	0·158385	0·192698
0·296685	0·248668	0·281709	0·236326	0·268152
0·377673	0·328837	0·358972	0·312772	0·341994
0·455864	0·406701	0·433848	0·387240	0·413779
0·530680	0·481711	0·505835	0·459261	0·483076
0·601568	0·553341	0·574456	0·528377	0·549467
0·668001	0·621093	0·639255	0·594153	0·612554
0·729489	0·684486	0·699799	0·656173	0·671957
0·785576	0·743079	0·755686	0·714044	0·727318
0·835847	0·796459	0·806544	0·767401	0·778306
0·879930	0·844253	0·852035	0·815906	0·824612
0 917498	0·886125	0·891856	0·859253	0·865960
0·948273	0·921781	0·925741	0·897167	0·902099
0·972028	0·950972	0·953466	0·929409	0·932813
0·988586	0·973493	0·974846	0·955775	0·957917
0·997830	0·989186	0·989739	0·976099	0·977260
	0·997945	0·998050	0·990252	0·990726
			0·998147	0·998238

3°. *Zeros of the Laguerre polynomials* $L_n(x)$.

$n = 1$	$n = 2$	$n = 3$	$n = 4$	$n = 5$
1·000000	0·585786	0·415775	0·322548	0·263560
	3·414214	2·294280	1·745761	1·413403
		6·289945	4·536620	3·596426
			9·395071	7·085810
				12·640801

$n = 6$	$n = 7$	$n = 8$	$n = 9$	$n = 10$
0·222847	0·193044	0·170280	0·152322	0·137793
1·188932	1·026665	0·903702	0·807220	0·729455
2·992736	2·567877	2·251087	2·005135	1·808343
5·775144	4·900353	4·266700	3·783474	3·401434
9·837467	8·182153	7·045905	6·204957	5·552496
15·982874	12·734180	10·758516	9·372985	8·330153
	19·395728	15·740679	13·466237	11·843786
		22·863132	18·833598	16·279258
			26·374072	21·996586
				29·920697

$n = 11$	$n = 12$	$n = 13$	$n = 14$	$n = 15$
0·125796	0·115722	0·107142	0·099748	0·093308
0·665418	0·611757	0·566132	0·526858	0·492692
1·647151	1·512610	1·398564	1·300629	1·215595
3·091138	2·833751	2·616597	2·430801	2·269950
5·029284	4·599228	4·238846	3·932103	3·667623
7·509888	6·844525	6·292256	5·825536	5·425337
10·605951	9·621317	8·815002	8·140240	7·565916
14·431614	13·006055	11·861404	10·916500	10·120229
19·178857	17·116855	15·510762	14·210805	13·130282
25·217709	22·151090	19·884636	18·104892	16·654408
33·497193	28·487967	25·182564	22·723382	20·776479
	37·099121	31·800386	28·272982	25·623894
		40·723009	35·149444	31·407519
			44·366082	38·530683
				48·026086

4°. *Zeros of the Hermite polynomials* $H_n(x)$.

$n = 1$	$n = 2$	$n = 3$	$n = 4$	$n = 5$
0·000000	0·707107	0·000000	0·524648	0·000000
		1·224745	1·650680	0·958572
				2·020183

$n = 6$	$n = 7$	$n = 8$	$n = 9$	$n = 10$
0·436077	0·000000	0·381187	0·000000	0·322901
1·335849	0·816288	1·157194	0·723551	1·036611
2·350605	1·673552	1·981657	1·468553	1·756684
	2·651961	2·930637	2·266581	2·532732
			3·190993	3·436159

$n = 11$	$n = 12$	$n = 13$	$n = 14$	$n = 15$
0·000000	0·314240	0·000000	0·291746	0·000000
0·656810	0·947788	0·605764	0·878714	0·565070
1·326557	1·597683	1·220055	1·476683	1·136116
2·025948	2·279507	1·853108	2·095183	1·719993
2·783290	3·020637	2·519736	2·748471	2·325732
3·668471	3·889725	3·246609	3·462657	2·967167
		4·101338	4·304449	3·669950
				4·499991

$n = 16$	$n = 17$	$n = 18$	$n = 19$	$n = 20$
0·273481	0·000000	0·258268	0·000000	0·245341
0·822951	0·531633	0·776683	0·503520	0·737474
1·380259	1·067649	1·300921	1·010368	1·234076
1·951788	1·612924	1·835532	1·524171	1·738538
2·546202	2·173503	2·386299	2·049232	2·254974
3·176999	2·757763	2·961378	2·591134	2·788806
3·869448	3·378932	3·573769	3·157849	3·347855
4·688739	4·061947	4·248118	3·762187	3·944764
	4·871345	5·048364	4·428533	4·603682
			5·220272	5·387481

5°. *Zeros of the Hermite polynomials* $h_n(x)$.

$n = 1$	$n = 2$	$n = 3$	$n = 4$	$n = 5$	$n = 6$
0·000000	1·000000	0·000000	0·741964	0·000000	0·616707
		1·732051	2·334414	1·355626	1·889176
				2·856970	3·324257

$n = 7$	$n = 8$	$n = 9$	$n = 10$	$n = 11$	$n = 12$
0·00000	0·539080	0·000000	0·484936	0·000000	0·444403
1·154405	1·636519	1·023256	1·465989	0·928869	1·340375
2·366759	2·802486	2·076848	2·484326	1·876035	2·259464
3·750440	4·144547	3·205429	3·581823	2·865123	3·223710
		4·512746	4·839463	3·936166	4·271826
				5·188001	5·500902

$n = 13$	$n = 14$	$n = 15$	$n = 16$	$n = 17$
0·000000	0·412590	0·000000	0·386761	0·000000
0·856680	1·242689	0·799129	1·163829	0·751843
1·725418	2·088345	1·606710	1·951980	1·509883
2·620690	2·963037	2·432437	2·760245	2·281020
3·563444	3·886925	3·289082	3·600874	3·073797
4·591398	4·896936	4·196208	4·492955	3·900066
5·800167	6·087409	5·190094	5·472226	4·778532
		6·363948	6·630878	5·744460
				6·889122

$n = 18$	$n = 19$	$n = 20$	$n = 21$	$n = 22$
0·365246	0·000000	0·346964	0·000000	0·331179
1·098395	0·712085	1·042945	0·678046	0·995162
1·839780	1·428877	1·745246	1·359765	1·664125
2·595834	2·155503	2·458664	2·049102	2·341760
3·374737	2·898051	3·189015	2·750593	3·032404
4·188020	3·664417	3·943967	3·469847	3·741496
5·054073	4·465873	4·734581	4·214344	4·476362
6·007746	5·320536	5·578739	4·994964	5·247725
7·139465	6·262891	6·510590	5·829382	6·073075
	7·382579	7·619049	6·751445	6·985981
			7·849383	8·074030

II. NUMERICAL TABLES

TABLE 1. COEFFICIENTS OF CERTAIN SERIES

n	$\dfrac{1}{n}$		$\displaystyle\sum_{k=1}^{n}\dfrac{1}{k}$	
1	$\dfrac{1}{1}$	1·00000	$\dfrac{1}{1}$	1·00000
2	$\dfrac{1}{2}$	0·50000	$1+\dfrac{1}{2}$	1·50000
3	$\dfrac{1}{3}$	0·33333	$1+\dfrac{1}{2}+\dfrac{1}{3}$	1·83333
4	$\dfrac{1}{4}$	0·25000	$1+\dfrac{1}{2}+\dfrac{1}{3}+\dfrac{1}{4}$	2·08333
5	$\dfrac{1}{5}$	0·20000	$1+\dfrac{1}{2}+\dots+\dfrac{1}{4}+\dfrac{1}{5}$	2·28333
6	$\dfrac{1}{6}$	0·16667	$1+\dfrac{1}{2}+\dots+\dfrac{1}{5}+\dfrac{1}{6}$	2·45000
7	$\dfrac{1}{7}$	0·14286	$1+\dfrac{1}{2}+\dots+\dfrac{1}{6}+\dfrac{1}{7}$	2·59286
8	$\dfrac{1}{8}$	0·12500	$1+\dfrac{1}{2}+\dots+\dfrac{1}{7}+\dfrac{1}{8}$	2·71786
9	$\dfrac{1}{9}$	0·11111	$1+\dfrac{1}{2}+\dots+\dfrac{1}{8}+\dfrac{1}{9}$	2·82897
10	$\dfrac{1}{10}$	0·10000	$1+\dfrac{1}{2}+\dots+\dfrac{1}{9}+\dfrac{1}{10}$	2·92897

Continuation of TABLE 1

n	$n!$		$\dfrac{1}{n!}$	
1	1	1	$\dfrac{1}{1}$	1·000 00
2	1 . 2	2	$\dfrac{1}{1 . 2}$	0·500 00
3	1 . 2 . 3	6	$\dfrac{1}{1 . 2 . 3}$	0·166 67
4	1 . 2 . 3 . 4	24	$\dfrac{1}{1 . 2 . 3 . 4}$	0·041 667
5	1 . 2 . 3 . 4 . 5	120	$\dfrac{1}{1 . 2 . 3 . 4 . 5}$	0·008 333 3
6	1 . 2 ... 5 . 6	720	$\dfrac{1}{1 . 2 ... 5 . 6}$	0·001 388 9
7	1 . 2 ... 6 . 7	5 040	$\dfrac{1}{1 . 2 ... 6 . 7}$	0·000 198 41
8	1 . 2 ... 7 . 8	40 320	$\dfrac{1}{1 . 2 ... 7 . 8}$	0·000 024 802
9	1 . 2 ... 8 . 9	362 880	$\dfrac{1}{1 . 2 ... 8 . 9}$	0·000 002 755 7
10	1 . 2 ... 9 . 10	3 628 800	$\dfrac{1}{1 . 2 ... 9 . 10}$	0·000 000 275 57

n	$(2n-1)!!$		$\dfrac{1}{(2n-1)!!}$	
1	1	1	$\dfrac{1}{2}$	1·000 00
2	1 . 3	3	$\dfrac{1}{1.3}$	0·333 33
3	1 . 3 . 5	15	$\dfrac{1}{1.3.5}$	0·066 667
4	1 . 3 . 5 . 7	105	$\dfrac{1}{1.3.5.7}$	0·009 523 9
5	1 . 3 . 5 . 7 . 9	945	$\dfrac{1}{1.3.5.7.9}$	0·001 058 2
6	1 . 3 … 9 . 11	10 395	$\dfrac{1}{1.3\ldots 9.11}$	0·000 096 2
7	1 . 3 … 11 . 13	135 135	$\dfrac{1}{1.3\ldots 11.13}$	0·000 007 4
8	1 . 3 … 13 . 15	2 027 025	$\dfrac{1}{1.3\ldots 13.15}$	0·000 000 493
9	1 . 3 … 15 . 17	34 459 425	$\dfrac{1}{1.3\ldots 15.17}$	0·000 000 029
10	1 . 3 … 17 . 19	654 729 075	$\dfrac{1}{1.3\ldots 17.19}$	0·000 000 002

Continuation of TABLE 1

n	$(2n)!!$		$\dfrac{1}{(2n)!!}$	
1	2	2	$\dfrac{1}{2}$	0·500 00
2	2 . 4	8	$\dfrac{1}{2 . 4}$	0·125 00
3	2 . 4 . 6	48	$\dfrac{1}{2 . 4 . 6}$	0·020 833
4	2 . 4 . 6 . 8	384	$\dfrac{1}{2 . 4 . 6 . 8}$	0·002 604 2
5	2 . 4 . 6 . 8 . 10	3 840	$\dfrac{1}{2 . 4 . 6 . 8 . 10}$	0·000 260 42
6	2 . 4 ... 10 . 12	46 080	$\dfrac{1}{2 . 4 ... 10 . 12}$	0·000 021 701
7	2 . 4 ... 12 . 14	645 120	$\dfrac{1}{2 . 4 ... 12 . 14}$	0·000 001 550
8	2 . 4 ... 14 . 16	10 321 920	$\dfrac{1}{2 . 4 ... 14 . 16}$	0·000 000 097
9	2 . 4 ... 16 . 18	185 794 560	$\dfrac{1}{2 . 4 ... 16 . 18}$	0·000 000 005
10	2 . 4 ... 18 . 20	3 715 891 200	$\dfrac{1}{2 . 4 ... 18 . 20}$	0·000 000 000

n	$\dfrac{n!}{(2n-1)!!}$		$\dfrac{2^n n!}{(2n+1)!!}$	
1	$\dfrac{1}{1.}$	1·00000	$\dfrac{2}{1.3}$	0·66667
2	$\dfrac{1.2}{1.3}$	0·66667	$\dfrac{2.4}{1.3.5}$	0·53333
3	$\dfrac{1.2.3}{1.3.5}$	0·40000	$\dfrac{2.4.6}{1.3.5.7}$	0·45714
4	$\dfrac{1.2.3.4}{1.3.5.7}$	0·22857	$\dfrac{2.4.6.8}{1.3.5.7.9}$	0·40635
5	$\dfrac{1.2.3.4.5}{1.3.5.7.9}$	0·12698	$\dfrac{2.4.6.8.10}{1.3.5.7.9.11}$	0·36941
6	$\dfrac{1.2\ldots5.6}{1.3\ldots9.11}$	0·06926	$\dfrac{2.4\ldots10.12}{1.3\ldots11.13}$	0·34099
7	$\dfrac{1.2\ldots6.7}{1.3\ldots11.13}$	0·03730	$\dfrac{2.4\ldots12.14}{1.3\ldots13.15}$	0·31826
8	$\dfrac{1.2\ldots7.8}{1.3\ldots13.15}$	0·01989	$\dfrac{2.4\ldots14.16}{1.3\ldots15.17}$	0·29954
9	$\dfrac{1.2\ldots8.9}{1.3\ldots15.17}$	0·01053	$\dfrac{2.4\ldots16.18}{1.3\ldots17.19}$	0·28377
10	$\dfrac{1.2\ldots9.10}{1.3\ldots17.19}$	0·00554	$\dfrac{2.4\ldots18.20}{1.3\ldots19.21}$	0·27026

Continuation of TABLE 1

n	$\dfrac{(2n-1)!!}{2^n n!}$		$\dfrac{(2n-1)!!}{2^n n!\,(2n+1)}$	
1	$\dfrac{1}{2}$	0·50000	$\dfrac{1}{2\,.\,3}$	0·166 667
2	$\dfrac{1\,.\,3}{2\,.\,4}$	0·37500	$\dfrac{1\,.\,3}{2\,.\,4\,.\,5}$	0·075 000
3	$\dfrac{1\,.\,3\,.\,5}{2\,.\,4\,.\,6}$	0·31250	$\dfrac{1\,.\,3\,.\,5}{2\,.\,4\,.\,6\,.\,7}$	0·044 643
4	$\dfrac{1\,.\,3\,.\,5\,.\,7}{2\,.\,4\,.\,6\,.\,8}$	0·27344	$\dfrac{1\,.\,3\,.\,5\,.\,7}{2\,.\,4\,.\,6\,.\,8\,.\,9}$	0·030 382
5	$\dfrac{1\,.\,3\,.\,5\,.\,7\,.\,9}{2\,.\,4\,.\,6\,.\,8\,.\,10}$	0·24609	$\dfrac{1\,.\,3\,.\,5\,.\,7\,.\,9}{2\,.4\,.6\,.8\,.10\,.11}$	0·022 372
6	$\dfrac{1\,.\,3\,\ldots\,9\,.\,11}{2\,.\,4\,\ldots\,10\,.\,12}$	0·22559	$\dfrac{1\,.\,3\,\ldots\,9\,.\,11}{2\,.\,4\,\ldots\,12\,.\,13}$	0·017 353
7	$\dfrac{1\,.\,3\,\ldots\,11\,.\,13}{2\,.\,4\,\ldots\,12\,.\,14}$	0·20947	$\dfrac{1\,.\,3\,\ldots\,11\,.\,13}{2\,.\,4\,\ldots\,14\,.\,15}$	0·013 965
8	$\dfrac{1\,.\,3\,\ldots\,13\,.\,15}{2\,.\,4\,\ldots\,14\,.\,16}$	0·19638	$\dfrac{1\,.\,3\,\ldots\,13\,.\,15}{2\,.\,4\,\ldots\,16\,.\,17}$	0·011 552
9	$\dfrac{1\,.\,3\,\ldots\,15\,.\,17}{2\,.\,4\,\ldots\,16\,.\,18}$	0·18547	$\dfrac{1\,.\,3\,\ldots\,15\,.\,17}{2\,.\,4\,\ldots\,18\,.\,19}$	0·009 761 6
10	$\dfrac{1\,.\,3\,\ldots\,17\,.\,19}{2\,.\,4\,\ldots\,18\,.\,20}$	0·17620	$\dfrac{1\,.\,3\,\ldots\,17\,.\,19}{2\,.\,4\,\ldots\,20\,.\,21}$	0·008 390 3

n	$\dfrac{(2n-1)!!}{2^{n+1}(n+1)!}$		$\dfrac{(2n-1)!!}{2^{n+1}(n+1)!\,(2n+3)}$	
1	$\dfrac{1}{2\,.\,4}$	0·125 00	$\dfrac{1}{2\,.\,4\,.\,5}$	0·025 000
2	$\dfrac{1\,.\,3}{2\,.\,4\,.\,6}$	0·062 500	$\dfrac{1\,.\,3}{2\,.\,4\,.\,6\,.\,7}$	0·008 928 6
3	$\dfrac{1\,.\,3\,.\,5}{2\,.\,4\,.\,6\,.\,8}$	0·039 062	$\dfrac{1\,.\,3\,.\,5}{2\,.\,4\,.\,6\,.\,8\,.\,9}$	0·004 340 3
4	$\dfrac{1\,.\,3\,.\,5\,.\,7}{2\,.\,4\,.\,6\,.\,8\,.\,10}$	0·027 344	$\dfrac{1\,.\,3\,.\,5\,.\,7}{2\,.\,4\ldots10\,.\,11}$	0·002 485 8
5	$\dfrac{1\,.\,3\,.\,5\,.\,7\,.\,9}{2\,.\,4\ldots10\,.\,12}$	0·020 508	$\dfrac{1\,.\,3\,.\,5\,.\,7\,.\,9}{2\,.\,4\ldots12\,.\,13}$	0·001 577 5
6	$\dfrac{1\,.\,3\ldots9\,.\,11}{2\,.\,4\ldots12\,.\,14}$	0·016 113	$\dfrac{1\,.\,3\ldots9\,.\,11}{2\,.\,4\ldots14\,.\,15}$	0·001 074 2
7	$\dfrac{1\,.\,3\ldots11\,.\,13}{2\,.\,4\ldots14\,.\,16}$	0·013 092	$\dfrac{1\,.\,3\ldots11\,.\,13}{2\,.\,4\ldots16\,.\,17}$	0·000 770 12
8	$\dfrac{1\,.\,3\ldots13\,.\,15}{2\,.\,4\ldots16\,.\,18}$	0·010 910	$\dfrac{1\,.\,3\ldots13\,.\,15}{2\,.\,4\ldots18\,.\,19}$	0·000 574 21
9	$\dfrac{1\,.\,3\ldots15\,.\,17}{2\,.\,4\ldots18\,.\,20}$	0·009 273 5	$\dfrac{1\,.\,3\ldots15\,.\,17}{2\,.\,4\ldots20\,.\,21}$	0·000 441 60
10	$\dfrac{1\,.\,3\ldots17\,.\,19}{2\,.\,4\ldots20\,.\,22}$	0·008 009 0	$\dfrac{1\,.\,3\ldots17\,.\,19}{2\,.\,4\ldots22\,.\,23}$	0·000 348 22

TABLE 2. BINOMIAL COEFFICIENTS $\left(\begin{smallmatrix} n \\ m \end{smallmatrix}\right)$

m \ n	1	2	3	4	5	6	7	8	9	10	11	12	13	14	15	16	17	18	19
0	1	1	1	1	1	1	1	1	1	1	1	1	1	1	1	1	1	1	1
1		2	3	4	5	6	7	8	9	10	11	12	13	14	15	16	17	18	19
2			3	6	10	15	21	28	36	45	55	66	78	91	105	120	136	153	171
3					10	20	35	56	84	120	165	220	286	364	455	560	680	816	969
4							35	70	126	210	330	495	715	1001	1365	1820	2380	3060	3876
5									126	252	462	792	1287	2002	3003	4368	6188	8568	11628
6											462	924	1716	3003	5005	8008	12,376	18,564	27,132
7													1716	3432	6435	11,440	19,448	31,824	50,388
8															6435	12,870	24,310	43,758	75,582
9																	24,310	48,620	92,378
10																			92,378

Note. This table gives only the first half of the binomial terms of Newton: the remaining (symmetric) coefficients are determined by the formula $C_n^m = C_n^{n-m}$ where $C_n^0 = 1$. A multiplier 10^k indicates that the number is approximate.

Continuation of TABLE 2

n / m	20	21	22	23	24	25	26	27	28
0	1	1	1	1	1	1	1	1	1
1	20	21	22	23	24	25	26	27	28
2	190	210	231	253	276	300	325	351	378
3	1140	1330	1540	1771	2024	2300	2600	2925	3276
4	4845	5985	7315	8855	10,626	12,650	14,950	17,550	20,475
5	15,504	20,349	26,334	33,649	42,504	53,130	65,780	80,730	98,280
6	38,760	54,264	74,613	100,947	134,596	177,100	230,230	296,010	376,740
7	77,520	116,280	170,544	245,157	346,104	480,700	657,800	888,030	1,184,040
8	125,970	203,490	319,770	490,314	735,471	1,081,575	1,562,275	2,220,075	3,108,105
9	167,960	293,930	497,420	817,190	1,307,504	2,042,975	3,124,550	4,686,825	6,906,900
10	184,756	352,716	646,646	1,144,066	1,961,256	3,268,760	5,311,735	8,436,285	13,123,110
11		352,716	705,432	1,352,078	2,496,144	4,457,400	7,726,160	13,037,895	21,474,180
12				1,352,078	2,704,156	5,200,300	9,657,700	17,383,860	30,421,755
13						5,200,300	10,400,600	20,058,300	37,442,160
14								20,058,300	40,116,600

m \ n	29	30	31	32	33	34	35
0	1	1	1	1	1	1	1
1	29	30	31	32	33	34	35
2	406	435	465	496	528	561	595
3	3654	4060	4495	4960	5456	5984	6545
4	23,751	27,405	31,465	35,960	40,920	46,376	52,360
5	118,755	142,506	169,911	201,376	237,336	278,256	324,632
6	475,020	593,775	736,281	906,192	1,107,568	1,345,904	1,623,160
7	1,560,780	2,035,800	2,629,575	3,365,856	4,272,048	5,379,616	6,724,520
8	4,292,145	5,852,925	7,888,725	10,518,300	13,884,156	18,156,204	23,535,820
9	10,015,005	14,307,150	20,160,075	28,048,800	38,567,100	52,451,256	70,607,460
10	20,030,010	30,045,015	44,352,165	64,512,240	92,561,040	$13,112,814 \times 10$	$18,357,940 \times 10$
11	34,597,290	54,627,300	84,672,315	$12,902,448 \times 10$	$19,353,672 \times 10$	28,609,776	41,722,590
12	51,895,935	86,493,225	$14,112,053 \times 10$	22,579,284	35,481,732	54,835,404	83,445,180
13	67,863,915	$11,975,985 \times 10$	20,625,308	34,737,360	57,316,644	92,798,376	$14,763,378 \times 10^2$
14	77,558,760	14,542,268	26,518,253	47,143,560	81,880,920	$13,919,756 \times 10^2$	23,199,594
15	77,558,760	15,511,752	30,054,020	56,572,272	$10,371,583 \times 10^2$	18,559,675	32,479,432
16			30,054,020	60,108,039	11,668,031	22,039,644	40,599,290
17					11,668,031	23,336,062	45,375,677
18							45,375,677

Continuation of TABLE 2

$\frac{n}{m}$	36	37	38	39	40
0	1	1	1	1	1
1	36	37	38	39	40
2	630	666	703	741	780
3	7140	7770	8436	9139	9880
4	58,905	66,045	73,815	82,251	91,390
5	376,992	435,897	501,942	575,757	658,008
6	1,947,792	2,324,784	2,760,681	3,262,623	3,838,380
7	8,347,680	10,295,472	12,620,256	15,380,937	18,643,560
8	30,260,340	38,608,020	48,903,492	61,523,748	76,904,685
9	94,143,280	$12,440,362\times10$	$16,301,164\times10$	$21,191,513\times10$	$27,343,888\times10$
10	$25,418,686\times10$	34,833,014	47,273,376	63,574,540	84,766,053
11	60,080,530	85,499,215	$12,033,233\times10^2$	$16,760,560\times10^2$	$23,118,014\times10^2$
12	$12,516,777\times10^2$	$18,524,830\times10^2$	27,074,751	39,107,974	55,868,535
13	23,107,896	35,624,673	54,149,503	81,224,254	$12,033,223\times10^3$
14	37,962,972	61,070,868	96,695,541	$15,084,504\times10^3$	23,206,930
15	55,679,026	93,641,998	$15,471,287\times10^3$	25,140,841	40,225,345
16	73,078,721	$12,875,775\times10^3$	22,239,974	37,711,261	62,852,102
17	85,974,966	15,905,369	28,781,143	51,021,118	88,732,379
18	90,751,353	17,672,632	33,578,001	62,359,144	$11,338,026\times10^4$
19		17,672,632	35,345,264	68,923,264	13,128,241
20				68,923,264	13,784,653

Continuation of TABLE 2

m \\ n	41	42	43	44	45
0	1	1	1	1	1
1	41	42	43	44	45
2	820	861	903	946	990
3	10,660	11,480	12,341	13,244	14,190
4	101,270	111,930	123,410	135,751	148,995
5	749,398	850,668	962,598	1,086,008	1,221,759
6	4,496,388	5,245,786	6,096,454	7,059,052	8,145,060
7	22,481,940	26,978,328	32,224,114	38,320,568	45,379,620
8	95,548,245	$11,803,019 \times 10$	$14,500,851 \times 10$	$17,723,263 \times 10$	$21,555,320 \times 10$
9	$35,034,357 \times 10$	44,589,181	56,392,200	70,893,051	88,616,314
10	$11,210,994 \times 10^2$	$14,714,430 \times 10^2$	$19,173,348 \times 10^2$	$24,812,568 \times 10^2$	$31,901,873 \times 10^2$
11	31,594,620	42,805,614	57,520,043	76,693,391	$10,150,596 \times 10^3$
12	78,986,549	$11,058,117 \times 10^3$	$15,338,678 \times 10^3$	$21,090,683 \times 10^3$	28,760,022
13	$17,620,076 \times 10^3$	25,518,731	36,576,848	51,915,526	73,006,209
14	35,240,153	52,860,229	78,378,960	$11,495,581 \times 10^4$	$16,687,133 \times 10^4$
15	63,432,275	98,672,428	$15,153,266 \times 10^4$	22,991,162	34,486,743
16	$10,307,745 \times 10^4$	$16,650,972 \times 10^4$	26,518,215	41,671,481	64,662,642
17	15,158,448	25,466,193	42,117,165	68,635,380	$11,030,686 \times 10^5$
18	20,211,264	35,369,712	60,835,905	$10,295,307 \times 10^5$	17,158,845
19	24,466,267	44,677,531	80,047,243	14,088,315	24,383,622
20	26,912,894	51,379,161	96,056,692	17,610,394	31,698,708
21	26,912,894	53,825,787	$10,520,495 \times 10^5$	20,126,164	37,736,558
22			10,520,495	21,040,990	41,167,154
23					41,167,154

Continuation of TABLE 2

m \ n	46	47	48	49	50
0	1	1	1	1	1
1	46	47	48	49	50
2	1035	1081	1128	1176	1225
3	15,180	16,215	17,296	18,424	19,600
4	163,185	178,365	194,580	211,876	230,300
5	1,370,754	1,533,939	1,712,304	1,906,884	2,118,760
6	9,366,819	10,737,573	12,271,512	13,983,816	15,890,700
7	53,524,680	62,891,499	73,629,072	85,900,584	99,884,400
8	$26{,}093{,}282 \times 10$	$31{,}445{,}750 \times 10$	$37{,}734{,}899 \times 10$	$45{,}097{,}807 \times 10$	$53{,}687{,}865 \times 10$
9	$11{,}017{,}163 \times 10^2$	$13{,}626{,}491 \times 10^2$	$16{,}771{,}066 \times 10^2$	$20{,}544{,}556 \times 10^2$	$25{,}054{,}337 \times 10^2$
10	40,763,504	51,780,668	65,407,159	82,178,225	$10{,}272{,}278 \times 10^3$
11	$13{,}340{,}783 \times 10^3$	$17{,}417{,}134 \times 10^3$	$22{,}595{,}200 \times 10^3$	$29{,}135{,}916 \times 10^3$	37,353,739
12	38,910,618	52,251,401	69,668,534	92,263,735	$12{,}139{,}965 \times 10^4$
13	$10{,}176{,}623 \times 10^4$	$14{,}067{,}685 \times 10^4$	$19{,}292{,}825 \times 10^4$	$26{,}259{,}678 \times 10^4$	35,486,052
14	23,987,754	34,164,377	48,232,062	67,524,887	93,784,566
15	51,173,876	75,161,630	$10{,}932{,}601 \times 10^5$	$15{,}755{,}807 \times 10^5$	$22{,}508{,}296 \times 10^5$
16	99,149,385	$15{,}032{,}326 \times 10^5$	22,548,489	33,481,090	49,236,897
17	$17{,}496{,}950 \times 10^5$	27,411,889	42,444,215	64,992,704	98,473,794
18	28,189,531	45,686,481	73,098,370	$11{,}554{,}258 \times 10^6$	$18{,}053{,}529 \times 10^6$
19	41,542,467	69,731,998	$11{,}541{,}848 \times 10^6$	18,851,685	30,405,943
20	56,082,330	97,624,797	16,735,679	28,277,527	47,129,212
21	69,435,266	$12{,}551{,}760 \times 10^6$	22,314,239	39,049,919	67,327,446
22	78,903,711	14,833,898	27,385,657	49,699,897	88,749,815
23	82,334,307	16,123,802	30,957,700	58,343,357	$10{,}804{,}325 \times 10^7$
24		16,123,802	32,247,604	63,205,303	12,154,866
25				63,205,303	12,641,061

TABLE 3. BINOMIAL COEFFICIENTS $\binom{\nu}{m}$

(where ν is negative or fractional)

$\dfrac{\quad m}{\nu\quad}$	1	2	3	4	5	6
-1	-1	$+1$	-1	$+1$	-1	$+1$
-2	-2	$+3$	-4	$+5$	-6	$+7$
-3	-3	$+6$	-10	$+15$	-21	$+28$
-4	-4	$+10$	-20	$+35$	-56	$+84$
-5	-5	$+15$	-35	$+70$	-126	$+210$
$-\dfrac{7}{2}$	$-\dfrac{7}{2}$	$+\dfrac{63}{8}$	$-\dfrac{231}{16}$	$+\dfrac{3003}{128}$	$-\dfrac{9009}{256}$	$+\dfrac{51\,051}{1024}$
$-\dfrac{5}{2}$	$-\dfrac{5}{2}$	$+\dfrac{35}{8}$	$-\dfrac{105}{16}$	$+\dfrac{1155}{128}$	$-\dfrac{3003}{256}$	$+\dfrac{15\,015}{1024}$
$-\dfrac{3}{2}$	$-\dfrac{3}{2}$	$+\dfrac{15}{8}$	$-\dfrac{35}{16}$	$+\dfrac{315}{128}$	$-\dfrac{693}{256}$	$+\dfrac{3003}{1024}$
$-\dfrac{1}{2}$	$-\dfrac{1}{2}$	$+\dfrac{3}{8}$	$-\dfrac{5}{16}$	$+\dfrac{35}{128}$	$-\dfrac{63}{256}$	$+\dfrac{231}{1024}$
$\dfrac{1}{2}$	$\dfrac{1}{2}$	$-\dfrac{1}{8}$	$+\dfrac{1}{16}$	$-\dfrac{5}{128}$	$+\dfrac{7}{256}$	$-\dfrac{21}{1024}$
$\dfrac{3}{2}$	$\dfrac{3}{2}$	$+\dfrac{3}{8}$	$-\dfrac{1}{16}$	$+\dfrac{3}{128}$	$-\dfrac{3}{256}$	$+\dfrac{7}{1024}$
$\dfrac{5}{2}$	$\dfrac{5}{2}$	$+\dfrac{15}{8}$	$+\dfrac{5}{16}$	$-\dfrac{5}{128}$	$+\dfrac{3}{256}$	$-\dfrac{5}{1024}$
$\dfrac{7}{2}$	$\dfrac{7}{2}$	$+\dfrac{35}{8}$	$+\dfrac{35}{16}$	$+\dfrac{35}{128}$	$-\dfrac{7}{256}$	$+\dfrac{7}{1024}$

Continuation of TABLE 3

v \ m	1	2	3	4	5	6
$-\dfrac{4}{3}$	$-\dfrac{4}{3}$	$+\dfrac{14}{9}$	$-\dfrac{140}{81}$	$+\dfrac{455}{243}$	$-\dfrac{1456}{729}$	$+\dfrac{13\,832}{6561}$
$-\dfrac{2}{3}$	$-\dfrac{2}{3}$	$+\dfrac{5}{9}$	$-\dfrac{40}{81}$	$+\dfrac{110}{243}$	$-\dfrac{308}{729}$	$+\dfrac{5236}{6561}$
$-\dfrac{1}{3}$	$-\dfrac{1}{3}$	$+\dfrac{2}{9}$	$-\dfrac{14}{81}$	$+\dfrac{35}{243}$	$-\dfrac{91}{729}$	$+\dfrac{728}{6561}$
$\dfrac{1}{3}$	$\dfrac{1}{3}$	$-\dfrac{1}{9}$	$+\dfrac{5}{81}$	$-\dfrac{10}{243}$	$+\dfrac{22}{729}$	$-\dfrac{154}{6561}$
$\dfrac{2}{3}$	$\dfrac{2}{3}$	$-\dfrac{1}{9}$	$+\dfrac{4}{81}$	$-\dfrac{7}{243}$	$+\dfrac{14}{729}$	$-\dfrac{91}{6561}$
$\dfrac{4}{3}$	$\dfrac{4}{3}$	$+\dfrac{2}{9}$	$-\dfrac{4}{81}$	$+\dfrac{5}{243}$	$-\dfrac{8}{729}$	$+\dfrac{44}{6561}$
$-\dfrac{5}{4}$	$-\dfrac{5}{4}$	$+\dfrac{45}{32}$	$-\dfrac{195}{128}$	$+\dfrac{3315}{2048}$	$-\dfrac{13\,923}{8192}$	$+\dfrac{348\,075}{32\,768}$
$-\dfrac{3}{4}$	$-\dfrac{3}{4}$	$+\dfrac{21}{32}$	$-\dfrac{77}{128}$	$+\dfrac{1155}{2048}$	$-\dfrac{4389}{8192}$	$+\dfrac{100\,947}{32\,768}$
$-\dfrac{1}{4}$	$-\dfrac{1}{4}$	$+\dfrac{5}{32}$	$-\dfrac{15}{128}$	$+\dfrac{195}{2048}$	$-\dfrac{663}{8192}$	$+\dfrac{13\,923}{32\,768}$
$\dfrac{1}{4}$	$\dfrac{1}{4}$	$-\dfrac{3}{32}$	$+\dfrac{7}{128}$	$-\dfrac{77}{2048}$	$+\dfrac{231}{8192}$	$-\dfrac{4389}{32\,768}$
$\dfrac{3}{4}$	$\dfrac{3}{4}$	$-\dfrac{3}{32}$	$+\dfrac{5}{128}$	$-\dfrac{45}{2048}$	$+\dfrac{117}{8192}$	$-\dfrac{1989}{32\,768}$
$\dfrac{5}{4}$	$\dfrac{5}{4}$	$+\dfrac{5}{32}$	$-\dfrac{5}{128}$	$+\dfrac{35}{2048}$	$-\dfrac{77}{8192}$	$+\dfrac{1155}{32\,768}$

TABLE 4. SUMS OF POWERS OF INTEGERS

n	$\sum_{k=1}^{n} k$	$\sum_{k=1}^{n} k^2$	$\sum_{k=1}^{n} k^3$	$\sum_{k=1}^{n} k^4$	$\sum_{k=1}^{n} k^5$
1	1	1	1	1	1
2	3	5	9	17	33
3	6	14	36	98	276
4	10	30	100	354	1300
5	15	55	225	979	4425
6	21	91	441	2275	12,201
7	28	140	784	4676	29,008
8	36	204	1296	8772	61,776
9	45	285	2025	15,333	120,825
10	55	385	3025	25,333	220,825
11	66	506	4356	39,974	381,876
12	78	650	6084	60,710	630,708
13	91	819	8281	89,271	1,002,001
14	105	1015	11,025	127,687	1,539,825
15	120	1240	14,400	178,312	2,299,200
16	136	1496	18,496	243,848	3,347,776
17	153	1785	23,409	327,369	4,767,633
18	171	2109	29,241	432,345	6,657,201
19	190	2470	36,100	562,666	9,133,300
20	210	2870	44,100	722,666	12,333,300
21	231	3311	53,361	917,147	16,417,401
22	253	3795	64,009	1,151,403	21,571,033
23	276	4324	76,176	1,431,244	28,007,376
24	300	4900	90,000	1,763,020	35,970,000
25	325	5525	105,625	2,153,645	45,735,625
26	351	6201	123,201	2,610,621	57,617,001
27	378	6930	142,884	3,142,062	71,965,908
28	406	7714	164,836	3,756,718	89,176,276
29	435	8555	189,225	4,463,999	109,687,425
30	465	9455	216,225	5,273,999	133,987,425
31	496	10,416	246,016	6,197,520	162,616,576
32	528	11,440	278,784	7,246,096	196,171,008
33	561	12,529	314,721	8,432,017	235,306,401
34	595	13,685	354,025	9,768,353	280,741,825
35	630	14,910	396,900	11,268,978	333,263,700
36	666	16,206	443,556	12,948,594	393,729,876
37	703	17,575	494,209	14,822,755	463,073,833
38	741	19,019	549,081	16,907,891	542,309,001
39	780	20,540	608,400	19,221,332	632,533,200
40	820	22,140	672,400	21,781,332	734,933,200
41	861	23,821	741,321	24,607,093	850,789,401
42	903	25,585	815,409	27,718,789	981,480,633
43	946	27,434	894,916	31,137,590	1,128,489,076
44	990	29,370	980,100	34,885,686	1,293,405,300
45	1035	31,395	1,071,225	38,986,311	1,477,933,425
46	1081	33,511	1,168,561	43,463,767	1,683,896,401
47	1128	35,720	1,272,384	48,343,448	1,913,241,408
48	1176	38,024	1,382,976	53,651,864	2,168,045,376
49	1225	40,425	1,500,625	59,416,665	2,450,520,625
50	1275	42,925	1,625,625	65,666,665	2,763,020,625

TABLE 5. GUDERMANNIAN (gd x)

x	gd x	x	gd x	x	gd x	x	gd x	x	gd x	x	gd x
0·00	0·00000	0·20	0·19868	0·40	0·38974	0·60	0·56694	0·80	0·72625	1·00	0·86579
01	01000	21	20847	41	39897	61	57535	81	73366	01	87223
02	02000	22	21825	42	40817	62	58372	82	74106	02	87863
03	03000	23	22800	43	41733	63	59204	83	74841	03	88499
04	03999	24	23773	44	42645	64	60031	84	75571	04	89130
05	04998	25	24744	45	43554	65	60854	85	76297	05	89756
06	05996	26	25712	46	44459	66	61672	86	77017	06	90377
07	06994	27	26678	47	45359	67	62486	87	77732	07	90993
08	07991	28	27641	48	46256	68	63294	88	78443	08	91604
09	08988	29	28602	49	47149	69	64098	89	79148	09	92211
10	09983	30	29560	50	48038	70	64897	90	79848	10	92812
11	10978	31	30515	51	48923	71	65692	91	80544	11	93410
12	11971	32	31467	52	49803	72	66487	92	81234	12	94002
13	12964	33	32417	53	50680	73	67266	93	81919	13	94589
14	13954	34	33363	54	51552	74	68045	94	82599	14	95172
15	14944	35	34307	55	52420	75	68824	95	83275	15	95750
16	15932	36	35247	56	53284	76	69590	96	83945	16	96323
17	16919	37	36184	57	54143	77	70355	97	84611	17	96892
18	17904	38	37117	58	54997	78	71115	98	85271	18	97455
0·19	0·18887	0·39	0·38047	0·59	0·55848	0·79	0·71870	0·99	0·85926	1·19	0·98015

x	gd x	x	gd x	x	gd x	x	gd x	x	gd x	x	gd x
1·20	0·98569	1·40	1·08725	1·60	1·17236	1·80	1·24316	2·00	1·30176	2·20	1·35009
21	99120	41	09188	61	17622	81	24636	01	30441	21	35227
22	0·99665	42	09647	62	18005	82	24954	02	30703	22	35443
23	1·00205	43	10101	63	18384	83	25268	03	30962	23	35656
24	00744	44	10552	64	18760	84	25579	04	31219	24	35868
25	01274	45	10999	65	19132	85	25888	05	31473	25	36077
26	01801	46	11441	66	19500	86	26193	06	31726	26	36285
27	02324	47	11880	67	19866	87	26496	07	31975	27	36490
28	02842	48	12315	68	20228	88	26795	08	32222	28	36694
29	03356	49	12746	69	20586	89	27092	09	32467	29	36895
30	03866	50	13173	70	20941	90	27386	10	32710	30	37095
31	04371	51	13596	71	21293	91	27677	11	32950	31	37292
32	04872	52	14015	72	21642	92	27966	12	33188	32	37488
33	05368	53	14431	73	21987	93	28251	13	33423	33	37682
34	05860	54	14843	74	22330	94	28534	14	33656	34	37873
35	06348	55	15251	75	22668	95	28814	15	33887	35	38063
36	06832	56	15655	76	23004	96	29092	16	34116	36	38251
37	07312	57	16056	77	23337	97	29367	17	34343	37	38438
38	07787	58	16453	78	23666	98	29640	18	34567	38	38622
1·39	1·08258	1·59	1·16846	1·79	1·23993	1·99	1·29909	2·19	1·34789	2·39	1·38805

Continuation of TABLE 5

x	gd x	x	gd x	x	gd x	x	gd x	x	gd x	x	gd x
2·40	1·38986	2·60	1·42252	2·80	1·44933	3·00	1·47130	3·20	1·48932	3·40	1·50407
41	39165	61	42399	81	45053	01	47229	21	49013	41	50474
42	39342	62	42545	82	45173	02	47327	22	49093	42	50540
43	39518	63	42689	83	45291	03	47424	23	49172	43	50605
44	39691	64	42832	84	45408	04	47520	24	49251	44	50669
45	39864	65	42973	85	45524	05	47615	25	49329	45	50733
46	40034	66	43113	86	45638	06	47709	26	49406	46	50796
47	40203	67	43251	87	45752	07	47802	27	49482	47	50858
48	40370	68	43388	88	45864	08	47894	28	49558	48	50920
49	40535	69	43524	89	45976	09	47986	29	49632	49	50981
50	40700	70	43659	90	46086	10	48076	30	49706	50	51042
51	40862	71	43792	91	46195	11	48165	31	49780	51	51102
52	41022	72	43924	92	46303	12	48254	32	49852	52	51161
53	41181	73	44054	93	46410	13	48342	33	49924	53	51220
54	41339	74	44183	94	46516	14	48428	34	49995	54	51279
55	41495	75	44311	95	46621	15	48514	35	50066	55	51336
56	41649	76	44438	96	46725	16	48600	36	50135	56	51393
57	41802	77	44564	97	46828	17	48684	37	50204	57	51450
58	41954	78	44688	98	46930	18	48767	38	50273	58	51506
2·59	1·42104	2·79	1·44811	2·99	1·47031	3·19	1·48850	3·39	1·50340	3·59	1·51561

x	gd x	x	gd x	x	gd x	x	gd x	x	gd x	x	gd x
3·60	1·51616	3·80	1·52606	4·00	1·53417	4·20	1·54081	4·40	1·54624	4·60	1·55069
61	51671	81	52651	01	53453	21	54111	41	54649	61	55089
62	51724	82	52695	02	53490	22	54140	42	54673	62	55109
63	51778	83	52738	03	53525	23	54169	43	54697	63	55129
64	51830	84	52782	04	53561	24	54198	44	54721	64	55148
65	51883	85	52824	05	53596	25	54227	45	54744	65	55167
66	51934	86	52867	06	53630	26	54255	46	54767	66	55186
67	51985	87	52909	07	53664	27	54283	47	54790	67	55205
68	52036	88	52950	08	53698	28	54311	48	54813	68	55224
69	52086	89	52991	09	53732	29	54339	49	54836	69	55242
70	52136	90	53032	10	53765	30	54366	50	54858	70	55261
71	52185	91	53072	11	53789	31	54393	51	54880	71	55279
72	52234	92	53112	12	53831	32	54420	52	54902	72	55297
73	52282	93	53151	13	53863	33	54446	53	54924	73	55314
74	52330	94	53190	14	53895	34	54472	54	54945	74	55332
75	52377	95	53229	15	53927	35	54498	55	54966	75	55350
76	52424	96	53267	16	53958	36	54524	56	54987	76	55367
77	52470	97	53305	17	53989	37	54550	57	55008	77	55384
78	52516	98	53343	18	54020	38	54575	58	55029	78	55400
3·79	1·52561	3·99	1·53380	4·19	1·54051	4·39	1·54600	4·59	1·55049	4·79	1·55417

Continuation of TABLE 5

x	gd x	x	gd x	x	gd x	x	gd x	x	gd x	x	gd x
4·80	1·55434	5·00	1·55732	5·20	1·55976	5·40	1·56176	5·60	1·56340	5·80	1·56474
81	55450	01	55745	21	55987	41	56185	61	56347	81	56480
82	55466	02	55759	22	55998	42	56194	62	56355	82	56486
83	55482	03	55772	23	56009	43	56203	63	56362	83	56492
84	55498	04	55785	24	56020	44	56212	64	56369	84	56498
85	55514	05	55798	25	56030	45	56220	65	56376	85	56504
86	55530	06	55811	26	56041	46	56229	66	56383	86	56509
87	55545	07	55823	27	56051	47	56238	67	56390	87	56515
88	55560	08	55836	28	56061	48	56246	68	56397	88	56521
89	55575	09	55848	29	56071	49	56254	69	56404	89	56526
90	55590	10	55860	30	56081	50	56262	70	56410	90	56532
91	55605	11	55872	31	56091	51	56270	71	56417	91	56537
92	55620	12	55884	32	56101	52	56278	72	56424	92	56543
93	55634	13	55896	33	56111	53	56286	73	56430	93	56548
94	55649	14	55908	34	56120	54	56294	74	56437	94	56553
95	55663	15	55920	35	56130	55	56302	75	56434	95	56558
96	55677	16	55931	36	56139	56	56310	76	56449	96	56564
97	55691	17	55943	37	56149	57	56318	77	56456	97	56569
98	55705	18	55954	38	56158	58	56325	78	56462	98	56574
4·99	1·55719	5·19	1·55965	5·39	1·56167	5·59	1·56333	5·79	1·56468	5·99	1·56579

x	gd x	x	gd x	x	gd x	x	gd x	x	gd x	x	gd x
6·00	1·565838	6·20	1·566737	6·40	1·567473	6·60	1·568076	6·80	1·568569	7·00	1·568973
01	565888	21	566778	41	567506	61	568103	81	568591	01	568991
02	565937	22	566818	42	567539	62	568129	82	568613	02	569009
03	565985	23	566857	43	567571	63	568156	83	568635	03	569026
04	566033	24	566897	44	567604	64	568182	84	568656	04	569044
05	566081	25	566935	45	567635	65	568208	85	568677	05	569062
06	566127	26	566974	46	567667	66	568234	86	568698	06	569079
07	566174	27	567012	47	567698	67	568260	87	568719	07	569096
08	566220	28	567050	48	567729	68	568285	88	568740	08	569113
09	566266	29	567087	49	567760	69	568310	89	568760	09	569130
10	566311	30	567124	50	567789	70	568336	90	568781	10	569146
11	566355	31	567160	51	567819	71	568359	91	568801	11	569163
12	566399	32	567196	52	567849	72	568383	92	568821	12	569179
13	566443	33	567232	53	567878	73	568407	93	568840	13	569195
14	566486	34	567267	54	567907	74	568431	94	568860	14	569211
15	566529	35	567303	55	567936	75	568455	95	568880	15	569227
16	566572	36	567338	56	567965	76	568478	96	568898	16	569242
17	566614	37	567372	57	567993	77	568501	97	568917	17	569258
18	566656	38	567406	58	568021	78	568524	98	568936	18	569273
6·19	1·566697	6·39	1·567440	6·59	1·568048	6·79	1·568546	6·99	1·568954	7·19	1·569288

Continuation of TABLE 5

x	gd x	x	gd x	x	gd x	x	gd x	x	gd x	x	gd x
7·20	1·569303	7·40	1·569574	7·60	1·569795	7·80	1·569977	8·00	1·570125	8·20	1·570247
21	569318	41	569586	61	569805	81	569985	01	570132	21	570252
22	569333	42	569598	62	569815	82	569993	02	570139	22	570258
23	569347	43	569610	63	569825	83	570001	03	570145	23	570263
24	569362	44	569622	64	569835	84	570009	04	570152	24	570269
25	569376	45	569633	65	569844	85	570017	05	570159	25	570274
26	569390	46	569645	66	569854	86	570025	06	570164	26	570279
27	569404	47	569656	67	569863	87	570032	07	570171	27	570284
28	569418	48	569668	68	569872	88	570040	08	570177	28	570289
29	569432	49	569679	69	569888	89	570047	09	570183	29	570294
30	569445	50	569690	70	569891	90	570055	10	570189	30	570299
31	569459	51	569701	71	569900	91	570062	11	570195	31	570304
32	569472	52	569712	72	569909	92	570069	12	570201	32	570309
33	569485	53	569723	73	569917	93	570077	13	570207	33	570314
34	569498	54	569734	74	569926	94	570084	14	570213	34	570319
35	569511	55	569744	75	569935	95	570091	15	570219	35	570324
36	569524	56	569755	76	569943	96	570098	16	570225	36	570328
37	569537	57	569765	77	569952	97	570105	17	570230	37	570333
38	569550	58	569775	78	569960	98	570112	18	570236	38	570338
7·39	1·569562	7·59	1·569785	7·79	1·569969	7·99	1·570119	8·19	1·570242	8·39	1·570342

Continuation of TABLE 5

x	gd x	x	gd x	x	gd x	x	gd x	x	gd x	x	gd x
8·40	1·570347	8·50	1·570389	8·60	1·570428	8·70	1·570463	8·80	1·570495	8·90	1·570524
41	570351	51	570393	61	570432	71	570466	81	570498	91	570526
42	570356	52	570397	62	570435	72	570470	82	570501	92	570529
43	570360	53	570401	63	570439	73	570473	83	570504	93	570532
44	570364	54	570405	64	570443	74	570476	84	570507	94	570534
45	570369	55	570409	65	570446	75	570479	85	570510	95	570537
46	570373	56	570413	66	570450	76	570483	86	570512	96	570539
47	570377	57	570417	67	570453	77	570486	87	570515	97	570542
48	570381	58	570421	68	570456	78	570489	88	570518	98	570544
8·49	1·570385	8·59	1·570424	8·69	1·570460	8·79	1·570492	8·89	1·570521	8·99	570547
										9·00	1·570550

TABLE 6. INVERSE GUDERMANNIAN (arg gd x)

x	arg gd x	x	arg gd x	x	arg gd x	x	arg gd x	x	arg gd x	x	arg gd x
0·00	0·00000	0·23	0·23206	0·46	0·47714	0·69	0·75233	0·92	1·08651	1·15	1·54384
01	01000	24	24234	47	48833	70	76535	93	10313	16	56860
02	02000	25	25265	48	49957	71	77848	94	11997	17	59394
03	03000	26	26298	49	51087	72	79172	95	13704	18	61987
04	04001	27	27334	50	52224	73	80508	96	15435	19	64645
05	05002	28	28373	51	53366	74	81856	97	17192	20	67370
06	06004	29	29415	52	54515	75	83217	98	18974	21	70166
07	07006	30	30462	53	55671	76	84590	0·99	20783	22	73037
08	08009	31	31509	54	56834	77	85976	1·00	22620	23	75987
09	09012	32	32561	55	58003	78	87376	01	24485	24	79022
10	10017	33	33616	56	59180	79	88790	02	26380	25	82147
11	11022	34	34675	57	60364	80	90218	03	28306	26	85367
12	12029	35	35737	58	61555	81	91660	04	30265	27	88689
13	13037	36	36804	59	62755	82	93118	05	32258	28	92120
14	14046	37	37874	60	63962	83	94592	06	34285	29	95667
15	15057	38	38949	61	65178	84	96082	07	36349	30	1·99340
16	16069	39	40028	62	66402	85	97589	08	38451	31	2·03147
17	17082	40	41111	63	67636	86	0·99113	09	40593	32	07100
18	18098	41	42199	64	68878	87	1·00654	10	42776	33	11210
19	19115	42	43292	65	70129	88	02215	11	45003	34	15491
20	20135	43	44390	66	71390	89	03794	12	47275	35	19959
21	21156	44	45493	67	72661	90	05392	13	49594	36	24630
0·22	0·22180	0·45	0·46600	0·68	0·73942	0·91	1·07011	1·14	1·51963	1·37	2·29524

Continuation of TABLE 6

x	arg gd x	x	arg gd x	x	arg gd x	x	arg gd x	x	arg gd x	x	arg gd x
1·38	2·34666	1·470	2·987	1·491	3·221	1·511	3·510	1·531	3·917	1·551	4·615
39	40080	471	2·997	492	234	512	527	532	942	552	667
40	45800	472	3·007	493	246	513	544	533	969	553	722
41	51861	473	017	494	259	514	561	534	3·995	554	780
42	58307	474	028	495	272	515	579.	535	4·023	555	841
43	65193	475	038	496	286	516	597	536	051	556	907
44	72587	476	048	497	299	517	615	537	080	557	4·976
45	80558	477	059	498	313	518	634	538	110	558	5·052
46	89219	478	070	499	327	519	653	539	141	559	133
47	2·98695	479	081	500	341	520	673	540	173	560	222
48	3·09160	480	092	501	355	521	693	541	206	561	319
49	3·20843	481	103	502	369	522	713	542	241	562	427
50	3·34068	482	114	503	384	523	734	543	276	563	547
51	3·49306	483	125	504	399	524	755	544	313	564	685
52	3·67286	484	137	505	414	525	777	545	351	565	5·844
53	3·89217	485	148	506	429	526	799	546	390	566	6·033
54	4·17343	486	160	507	445	527	821	547	431	567	6·267
55	4·56609	487	172	508	461	528	844	548	474	568	6·573
56	5·22169	488	184	509	477	529	868	549	519	569	7·015
1·57	7·82864	489	196	1·510	3·493	1·530	3·892	1·550	4·566	1·570	7·829
		1·490	3·208								

TABLE 7. LEGENDRE POLYNOMIALS $P_n(x)$

(cf. Appendix I, § 4.1, 1° and Appendix I, § 4.5, 1°)

x \ n	2	3	4	5	6	7
0·00	−0·5000	+0·0000	+0·3750	+0·0000	−0·3125	−0·0000
01	4998	−0·0150	3746	0187	3118	0219
02	4994	0300	3735	0374	3099	0436
03	4986	0449	3716	0560	3066	0651
04	4976	0598	3690	0744	3021	0862
05	4962	0747	3657	0927	2962	1069
06	4946	0895	3616	1106	2891	1270
07	4926	1041	3567	1283	2808	1464
08	4904	1187	3512	1455	2713	1651
09	4878	1332	3449	1624	2606	1828
10	4850	1475	3379	1788	2488	1995
11	4818	1617	3303	1947	2360	2151
12	4784	1757	3219	2101	2220	2295
13	4746	1895	3129	2248	2071	2427
14	4706	2031	3032	2389	1913	2545
15	4662	2166	2928	2523	1746	2649
16	4616	2298	2819	2650	1572	2738
17	4566	2427	2703	2769	1389	2812
18	4514	2554	2581	2880	1201	2870
19	4458	2679	2453	2982	1006	2911
20	4400	2800	2320	3075	0806	2935
21	4338	2918	2181	3159	0601	2943
22	4274	3034	2037	3234	0394	2933
23	4206	3146	1889	3299	−0·0183	2906
24	4136	3254	1735	3353	+0·0029	2861
25	4062	3359	1577	3397	0243	2799
26	3986	3461	1415	3431	0456	2720
27	3906	3558	1249	3453	0669	2625
28	3824	3651	1079	3465	0879	2512
29	3738	3740	0906	3465	1087	2384
30	3650	3825	0729	3454	1292	2241
31	3558	3905	0550	3431	1492	2081
32	3464	3981	0369	3397	1686	1910
33	3366	4052	0185	3351	1873	1724
0·34	−0·3266	−0·4117	+0·0000	+0·3294	+0·2053	−0·1527

n x	2	3	4	5	6	7
0·35	−0·3162	−0·4178	−0·0187	+0·3225	+0·2225	−0·1318
36	3056	4234	0375	3144	2388	1098
37	2946	4284	0564	3051	2540	0870
38	2834	4328	0753	2948	2681	0635
39	2718	4367	0942	2833	2810	0393
40	2600	4400	1130	2706	2926	−0·0146
41	2478	4427	1317	2569	3029	+0·0104
42	2354	4448	1504	2421	3118	0356
43	2226	4462	1688	2263	3191	0608
44	2096	4470	1870	2095	3249	0859
45	1962	4472	2050	1917	3290	1106
46	1826	4467	2226	1730	3314	1348
47	1686	4454	2399	1534	3321	1584
48	1544	4435	2568	1330	3310	1811
49	1398	4409	2732	1118	3280	2027
50	1250	4375	2891	0898	3232	2231
51	1098	4334	3044	0673	3166	2422
52	0944	4285	3191	0441	3080	2596
53	0786	4228	3332	+0·0204	2975	2753
54	0626	4163	3465	−0·0037	2851	2891
55	0462	4091	3590	0282	2708	3007
56	0296	4010	3707	0529	2546	3102
57	−0·0126	3920	3815	0779	2366	3172
58	+0·0046	3822	3914	1028	2168	3217
59	0222	3716	4002	1278	1953	3235
60	0400	3600	4080	1526	1721	3226
61	0582	3475	4146	1772	1473	3188
62	0766	3342	4200	2014	1211	3121
63	0954	3199	4242	2251	0935	3023
·64	1144	3046	4270	2482	0646	2895
65	1338	2884	4284	2705	0347	2737
66	1534	2713	4284	2919	+0·0038	2548
67	1734	2531	4268	3122	−0·0278	2329
68	1936	2339	4236	3313	0601	2081
0·69	+0·2142	−0·2137	−0·4187	−0·3490	−0·0926	+0·1805

n \\ x	2	3	4	5	6	7
0·70	+0·2350	−0·1925	−0·4121	−0·3652	−0·1253	+0·1502
71	2562	1702	4036	3796	1578	1173
72	2776	1469	3933	3922	1899	0822
73	2994	1225	3810	4026	2214	0450
74	3214	0969	3666	4107	2518	+0·0061
75	3438	0703	3501	4164	2808	−0·0342
76	3664	0426	3314	4193	3081	0754
77	3894	−0·0137	3104	4193	3333	1171
78	4126	+0·0164	2871	4162	3559	1588
79	4362	0476	2613	4097	3756	1999
80	4600	0800	2330	3995	3918	2397
81	4842	1136	2021	3855	4041	2774
82	5086	1484	1685	3674	4119	3124
83	5334	1845	1321	3449	4147	3437
84	5584	2218	0928	3177	4120	3703
85	5838	2603	0506	2857	4030	3913
86	6094	3001	−0·0053	2484	3872	4055
87	6354	3413	+0·0431	2056	3638	4116
88	6616	3837	0947	1570	3322	4083
89	6882	4274	1496	1023	2916	3942
90	7150	4725	2079	−0·0411	2412	3678
91	7422	5189	2698	+0·0268	1802	3274
92	7696	5667	3352	1017	1077	2713
93	7974	6159	4044	1842	−0·0229	1975
94	8254	6665	4773	2744	+0·0751	−0·1040
95	8538	7184	5541	3727	1875	+0·0112
96	8824	7718	6349	4796	3151	1506
97	9114	8267	7198	5954	4590	3165
98	9406	8830	8089	7204	6204	5115
0·99	0·9702	0·9407	0·9022	0·8552	0·8003	0·7384
1·00	+1·0000	+1·0000	+1·0000	+1·0000	+1·0000	+1·0000

TABLE 8. LAGUERRE POLYNOMIALS $(1/n!)L_n(x)$
(cf. Appendix I, § 4.1, 10° and Appendix I, § 4.5, 9°)

x \ n	2	3	4	5	6	7
0·0	1·0000	1·0000	1·0000	1·0000	1·0000	1·0000
0·1	0·8050	0·7148	0·6293	0·5484	0·4717	0·3993
0·2	6200	4587	3147	0·1870	0·0743	—0·0244
0·3	4450	2305	0·0523	—0·0933	—0·2101	3011
0·4	2800	0·0293	—0·1616	3014	3978	4578
0·5	0·1250	—0·1458	3307	4456	5041	5183
0·6	—0·0200	2960	4586	5336	5428	5042
0·7	1550	4222	5487	5730	5265	4340
0·8	2800	5253	6043	5707	4667	3242
0·9	3950	6065	6287	5332	3737	1890
1·0	5000	6667	6250	4667	2569	—0·0405
1·1	5950	7068	5963	3767	—0·1247	0·1110
1·2	6800	7280	5456	2687	0·0157	2569
1·3	7550	7312	4757	1476	1578	3902
1·4	8200	7173	3893	—0·0178	2959	5056
1·5	8750	6875	2891	0·1164	4252	5988
1·6	9200	6427	1776	2513	5417	6668
1·7	9550	5838	—0·0573	3834	6420	7078
1·8	9800	5120	0·0694	5095	7235	7208
1·9	—0·9950	—0·4282	0·2003	0·6270	0·7840	0·7058

Continuation of TABLE 8

n / x	2	3	4	5	6	7
2·0	−1·0000	−0·3333	0·3333	0·7333	0·8222	0·6635
2·1	9950	2285	4663	8263	8371	5952
2·2	9800	−0·1147	5974	9042	8283	5030
2·3	9550	0·0072	7247	0·9653	7958	3891
2·4	9200	1360	8464	1·0084	7401	2564
2·5	8750	2708	0·9609	0325	6620	0·1080
2·6	8200	4107	1·0667	0369	5627	−0·0528
2·7	7550	5545	1623	1·0209	4437	2222
2·8	6800	7013	2464	0·9845	3068	3968
2·9	5950	0·8502	3177	9274	0·1540	5728
3·0	5000	1·0000	3750	8500	−0·0125	7464
3·1	3950	1498	4173	7526	1902	−0·9141
3·2	2800	2987	4437	6358	3766	−1·0722
3·3	1550	4455	4533	5004	5689	2173
3·4	−0·0200	5893	4454	3474	7645	3462
3·5	0·1250	7292	4193	0·1779	−0·9604	4558
3·6	2800	8640	3744	−0·0068	−1·1538	5435
3·7	4450	1·9928	3103	2053	3417	6066
3·8	6200	2·1147	2267	4159	5214	6430
3·9	0·8050	2·2285	1·1233	−0·6370	−1·6899	−1·6509

n \\ x	2	3	4	5	6	7
4·0	1·0000	2·3333	1·0000	−0·8667	−1·8444	−1·6286
4·1	2050	4282	0·8567	−1·1030	−1·9823	5750
4·2	4200	5120	6934	3439	−2·1010	4893
4·3	6450	5838	5103	5873	1978	3710
4·4	1·8800	6427	3077	−1·8310	2706	2201
4·5	2·1250	6875	0·0859	−2·0727	3170	−1·0369
4·6	3800	7173	−0·1546	3099	3351	−0·8222
4·7	6450	7312	4133	5404	3230	5769
4·8	2·9200	7280	6896	7617	2791	3026
4·9	3·2050	7068	−0·9827	−2·9713	2019	−0·0011
5·0	5000	6667	−1·2917	−3·1667	−2·0903	0·3254
5·1	3·8050	6065	6157	3454	−1·9433	0·6744
5·2	4·1200	5253	−1·9536	5050	7602	1·0430
5·3	4450	4222	−2·3043	6429	5405	4280
5·4	4·7800	2960	−2·6666	7568	−1·2841	1·8259
5·5	5·1250	2·1458	−3·0391	8440	−0·9911	2·2329
5·6	4800	1·9707	4203	9023	6619	2·6452
5·7	5·8450	7695	−3·8087	9293	−0·2970	3·0582
5·8	6·2200	5413	−4·2026	9227	0·1025	4677
5·9	6·6050	1·2852	−4·6003	−3·8803	0·5353	3·8690

Continuation of TABLE 8

$\dfrac{n}{a}$	2	3	4	5	6	7
6·0	7·0000	1·0000	−5·0000	−3·8000	1·0000	4·2571
6·1	4050	0·6848	3997	6797	1·4947	6273
6·2	7·8200	0·3387	−5·7973	5174	2·0171	4·9744
6·3	8·2450	−0·0395	−6·1907	3114	2·5650	5·2934
6·4	8·6800	4507	5776	−3·0598	3·1355	5790
6·5	9·1250	−0·8958	−6·9557	−2·7612	3·7255	5·8262
6·6	9·5800	−1·3760	−7·3226	4140	4·3319	6·0297
6·7	10·0450	−1·8922	−7·6757	−2·0171	4·9508	1847
6·8	10·5200	−2·4453	−8·0123	−1·5691	5·5785	2859
6·9	11·0050	−3·0365	3297	−1·0693	6·2107	3287
7·0	11·5000	−3·6667	6250	−0·5167	6·8431	3083
7·1	12·0050	−4·3368	−8·8953	0·0892	7·4708	2203
7·2	12·5200	−5·0480	−9·1376	0·7489	8·0889	6·0604
7·3	13·0450	−5·8012	3487	1·4624	8·6924	5·8246
7·4	13·5800	−6·5973	5253	2·2298	9·2756	5092
7·5	14·1250	−7·4375	6641	3·0508	9·8330	5·1110
7·6	14·6800	−8·3227	7616	3·9249	10·3588	4·6269
7·7	15·2450	−9·2538	8143	4·8513	10·8468	4·0543
7·8	15·8200	−10·2320	8186	5·8291	11·2910	3·3912
7·9	16·4050	−11·2582	−9·7707	6·8570	11·6850	2·6359

x \ n	2	3	4	5	6	7
8·0	17·0000	−12·3333	−9·6667	7·9333	12·0222	1·7873
8·1	17·6050	−13·4585	5027	9·0563	2961	0·8447
8·2	18·2200	−14·6347	−9·2746	10·2238	4999	−0·1919
8·3	18·8450	−15·8628	−8·9783	11·4333	6269	−1·3219
8·4	19·4800	−17·1440	6096	12·6820	6702	−2·5442
8·5	20·1250	−18·4792	−8·1641	13·9669	6229	−3·8569
8·6	20·7800	−19·8693	−7·6373	15·2845	4782	−5·2576
8·7	21·4450	−21·3155	−7·0247	16·6309	12·2291	−6·7429
8·8	22·1200	−22·8187	−6·3216	18·0021	11·8688	−8·3091
8·9	22·8050	−24·3798	−5·5233	19·3934	11·3905	−9·9514
9·0	23·5000	−26·0000	−4·6250	20·8000	10·7875	−11·6643
9·1	24·2050	−27·6802	−3·6217	22·2166	10·0533	−13·4416
9·2	24·9200	−29·4213	−2·5083	23·6374	9·1814	−15·2764
9·3	25·6450	−31·2245	−1·2797	25·0564	8·1657	−17·1607
9·4	26·3800	−33·0907	0·0694	26·4670	7·0000	−19·0860
9·5	27·1250	−35·0208	1·5443	27·8622	5·6787	−21·0426
9·6	27·8800	−37·0160	3·1504	29·2348	4·1961	−23·0202
9·7	28·6450	−39·0772	4·8933	30·5767	2·5472	−25·0078
9·8	29·4200	−41·2053	6·7787	31·8797	0·7270	−26·9931
9·9	30·2050	−43·4015	8·8123	33·1350	−1·2689	−28·9633

Continuation of TABLE 8

n / x	2	3	4	5	6	7
10·0	31·0000	−45·6667	11·0000	34·3333	−3·4444	−30·9048
10·2	32·6200	−50·4080	15·8614	36·5197	−8·3485	−34·6420
10·4	34·2800	−55·4373	21·4117	38·3546	−14·0077	−38·0782
10·6	35·9800	−60·7627	27·7014	39·7457	−20·4348	−41·0739
10·8	37·7200	−66·3920	34·7824	40·5919	−27·6323	−43·4775
11·0	39·5000	−72·3333	42·7083	40·7833	−35·5903	−45·1258
11·2	41·3200	−78·5947	51·5344	40·2006	−44·2854	−45·8453
11·4	43·1800	−85·1840	61·3174	38·7148	−53·6788	−45·4536
11·6	45·0800	−92·1093	72·1157	36·1873	−63·7152	−43·7607
11·8	47·0200	−99·3787	83·9894	32·4689	−74·3203	−40·5711
12·0	49·0000	−107·0000	97·0000	27·4000	−85·4000	−35·6857
12·2	51·0200	−114·9813	111·2107	20·8102	−96·8376	−28·9045
12·4	53·0800	−123·3307	126·6864	12·5178	−108·4928	−20·0289
12·6	55·1800	−132·0560	143·4934	2·3296	−120·1990	−8·8653
12·8	57·3200	−141·1653	161·6997	−9·9595	−131·7619	4·7721
13·0	59·5000	−150·6667	181·3750	−24·5667	−142·9569	21·0571
13·2	61·7200	−160·5680	202·5904	−41·7215	−153·5274	40·1478
13·4	63·9800	−170·8773	225·4187	−61·6666	−163·1823	62·1818
13·6	66·2800	−181·6027	249·9344	−84·6576	−171·5937	87·2716
13·8	68·6200	−192·7520	276·2134	−110·9633	−178·3950	115·4994

n / x	2	3	4	5	6	7
14·0	71·0000	−204·3333	304·3333	−140·8667	−183·1778	146·9111
14·2	73·4200	−216·3547	334·3734	−174·6646	−185·4900	181·5108
14·4	75·8800	−228·8240	366·4144	−212·6684	−184·8333	219·2538
14·6	78·3800	−241·7493	400·5387	−255·2039	−180·6599	260·0399
14·8	80·9200	−255·1387	436·8304	−302·6123	−172·3709	303·7059
15·0	83·5000	−269·0000	475·3750	−355·2500	−159·3125	350·0179
15·2	86·1200	−283·3413	516·2597	−413·4890	−140·7741	398·6624
15·4	88·7800	−298·1707	559·5734	−477·7174	−115·9851	449·2384
15·6	91·4800	−313·4960	605·4064	−548·3396	−84·1116	501·2469
15·8	94·2200	−329·3253	653·8507	−625·7767	−44·2542	554·0817
16·0	97·0000	−345·6667	705·0000	−710·4667	4·5556	607·0190
16·2	99·8200	−362·5280	758·9494	−802·8647	63·3583	659·2060
16·4	102·6800	−379·9173	815·7957	−903·4438	133·2697	709·6494
16·6	105·5800	−397·8427	875·6374	−1012·6947	215·4839	757·2037
16·8	108·5200	−416·3120	938·5744	−1131·1265	311·2769	800·5581
17·0	111·5000	−435·3333	1004·7083	−1259·2667	422·0097	838·2230
17·2	114·5200	−454·9147	1074·1424	−1397·6618	549·1319	868·5167
17·4	117·5800	−475·0640	1146·9814	−1546·8776	694·1849	889·5503
17·6	120·6800	−495·7893	1223·3317	−1707·4991	858·8059	899·2125
17·8	123·8200	−517·0987	1303·3014	−1880·1315	1044·7312	895·1542

Continuation of TABLE 8

$\frac{n}{x}$	2	3	4	5	6	7
18·0	127·0000	−539·0000	1387·0000	−2065·4000	1253·8000	874·7714
18·2	130·2200	−561·5013	1474·5387	−2263·9502	1487·9580	835·1885
18·4	133·4800	−584·6107	1566·0304	−2476·4486	1749·2613	773·2401
18·6	136·7800	−608·3360	1661·5894	−2703·5828	2039·8804	685·4524
18·8	140·1200	−632·6853	1761·3317	−2946·0619	2362·1041	568·0240
19·0	143·5000	−657·6667	1865·3750	−3204·6167	2718·3431	416·8060
19·2	146·9200	−683·2880	1973·8384	−3479·9999	3111·1346	227·2807
19·4	150·3800	−709·5573	2086·8427	−3772·9870	3543·1462	−5·4591
19·6	153·8800	−736·4827	2204·5104	−4084·3759	4017·1802	−286·7334
19·8	157·4200	−654·0720	2326·9654	−4414·9877	4536·1774	−622·2972
20·0	161·0000	−792·3333	2454·3333	−4765·6667	5103·2222	−1018·3651

TABLE 9. HERMITE POLYNOMIALS $(-1)^n h_n(x)$
(cf. Appendix I, § 4.1, 12°)

x \ n	2	3	4	5	6
0·00	−1·0000	0·00000	3·00000	0·00000	−15·00000
01	−0·9999	03000	2·99940	−0·14999	−14·99550
02	9996	05999	99760	29992	98200
03	9991	08997	99460	44973	95951
04	9984	11994	99040	59936	92804
05	9975	14988	98501	74875	88759
06	9964	17978	97841	−0·89784	83819
07	9951	20966	97062	−1·04657	77986
08	9936	23949	96164	19488	71261
09	9919	26927	95147	34272	63648
10	9900	29900	94010	49001	55150
11	9879	32867	92755	63671	45769
12	9856	35827	91381	78274	35511
13	9831	38780	89889	−1·92807	24378
14	9804	41726	88273	−2·07261	−14·12375
15	9775	44662	86551	21633	−13·99508
16	9744	47590	84706	35914	85781
17	9711	50509	82744	50101	71200
18	9676	53417	80665	64187	55771
19	9639	56314	78470	78166	39500
0·20	−0·9600	0·59200	2·76160	−2·92032	−13·22394

Continuation of TABLE 9

n / x	2	3	4	5	6
0·21	−0·9559	0·62074	2·73734	−3·05780	−13·04459
22	9516	64935	71194	19404	−12·85703
23	9471	67783	68540	32897	66133
24	9424	70618	65772	46256	45758
25	9375	73438	62891	59473	24585
26	9324	76242	59897	72543	−12·02624
27	9271	79032	56791	85460	−11·79883
28	9216	81805	53575	−3·98220	56372
29	9159	84561	50247	−4·10816	32100
30	9100	87300	46810	23243	−11·07077
31	9039	90021	43264	35495	−10·81314
32	8976	92723	39609	47568	54821
33	8911	95406	35846	59454	−10·27610
34	8844	0·98070	31976	71150	−9·99691
35	8775	1·00713	28001	82650	71076
36	8704	03334	23920	−4·93949	41777
37	8631	05935	19734	−5·05040	−9·11806
38	8556	08513	15445	15920	−8·81176
39	8479	11068	11053	26583	49900
40	8400	13600	06560	37024	−8·17990
41	8319	16108	2·01966	47238	−7·85461
0·42	−0·8236	1·18591	1·97272	−5·57219	−7·52327

Continuation of TABLE 9

x \ n	2	3	4	5	6
0·43	−0·8151	1·21049	1·92479	−5·66963	−7·18600
44	8064	23482	87588	76465	−6·84296
45	7975	25888	82601	85720	49429
46	7884	28266	77517	−5·94724	−5·14014
47	7791	30618	72340	−6·03470	−5·78067
48	7696	32941	67068	11956	41603
49	7599	35235	61708	20176	−5·04638
50	7500	37500	56250	28125	−4·67188
51	7399	39735	50705	35799	−4·29268
52	7296	41939	45072	43194	−3·90897
53	7191	44112	39350	50305	52091
54	7084	46254	33543	57128	−3·12866
55	6975	48363	27651	63658	−2·73241
56	6864	50438	21674	69891	−2·33233
57	6751	52481	15616	75824	−1·92860
58	6636	54489	09476	81452	52141
59	6519	56462	1·03257	86770	−1·11092
60	6400	58400	0·96960	91776	−0·69734
61	6279	60302	90586	−6·96465	−0·28086
62	6156	62167	84136	−7·00833	0·13835
63	6031	63995	77613	04877	56008
0·64	−0·5904	1·65786	0·71017	−7·08593	0·98414

Continuation of TABLE 9

x	2	3	4	5	6
0·65	−0·5775	1·67538	0·64351	−7·11978	1·41033
66	5644	69250	57615	15027	1·83844
67	5511	70924	50811	17738	2·26829
68	5376	72557	43941	20107	2·69966
69	5239	74149	37007	22131	3·13235
70	5100	75700	30010	23807	3·56615
71	4959	77209	22952	25131	4·00085
72	4816	78675	15834	26101	43624
73	4671	80098	08658	26714	4·87210
74	4524	81478	+0·01427	26966	5·30822
75	4375	82812	−0·05859	26855	5·74438
76	4224	84102	13198	26379	6·18037
77	4071	85347	20587	25535	6·61597
78	3916	86545	28025	24320	7·05094
79	3759	87696	35510	22732	48508
80	3600	88800	43040	20768	7·91814
81	3439	89856	50613	18427	8·34992
82	3276	90863	58228	15706	8·78018
83	3111	91821	65882	12603	9·20869
84	2944	92730	73573	09117	9·63523
85	2775	93588	81299	05246	10·05956
86	−0·2604	1·94394	−0·89059	−7·00987	10·48144

x \ n	2	3	4	5	6
0·87	−0·2431	1·95150	−0·96850	−6·96339	10·90066
88	2256	95853	−1·04670	91301	11·31697
89	2079	96503	12518	85872	11·73015
90	1900	97100	20890	80049	12·13994
91	1719	97643	28285	73832	54613
92	1536	98131	36201	67220	12·94846
93	1351	98564	44135	60212	13·34671
94	1164	98942	52085	52806	13·74064
95	0975	99262	60050	45003	14·13000
96	0784	99526	68025	36801	51456
97	0591	99733	76011	28200	14·89408
98	0396	99881	84003	19200	15·26832
99	−0·0199	1·99970	−1·92000	09800	15·63704
1·00	+0·0000	2·00000	−2·00000	−6·00000	16·00000
01	0201	1·99970	08000	−5·89800	35696
02	0404	99880	16000	79200	16·70768
03	0609	99727	23989	68200	17·05192
04	0816	99514	31974	56801	38944
05	1025	99238	39949	45003	17·72000
06	1236	98898	47912	32807	18·04336
07	1449	98496	55860	20212	35929
1·08	0·1664	1·98029	−2·63791	−5·07221	18·66754

Continuation of Table 9

x \ n	2	3	4	5	6
1·09	0·1881	1·97497	−2·71702	−4·93833	18·96788
10	2100	96900	79590	80051	19·26006
11	2321	96237	87453	65875	54386
12	2544	95507	−2·95288	51306	19·81903
13	2769	94710	−3·03093	36347	20·08535
14	2996	93846	10864	20997	34257
15	3225	92912	18599	−4·05261	59047
16	3456	91910	26296	−3·89138	20·82881
17	3689	90839	33951	72632	21·05736
18	3924	89697	41562	55744	27589
19	4161	88484	49126	38476	48417
20	4400	87200	56640	20832	68198
21	4641	85844	64101	−3·02813	21·86910
22	4884	84415	71507	−2·84423	22·04529
23	5129	82913	78853	65664	21033
24	5376	81338	86139	46538	36401
25	5625	79688	−3·93359	27051	50610
26	5876	77962	−4·00513	−2·07204	63640
27	6129	76162	07595	−1·87001	75468
28	6384	74285	14605	66445	86073
29	6641	72331	21537	45542	22·95434
1·30	0·6900	1·70300	−4·28390	−1·24298	23·03531

x \\ n	2	3	4	5	6
1·31	0·7161	1·68191	−4·35160	−1·02704	23·10342
32	7424	66003	41844	−0·80778	15849
33	7689	63736	48439	58521	20029
34	7956	63390	54942	35936	22865
35	8225	58962	61349	−0·13028	24335
36	8496	56454	67658	+0·10197	24422
37	8769	53865	73865	33736	23105
38	9044	51193	79966	57582	20367
39	9321	48438	85959	0·81731	16189
40	9600	45600	91840	1·06176	10554
41	0·9881	42678	−4·97606	30913	23·03442
42	1·0164	39671	−5·03253	55935	22·94838
43	0449	36579	08778	1·81236	84725
44	0736	33402	14178	2·06810	73085
45	1025	30138	19449	32652	59902
46	1316	26786	24588	58753	45161
47	1609	23348	29591	2·85108	28847
48	1904	19821	34455	3·11710	22·10943
49	2201	16205	39176	38551	21·91437
50	2500	12500	43750	65625	70312
51	2801	08705	48174	3·92924	47557
1·52	1·3104	1·04819	−5·52445	4·20440	21·23157

Continuation of Table 9

n / x	2	3	4	5	6
1·53	1·3409	1·00842	−5·56559	4·48166	20·97100
54	3716	0·96774	60511	4·76093	69373
55	4025	92612	64299	5·04214	39965
56	4336	88358	67919	32520	20·08864
57	4649	84011	71367	61003	19·76059
58	4964	79569	74639	5·89654	41540
59	5281	75032	77731	6·18464	19·05298
60	5600	70400	80640	47424	18·67322
61	5921	65672	83362	6·76525	18·27604
62	6244	60847	85892	7·05757	17·86136
63	6569	55925	88228	35111	17·42911
64	6896	50906	90365	64577	16·97920
65	7225	45788	92299	7·94144	51159
66	7556	40570	94027	8·23803	16·02621
67	7889	35254	95544	53543	15·52301
68	8224	29837	96846	8·83354	15·00195
69	8561	24319	97929	9·13224	14·46298
70	8900	18700	98790	43143	13·90607
71	9241	12979	99424	9·73099	13·33120
72	9584	07155	99827	10·03082	12·73834
73	1·9929	0·01228	99995	33078	12·12750
1·74	2·0276	−0·04802	−5·99924	10·63077	11·49865

n / x	2	3	4	5	6
1·75	2·0625	−0·10938	−5·99609	10·93066	10·85181
76	0976	17178	99047	11·23034	10·18698
77	1329	23523	98234	52967	9·50417
78	1684	29975	97164	11·82853	8·80342
79	2041	36534	95834	12·12679	8·08476
80	2400	43200	94240	42432	7·34822
81	2761	49974	92377	12·72099	6·59386
82	3124	56857	90241	13·01665	5·82173
83	3489	63849	87827	31118	5·03188
84	3856	70950	85131	60443	4·22441
85	4225	78162	82149	13·89626	3·39938
86	4596	85486	78877	14·18653	2·55689
87	4969	−0·92920	75309	47509	1·69703
88	5344	−1·00467	71442	14·76179	0·81992
89	5721	08127	67270	15·04648	−0·07434
90	6100	15900	62790	32901	−0·98562
91	6481	23787	57997	60922	−1·91378
92	6864	31789	52886	15·88695	−2·85868
93	7249	39906	46452	16·16205	−3·82016
94	7636	48138	41692	43435	−4·79807
95	8025	56488	35599	70369	−5·79222
1·96	2·8416	−1·64954	−5·29171	16·96990	−6·80245

Continuation of TABLE 9

x \ n	2	3	4	5	6
1·97	2·8809	−1·73537	−5·22402	17·23280	−7·82854
98	9204	82239	15286	49224	−8·87031
1·99	2·9603	−1·91060	07821	17·74803	−9·92754
2·00	3·0000	−2·00000	−5·00000	18·00000	−11·00000
01	0401	09060	−4·91819	24791	−12·08746
02	0804	18241	83274	49176	−13·18967
03	1209	27543	74358	73119	−14·30638
04	1616	39966	65069	18·96605	−15·43732
05	2025	46512	55399	19·19619	−16·58221
06	2436	56182	45346	42139	−17·74077
07	2849	65974	34903	64147	−18·91268
08	3264	75891	24066	19·85623	−20·09764
09	3681	85933	12830	20·06547	−21·29532
10	4100	−2·96100	−4·01190	26899	−22·50538
11	4521	−3·06393	−3·89141	46659	−23·72748
12	4944	16813	76677	65806	−24·96125
13	5369	27360	63794	20·84320	−26·20632
14	5796	38034	50486	21·02178	−27·46230
15	6225	48838	36749	19361	−28·72880
16	6656	59770	22578	35846	−30·00539
17	7089	70831	−3·07966	51612	−31·29167
2·18	3·7524	−3·82023	−2·92909	21·66635	−32·58718

Continuation of TABLE 9

x \ n	2	3	4	5	6
2.19	3.7961	-3.93346	-2.77402	21.80895	-33.89148
20	8400	-4.04800	61440	21.94368	-35.20410
21	8841	16386	45017	22.07031	-36.52456
22	9284	28105	28127	18862	-37.85237
23	3.9729	39957	-2.10767	29836	-39.18702
24	4.0176	51942	-1.92929	39931	-40.52799
25	0625	64062	74609	49121	-41.87476
26	1076	76318	55802	57383	-43.22675
27	1529	-4.88708	36502	64693	-44.58343
28	1984	-5.01235	-1.16704	71025	-45.94419
29	2441	13899	-0.96402	76355	-47.30846
30	2900	26700	75590	80657	-48.67561
31	3361	39639	54264	83905	-50.04503
32	3824	52717	32417	86075	-51.41608
33	4289	65934	-0.10044	87138	-52.78810
34	4756	79290	0.12860	87070	-54.16042
35	5225	-5.92788	36301	85844	-55.53235
36	5696	-6.06426	60284	83431	-56.90320
37	6169	20205	0.84817	79806	-58.27223
38	6644	34127	1.09903	74240	-59.63872
2.39	4.7121	-6.48192	1.35549	22.68806	-61.00190

Continuation of TABLE 9

n / x	2	3	4	5	6
2·40	4·7600	−6·62400	1·61760	22·61376	−62·36102
41	8081	76752	1·88543	52621	−63·71529
42	8564	−6·91249	2·15902	42512	−65·06390
43	9049	−7·05891	43844	31021	−66·40603
44	4·9536	20678	2·72375	18118	−67·74084
45	5·0025	35612	3·01501	22·03773	−69·06748
46	0516	50694	31226	21·87958	−70·38507
47	1009	65922	61558	70641	−71·69273
48	1504	81299	3·92502	51792	−72·98954
49	2001	−7·96825	4·24064	31380	−74·27457
50	2500	−8·12500	56250	21·09375	−75·54688
51	3001	28325	4·89066	20·85745	−76·80549
52	3504	44301	5·22518	60458	−78·04944
53	4009	60428	56612	33482	−79·27770
54	4516	76706	5·91354	20·04786	−80·48927
55	5025	−8·93138	6·26751	19·74336	−81·68310
56	5536	−9·09722	62807	42100	−82·85812
57	6049	26459	6·99530	19·08044	−84·01325
58	6564	43351	7·36926	18·72135	−85·14740
59	7081	60398	7·75001	18·34340	−86·25944
60	7600	77600	8·13760	17·94624	−87·34822
2·61	5·8121	−9·94958	8·53211	17·52953	−88·41260

n \ x	2	3	4	5	6
2·62	5·8644	−10·12473	8·93359	17·09291	−89·45137
63	9169	30145	9·34211	16·63605	−90·46334
64	5·9696	47974	9·75772	16·15858	−91·44728
65	6·0225	65962	10·18051	15·66016	−92·40195
66	0756	−10·84110	10·61052	15·14041	−93·32608
67	1289	−11·02416	11·04782	14·59899	−94·21837
68	1824	20883	11·49247	14·03551	−95·07751
69	2361	39511	11·94454	13·44961	−95·90218
70	2900	58300	12·40410	12·84093	−96·69101
71	3441	77251	12·87120	12·20908	−97·44263
72	3984	−11·96365	13·34592	11·55368	−98·15563
73	4529	−12·15642	13·82832	10·87436	−98·82859
74	5076	35082	14·31846	10·17072	−99·46007
75	5625	54688	14·81641	9·44238	−100·04858
76	6176	74458	15·32223	8·68895	−100·59265
77	6729	−12·94393	15·83600	7·91003	−101·09075
78	7284	−13·14495	16·35777	7·10522	54134
79	7841	34764	16·88761	6·27412	−101·94285
80	8400	55200	17·42560	5·41632	−102·29370
81	8961	75804	17·97180	4·53142	59226
82	6·9524	−13·96577	18·52627	3·61900	−102·83692
2·83	7·0089	−14·17519	19·08908	2·67865	−103·02599

APPENDIX II

Continuation of TABLE 9

x \ n	2	3	4	5	6
2·84	7·0656	—14·38630	19·66030	1·70995	—103·15779
85	1225	59912	20·24001	0·71248	23061
86	1796	—14·81366	20·82826	—0·31419	24270
87	2369	—15·02990	21·42512	—1·37048	19231
88	2944	24787	22·03067	—2·45685	—103·07764
89	3521	46757	22·64497	—3·57370	—102·89688
90	4100	68900	23·26810	—4·72149	64818
91	4681	—15·91217	23·90012	—5·90066	—102·32967
92	5264	—16·13709	24·54110	—7·11165	—101·93946
93	5849	36376	25·19111	—8·35492	—101·47563
94	6436	59218	25·85022	—9·63091	—100·93622
95	7025	—16·82238	26·51851	—10·94009	—100·31926
96	7616	—17·05434	27·19603	—12·28292	—99·62273
97	8209	28807	27·88288	—13·65985	—98·84462
98	8804	52359	28·57910	—15·07136	—97·98286
2·99	7·9401	—17·76090	29·28479	—16·51792	—97·03536
3·00	8·0000	—18·00000	30·00000	—18·00000	—96·00000
01	0601	24090	30·72481	—19·51808	—94·87464
02	1204	48361	31·45930	—21·07264	—93·65710
3·03	8·1809	—18·72813	32·20352	—22·66417	—92·34518

x \ n	2	3	4	5	6
3·04	8·2416	—18·97446	32·95757	—24·29316	—90·93665
05	3025	—19·22262	33·72151	—25·96009	—89·42924
06	3636	47262	34·49540	—27·66548	—87·82067
07	4249	72444	35·27934	—29·40980	—86·10861
08	4864	—19·97811	36·07338	—31·19358	—84·29071
09	5481	—20·23363	36·87761	—33·01731	—82·36458
10	6100	49100	37·69210	—34·88151	—80·32782
11	6721	—20·75023	38·51692	—36·78669	—78·17798
12	7344	—21·01133	39·35214	—38·73338	—75·91259
13	7969	27430	40·19785	—40·72208	—73·52913
14	8596	53914	41·05411	—42·75334	—71·02509
15	9225	—21·80588	41·92101	—44·82767	—68·39787
16	8·9856	—22·07450	42·79861	—46·94562	—65·64489
17	9·0489	34501	43·68699	—49·10771	—62·76351
18	1124	61743	44·58623	—51·31450	—59·75107
19	1761	—22·89176	45·49641	—53·56652	—56·60487
20	2400	—23·16800	46·41760	—55·84432	—53·32218
21	3041	44616	47·34988	—58·20846	—49·90023
22	3684	—23·72625	48·29332	—60·59949	—46·33622
23	4329	—24·00827	49·24800	—63·03798	—42·62734
24	4976	29222	50·21401	—65·52448	—38·77070
3·25	9·5625	—24·57812	51·19141	—68·05957	—34·76343

Continuation of TABLE 9

x \ n	2	3	4	5	6
3·26	9·6276	—24·86598	52·18028	—70·64381	—30·60257
27	6929	—25·15578	53·18071	—73·27779	—26·28518
28	7584	44755	54·19277	—75·96208	—21·80823
29	8241	—25·74129	55·21654	—78·69726	—17·16871
30	8900	—26·03700	56·25210	—81·48393	—12·36353
31	9·9561	33469	57·29953	—84·32267	—7·38959
32	10·0224	63437	58·35890	—87·21408	—2·24376
33	0889	—26·93604	59·43030	—90·15876	3·07716
34	1556	—27·23970	60·51381	—93·15731	8·57637
35	2225	54538	61·60951	—96·21035	14·25713
36	2896	—27·85306	62·71747	—99·31847	20·12272
37	3569	—28·16275	63·83778	—102·48230	26·17646
38	4244	47447	64·97052	—105·70245	32·42172
39	4921	—28·78822	66·11576	—108·97956	38·86189
40	5600	—29·10400	67·27360	—112·31424	45·50042
41	6281	42182	68·44411	—115·70713	52·34076
42	6964	—29·74169	69·62737	—119·15886	59·38645
43	7649	—30·06361	70·82347	—122·67008	66·64102
44	8336	38758	72·03249	—126·24143	74·10806
45	9025	—30·71362	73·25451	—129·87355	81·79120
46	10·9716	—31·04174	74·48961	—133·56709	89·69411
3·47	11·0409	—31·37192	75·73787	—137·32273	97·82050

n / x	2	3	4	5	6
3·48	11·1104	−31·70419	76·99939	−141·14110	106·17410
49	1801	−32·03855	78·27424	−145·02289	114·75870
50	2500	37500	79·56250	−148·96875	123·57812
51	3201	−32·71355	80·86426	−152·97936	132·63624
52	3904	−33·05421	82·17961	−157·05540	141·93696
53	4609	39700	83·50863	−161·19755	151·48421
54	5316	−33·74186	84·85140	−165·40649	161·28200
55	6025	−34·08888	86·20801	−169·68292	171·33434
56	6736	43802	87·57854	−174·02753	181·64531
57	7449	−34·78929	88·96308	−178·44101	192·21902
58	8164	−35·14271	90·36171	−182·92407	203·05963
59	8881	49828	91·77452	−187·47742	214·17132
60	11·9600	−35·85600	93·20160	−192·10176	225·55834
61	12·0321	−36·21588	94·64303	−196·79782	237·22496
62	1044	57793	96·09890	−201·56630	249·17552
63	1769	−36·94215	97·56929	−206·40795	261·41438
64	2496	−37·30854	99·05430	−211·32348	273·94595
65	3225	−37·67712	100·55401	−216·31362	286·77469
66	3956	−38·04790	102·06850	−221·37912	299·90510
67	4689	42086	103·59787	−226·52072	313·34171
68	5424	−38·79603	105·14220	−231·73916	327·08912
3·69	12·6161	−39·17341	106·70158	−237·03519	341·5196

APPENDIX II

Continuation of TABLE 9

x \ n	2	3	4	5	6
3·70	12·6900	−39·55300	108·27610	−242·40957	355·53491
71	7641	−39·93481	109·86585	−247·86306	370·24269
72	8384	−40·31885	111·47091	−253·39641	385·28007
73	9129	−40·70512	113·09139	−259·01040	400·65187
74	12·9876	−41·09362	114·72735	−264·70581	416·36295
75	13·0625	48438	116·37891	−270·48340	432·41821
76	1376	−41·87738	118·04613	−276·34396	448·82262
77	2129	−42·27263	119·72913	−282·28827	465·58116
78	2884	−42·67015	121·42797	−288·31714	482·69890
79	3641	−43·06994	123·14277	−294·43134	500·18093
80	4400	47200	124·87360	−300·63168	518·03238
81	5161	−43·87634	126·62056	−306·91897	536·25847
82	5924	−44·28297	128·38374	−313·29401	554·86442
83	6689	−44·69189	130·16323	−319·75761	573·85552
84	7456	−45·10310	131·95912	−326·31060	593·23712
85	8225	51662	133·77151	−332·95380	613·01460
86	8996	−45·93246	135·60048	−339·68803	633·19339
87	13·9769	−46·35060	137·44613	−346·51413	653·77900
88	14·0544	−46·77107	139·30856	−353·43292	674·77694
89	1321	−47·19387	141·18785	−360·44526	696·19282
90	2100	−47·61900	143·08410	−367·55200	718·03226
3·91	14·2881	−48·04647	144·99740	−374·75396	740·30096

Continuation of TABLE 9

x \ n	2	3	4	5	6
3·92	14·3664	−48·47629	146·92785	−382·05202	763·00466
93	4449	−48·90846	148·87554	−389·44703	786·14914
94	5236	−49·34298	150·84056	−396·93986	809·74026
95	6025	−49·77988	152·82301	−404·53137	833·78390
96	6816	−50·21914	154·82298	−412·22245	858·28601
97	7609	−50·66077	156·84057	−420·01397	883·25260
98	8404	−51·10479	158·87587	−427·90680	908·68972
3·99	14·9201	−51·55120	160·92898	−435·90185	934·60346
4·00	15·0000	−52·00000	163·00000	−444·00000	961·00000

BIBLIOGRAPHY[†]

"Library of Mathematical Handbooks", edited by L. A. Lyusternik and A. R. Yanpol'skii.

L. A. LYUSTERNIK and A. R. YANPOL'SKII. *Mathematical Analysis—Functions, Limits, Series, Continued Fractions* (*Mathematicheskii analiz — funktsii, predely, ryady, tsepnyye drobi*). Fizmatgiz, Moscow, 1961. English translation, Pergamon Press, Oxford, 1965.

II. I. G. ARAMANOVICH, R. S. GUTER *et al. Mathematical Analysis — Differentiation and Integration* (*Matematicheskii analiz — differentsirovaniye i integrirovaniye*). Fizmatgiz, Moscow, 1961. English translation, Pergamon Press, Oxford, 1965.

1. O. S. BAKALYAYEV. General conclusions of theorems on the summation of trigonometric and hyperbolic functions and their inverses (Uzagol'nennya teorem dodavannya trigonometrichnikh, giperbolichnikh i obernenikh im funktsii). (In Ukrainian) *Nauk. zapiski zap. derzh. ped. inst.*, t. 1, Derzh uch-ped. vid. "Radyans'ka shkola", Kiev, 1952.

2. È. G. BELAGA. Certain questions concerning the computation of polynomials. (In Russian) *Dokl. Akad. Nauk SSSR* **123**, No. 5 (1958).

3. V. N. BONDARENKO, I. T. PLOTNIKOV and P. P. POLOZOV. *Programming for the Digital Computing Machine "Ural"* (*Programmirovaniye dlya tsifrovoi vyschislitel'noi mashiny "Ural"*), Moscow, 1957.

4. N. M. BURUNOVA. *Handbook of Mathematical Tables*. Supplement 1, Tables of Functions (*Spravochnik po matematicheskim tablitsam*, Dopolneniye 1, Tablitsy funktsii). Izd. Akad. Nauk SSSR, Moscow, 1959. English translation by D. G. Fry published as *A Guide to Mathematical Tables*, Supplement 1, Pergamon Press, Oxford, 1960.

5. A. D. BOOTH and K. V. H. BOOTH. *Automatic Digital Machines* (*Avtomaticheskiye tsifrovyye mashiny*). Fizmatgiz, Moscow, 1959. Translated from *Automatic Digital Calculators* (2nd ed.), Butterworths, London, 1956.

6. G. N. WATSON. *Theory of Bessel Functions* (*Teoriya besselevykh funktsii*), vol. 1. Foreign Literature Publishing House, Moscow, 1949. Translated

---

† For this edition, bibliographic details have been added of English (and German) translations of some of the Russian, Italian and German works cited. Also, details have been added of English, German, Italian or Latin originals of those works which are cited in Russian translations. However, any translation listed might correspond to some edition of its original version other than that given here (G. J. T.).

from *A Treatise on the Theory of Bessel Functions* (2nd ed.), C.U.P., Cambridge, 1944.

7. YE. A. VOLKOV. *New Formulae for Computing Elementary Functions on BESM* (*Novyye formuly dlya vychisleniya elementarnykh funktsii na BESM*). Moscow, 1957.

8. V. L. GONCHAROV. *The Theory of Interpolation and Approximation of Functions* (*Teoriya interpolirovaniya i priblizheniya funktsii*). Gostekhizdat, Moscow–Leningrad, 1934.

9. N. M. GYUNTER and R. O. KUZ'MIN. *Collection of Problems in Higher Mathematics* (*Sbornik zadach po vysshei matematike*), vol. 3. Gostekhizdat, Moscow—Leningrad, 1947.

10. YE. A. ZHOGOLEV, G. S. ROSLYAKOV and N. P. TRIFONOV. *Computational Methods and Programming. A Collection of Works from the Computational Centre of the Moscow State University* (*Vychislitel'nyye metody i programmirovaniye. Sb. rabot vychislitel'nogo tsentra MGU*), Moscow, 1961.

11. YE. A. ZHOGOLEV, G. S. ROSLYAKOV, N. P. TRIFONOV and M. R. SHURA-BURA. *A System of Standard Sub-Programs* (*Sistema standartnykh podprogramm*). Fizmatgiz, Moscow, 1958.

12. V. L. ZAGUSKIN. *Handbook of Numerical Methods for the Solution of Algebraic and Transcendental Equations* (*Spravochnik po chislennym metodam resheniya algebraicheskikh i transtsendentnykh uravnenii*). Fizmatgiz, Moscow, 1960. English translation by G. O. Harding, published as *Handbook of Numerical Methods for Solution of Equations*, Pergamon Press, Oxford, 1961.

13. S. N. ZUKHOVITSKII. Some generalizations of the concept of Chebyshev alternance (In Russian). *Dokl. Akad. Nauk Ukr. SSR* 5, 419—424 (1955).

14. YU. L. KETKOV. On the computation of polynomials (In Russian). *Izv. Vyssh. Uchebn. Zaved. Radiofizika* 1, No. 4 (1958).

15. R. O. KUZ'MIN. *Bessel Functions* (*Besselevy funktsii*). United Scientific and Technical Press, Moscow–Leningrad, 1935.

16. A. V. LEBEDEV and R. M. FEDOROVA. *Handbook of Mathematical Tables* (*Spravochnik po matematicheskim tablitsam*). Izd. Akad. Nauk SSSR, Moscow, 1956. English translation by D. G. Fry, published as *A Guide to Mathematical Tables*, Pergamon Press, Oxford, 1960.

17. C. LANCZOS. *Practical Methods of Applied Analysis* (*Prakticheskiye metody prikladnogo analiza*). Fizmatgiz, Moscow, 1961. Translated from *Applied Analysis*, Pitman, London, 1957.

18. V. S. LINSKII. The computation of elementary functions on automatic digital machines (In Russian). *Sb. Vychislit. Matem.* vyp. 2, 90—119 (1957).

19. L. A. LYUSTERNIK. On the computation of values of a function of a single variable (In Russian). *Matem. Prosveshch.* vyp. 3, 63—76 (1958); vyp. 4, 3—23 (1959).

20. L. A. LYUSTERNIK, A. A. ABRAMOV, V. I. SHESTAKOV and M. R. SHURA-BURA. *The Solution of Mathematical Problems on Automatic Digital Machines. Programming for High-Speed Computing Machines* (*Resheniye matematicheskikh zadach na avtomaticheskikh tsifrovykh*

238   BIBLIOGRAPHY

    mashinakh. Programmirovaniye dlya bystrodeistvuyushchikh schetnykh mashin). Izd. Akad. Nauk SSSR, Moscow, 1952.

21. YE. P. NOVODVORSKII and YE. M. PINSKER. A process of equalization of maxima (In Russian). *Uspekhi Matem. Nauk* **6**, No. 6 (46), 174—181 (1951). An English translation is available from Professor A. Shenitzer, New York University.

22. S. I. NOVOSELOV. *Special Course of Trigonometry (Spetsial'nyi kurs trigonometrii).* Izd. "Sovetskaya Nauka", Moscow, 1951.

23. V. YA. PAN. Some schemes for computing polynomials with real coefficients (In Russian). *Dokl. Akad. Nauk SSSR* **127**, No. 2, 266—269 (1959).

24. G. PÓLYA and G. SZEGÖ. *Problems and Theorems from Analysis (Zadachi i teoremy iz analiza)*, vol. 1. Fizmatgiz, Moscow, 1959. Translated from *Aufgaben und Lehrsätzen aus der Analysis I, II*, Berlin, 1925.

25. YE. YA. REMEZ. *General Computational Methods of Chebyshev Approximation. Problems with Real Parameters Entering Linearly (Obshchiye vychislitel'nyye metody chebyschevskikh priblizhenii. Zadachi s lineinoi vkhodyashchimi veshchestvennymi parametrami)*, Kiev, 1957.

26. I. M. RYZHIK and I. S. GRADSHTEIN. *Tables of Integrals, Sums, Series and Products (Tablitsy integralov, summ, ryadov i proizvedenii).* Gostekhizdat, Moscow—Leningrad, 1951 (later edition 1962). A German-English version of the 3rd Russian edition was published as *Tables of Series, Products and Integrals*, by I. M. Ryshik and I. S. Gradstein, VEB Deutscher Verlag der Wissenschaft, Berlin, 1957.

27. V. I. SMIRNOV. *A Course of Higher Mathematics (Kurs vysshei matematiki)*, vol. 3(ii), (4th ed.). Gostekhizdat, Moscow–Leningrad, 1950. German translation published as *Lehrgang der höheren Mathematik*, 5 vols., Berlin, 1961—63. English translation by D.E. Brown of Russian edition (published 1957 by Fizmatgiz, Moscow) published as *Complex Variables/Special Functions* by Pergamon Press, Oxford, 1964.

28. J. M. STESIN. Inversion of orthogonal expansions in a sequence of fractions (In Russian). *Sb. Vyschislit. Matem*, vyp. 1, 119 (1959).

29. J. TODD. Motives for working in the field of numerical analysis (In Russian). *Matem. Prosveshch.*, vyp. 1, 75 (1957). Translated from Motivations for working in numerical analysis, *Comm. Pure and Appl. Math.* **8**, 97—116 (1955).

30. E. T. WHITTAKER and G. N. WATSON. *A Course of Modern Analysis (Kurs sovremennogo analiza)*, vol. 2. Gostekhizdat, Moscow—Leningrad, 1934 (later edition 1963). Translated from *A Course of Modern Analysis*, C.U.P., Cambridge, 1915.

31. E. T. WHITTAKER and G. ROBINSON. *Mathematical Processing of the Results of Observations (Matematicheskaya obrabotka resul'tatov nablyudenii).* Gostekhizdat, Moscow—Leningrad, 1933. Translated from *The Calculus of Observations* (2nd ed.), Blackie, Glasgow, 1924.

32. G. M. FIKHTENGOL'TS. *A Course of Differential and Integral Calculus. (Kurs differentsial'nogo i integral'nogo ischisleniya)*, vols. II and III. Gostekhizdat, Moscow–Leningrad, 1948 and 1949 (later edition 1959 and 1960). English translation published as *Fundamentals of Mathematical Analysis*, vols. 1 and 2, Pergamon Press, Oxford, 1965.

33. A. N. KHOVANSKII. *The Lambert–Oberreit Method* (In Russian). Preprint.

34. A. N. KHOVANSKII. *Applications of Continued Fractions, and Their Generalizations, to Problems of Approximate Analysis (Prilozheniye tsepnykh drobei i ikh obobshchenii, k voprosam priblizhennogo analiza)*. Gostekhizdat, Moscow, 1956.

35. P. L. CHEBYSHEV. *Complete Collected Works (Polnoye sobraniye sochinenii)*, vols. I–V. Izd. Akad. Nauk SSSR, Moscow–Leningrad, 1944–1951.

36. L. EULER. *Introduction to the Analysis of the Infinitely Small (Vvedeniye v analiz beskonechno malykh)*. United Scientific and Technical Press, Moscow–Leningrad, 1936. Translated from *Introductio in Analysin Infinitorum*, Lausanne, 1748.

37. E. JAHNKE and F. EMDE. *Tables of Functions, with Formulae and Curves (Tablitsy funktsii s formulami i krivymi)*. Fizmatgiz, Moscow, 1959. The sixth English–German edition, revised by F. Lösch, was published as *Tables of Functions*, McGraw-Hill, New York, 1960.

38. A. R. YANPOL'SKII. *Hyperbolic Functions (Giperbolicheskiye funktsii)*. Fizmatgiz, Moscow, 1960.

39. E. P. ADAMS and R. L. HIPPISLEY. *Smithsonian Mathematical Formulae and Tables of Elliptic Functions*. Smithsonian Institute, Washington, 1922 (reprinted 1939, 1947).

40. W. BARTH. Ein iterations Verfahren zur Approximation durch Polynome, *Z. Angew. Math. und Mech.* **38**, 258–260 (1958).

41. R. W. BEMER. A machine method for square-root computation, *Comm. Assoc. Comp. Mach.* **1**, No. 1, 6–7 (1958).

42. A. D. BOOTH. A note on approximating polynomials for trigonometric functions, *MTAC* **9**, No. 49, 21–23 (1955).

43. T. I. BROMWICH. *An Introduction to the Theory of Infinite Series*, London, 1926.

44. CHIH-BING LING. Tables of values of 16 integrals of algebraic–hyperbolic type, *MTAC* **11**, No. 59, 160–166 (1957).

45. E. G. H. COMFORT. Table Errata, 265: "E. P. Adams, Smithsonian mathematical formulae and tables of elliptic functions, 2nd reprint, The Smithsonian Institute, Washington D. C., 1947, 139", *MTAC* **12**, No. 63, 262 (1958).

46. C. F. GAUSS. *Werke*, Bd. III. Göttingen, 1876.

47. C. W. CLENSHAW. Polynomial approximations to elementary functions, *MTAC* **8**, No. 47, 143–147 (1954).

48. C. HASTINGS. Analytical approximations, *MTAC* **7**, No. 41, 67–69 (1953).

49. C. HASTINGS, J. T. HAYWARD and J. P. WONG. *Approximations for Digital Computers*. Princeton University Press, Princeton, 1955.

50. C. HASTINGS and J. P. WONG. Analytical approximations, *MTAC* **8**, No. 45, 46–47 (1954).

51. HORVATH. Sur les valeurs approximatives et rationelles des radicaux de forme $\sqrt{a^2 + b^2 + c^2}$ et $\sqrt{a^2 + b^2}$, *L'Institut. Journ. univ. Sci. Soc. savantes en France et a l'etranger*, section I, Sci. math. phys. et natur. (Paris) **36**, 1, 67–69 (1868).

52. L. B. W. JOLLEY. *Summation of Series.* Chapman & Hall, London, 1925.

53. W. B. JORDAN. An iterative process, *MTAC* 5, No. 35, 183 (1951).

54. S. KAPLAN. On finding the square root of a complex number, *MTAC* 4. No. 31, 177—178 (1950).

55. E. G. KOGBETLIANTZ. Computation of e^N for $-\infty < N < +\infty$ using an electronic computer, *IBM Journal of Research and Development* 1, No. 1, 110–115 (1957).

56. E. G. KOGBETLIANTZ. Computation of arc tan N for $-\infty < N < +\infty$ using an electronic computer, *IBM Journal of Research and Development* 2, No. 1, 43—53 (1958).

57. E. G. KOGBETLIANTZ. Computation of $\sin N$, $\cos N$ and $\sqrt[m]{N}$ using an electronic computer, *IBM Journal of Research and Development* 3, No. 2 (1959).

58. Z. KOPAL. Operational methods in numerical analysis based on rational approximations, *On Numerical Approximations. Proceedings of a Symposium Conducted by the Mathematical Research Center, United States Army, at the University of Wisconsin, Madison, April 21-23, 1958.* Publication number I, 25–43, University of Wisconsin Press, Madison, 1959.

59. J. H. LAMBERT. *Deutscher gelearter Briefswechsel herausgeg. von Joh. Bernouilli,* Bd. IV. Berlin, 1784.

60. L. R. LANGDON. Approximating functions for digital computers, *Industr. Math.* 6, 79–96 (1955).

61. W. LÁSKA. *Sammlung von Formeln der reinen und angewandten Mathematik,* Friedrich Viewig und Sohn, Braunschweig, 1888—94.

62. E.LOMMEL.*Studien über die Bessel'shen Funktionen,*Teubner,Leipzig,1868.

63. Y. L. LUKE. On the computation of Log Z and Arctan Z, *MTAC* 11, No. 57, 16—18 (1957).

64. N. MACON. A continued fraction to e^x, *MTAC* 9, No. 52, 194—195 (1955).

65. N. MACON. On the computation of exponential and hyperbolic functions using continued fractions, *JACM* 2, No. 4, 262—266 (1955).

66. W. MAGNUS and F. OBERHETTINGER. *Formeln und Sätze für die speziellen Funktionen der mathematischen Physik.* Springer-Verlag, Berlin-Gottingen–Heidelberg, 1948. English translation by J. Werner published as *Formulae and Theorems for the Special Functions of Mathematical Physics,* Chelsea, New York, 1949.

67. F. D. MURNAGHAND and J. W. WRENCH. The determination of the Chebyshev approximating polynomial for a differentiable function, *MTAC* 13, No. 67, 185—193 (1959).

68. L. OBERREIT. *Leipziger Magazin zur Naturkunde, Mathematik und Oekonomie viertes Stück,* 1781.

69. I. E. PERLIN and J. R. GARRET. High precision calculation of Arc sin x, Arc cos x and Arc tan x, *Math. of Comp.* 14, No. 71, 270—274 (1960).

70. J.V. PONCELET. *Cours de mecanique appliquée aux machines.* Metz, 1828.

71. J.V. PONCELET. *Traite de mecanique appliquée aux machines.* Liege, 1844.

72. J. V. PONCELET. Sur la valeur approchée lineaire et rationelle des

radicaux de la forme $\sqrt{a^2+b^2}$, $\sqrt{a^2-b^2}$ etc., *Journ. reine und angew. Math.* **13**, Heft 4, 277–291 (1835).

73. RENE DE VOGELAERE. Remarks on the paper "Tchebysheff approximations for power series", *JACM* **6**, No. 1, 111−114 (1959).

74. D. SHANKS. A logarithm algorithm, *MTAC* **8**, No. 46, 60−64 (1954).

75. A. SCHENITZER. Tchebyshev approximation of a continuous function by a class of functions, *JACM* **4**, No. 1, 30−35 (1957).

76. J. SUGAI. Extraction of roots by repeated subtractions for digital computers, *Comm. Assoc. Comp. Mach.* **1**, No. 12, 6−8 (1958).

77. D. TEICHROEW. Use of continued fractions in high speed computing, *MTAC* **6**, No. 39, 127−132 (1952).

78. M. VIONNET. Approximation de Tchebycheff d'ordre n des fonctions $\sin x$, $\sin x/x$, $\cos x$ et $\exp x$, *Chiffres, Revue de L'Association Francaises de Calcul* **2**, 77−96 (1959).

79. W. G. WADEY. Two square-root approximations, *Comm. Assoc. Comp. Mach.* **1**, No. 11, 13−14 (1958).

80. H. S. WALL. *Continued Fractions.* van Nostrand, New York, 1948.

81. P. WYNN. The rational approximation of functions which are formally defined by a power series expansion, *Math. of Comp.* **14**, No. 70, 147−186 (1960).

REFERENCES FOR THE APPENDICES

APPENDIX I

1. D. JACKSON. *Fourier Series and Orthogonal Polynomials* (*Ryady Fur'e i ortogonal'nyye polinomy*). Foreign Literature Publishing House, Moscow, 1948. Translated from *Fourier Series and Orthogonal Polynomials*, Carus Mathematical Monograph 6, Mathematical Association of America, 1941.

2. E. KAMKE. *Handbook for Ordinary Differential Equations* (*Spravochnik po obyknovennym differentsial'nym uravneniyam*). Foreign Literature Publishing House, Moscow, 1951 (later edition, Fizmatgiz, Moscow, 1961). Translated from *Differentialgleichungen Lösungsmethoden und Lösungen. I. Gewöhnliche Differentialgleichungen* (3rd ed.), Becker & Erler, Leipzig, 1944.

3. L. M. MILNE-THOMSON and L. J. COMRIE. *Four-figure Mathematical Tables* (*Chetyrekhznachnyye matematicheskiye tablitsy*). Fizmatgiz, Moscow, 1961. Translated from *Standard Four-Figure Mathematical Tables*, Macmillan, London, 1931.

4. Same as Ref. 26 in main Bibliography.

5. E. C. TITCHMARSH. *The Theory of Functions* (*Teoriya funktsii*). Gostekhizdat, Moscow, 1951. Translated from *The Theory of Functions*, O.U.P., Oxford, 1932.

6. F. G. TRICOMI. *Lectures on Partial Differential Equations (Lektsii po uravneniyam v chastnykh proizvodnykh)*. Foreign Literature Publishing House, Moscow, 1957. Translated from *Equazioni a Derivate Parziali*, Edizioni Cremonese, Rome, 1957.

7. Same as Ref. 30 in main Bibliography.

8. Same as Ref. 32 in main Bibliography.

9. G. H. HARDY. *Divergent Series (Raskhodyashchiyesya ryady)*. Foreign Literature Publishing House, Moscow, 1951. Translated from *Divergent Series*, O.U.P., Oxford, 1949.

10. YA. N. SHPIL'REIN. *Tables of Special Functions (Tablitsy spetsial'nykh funktsii)*, vol. 2. Gostekhizdat, Moscow, 1934.

11. I. YA. SHTAYERMAN. *Hyperbolic Functions (Giperbolicheskiye funktsii)*. Gostekhizdat, Moscow, 1935.

12. Same as Ref. 37 in main Bibliography.

13. Same as Ref. 38 in main Bibliography.

14. Same as Ref. 66 in main Bibliography.

APPENDIX II

15. P. P. ANDREYEV. *Mathematical Tables (Matematicheskiye tablitsy)*. Gostekhizdat, Moscow, 1951.

16. J. BAUSCHINGER and J. PETERS. *Tables of Logarithms of Numbers and Trigonometric Functions with Eight Decimal Figures (Tablitsy logarifmov chisel i trigonometricheskikh funktsii s vosem'yu desyatichnymi znakami)*. Gosgeodesizdat, Moscow, 1942—44. Translated from *Logarithmische trigonometrische Tafeln mit acht Dezimalstellen*. Engelmann, Leipzig, 1910—1911 (American edition published in New York, 1957).

17. V. M. BRADIS. *Four figure Mathematical Tables (Chetyrekhznachnyye matematicheskiye tablitsy)* (28th ed.). Uchpedgiz, Moscow, 1957.

18. K. BREMIKER. *Logarithmic-Trigonometric Tables with Six Decimal Figures, with a Supplement by L. S. Khrenov (Logarifmo-trigonometricheskiye tablitsy s shest'yu desyatichnymi znakami, s dop. L. S. Khrenova)*. Fizmatgiz, Moscow, 1962. Translated from *Logarithmische trigonometrische Tafeln mit sechs Dezimalstellen*, Witwer, Stuttgart, 1852 (22nd ed.1950). Twelfth edition published as *Tables of the Common Logarithms ... to Six Places of Decimals*, Wittwer, Stutgart, 1922.

19. I. N. BRONSHTEIN and K. A. SEMENDYAYEV. *Handbook of Mathematics for Engineers and Refresher Colleges (Spravochnik po matematike dlya inzhenerov i uchashchikhsya vtuzov)*(9th ed.). Fizmatgiz, Moscow, 1962.

20. C. C. BRUHNS. *Tables of Logarithms of Numbers and Trigonometric Functions with Seven Decimal Figures (Tablitsy logarifmov chisel i trigonometricheskikh funktsii s sem'yu desyatichnymi znakami)*. Izd. Redbyuro GUGK pri SNK SSSR, Moscow, 1939. Translated from "Neues logarithmisch–trigonometrisches Handbuch auf sieben Dezimalen", 1870. Thirteenth edition published as *A New Manual of*

Logarithms to Seven Places of Decimals, Chapman & Hall, London, 1922.

21. G. VEGA. *Logarithmic trigonometric Handbook — Seven-Figure Tables (Logarifmicheski—trigonometricheskoye rukovodstvo (semiznachnyye tablitsy))*. State Scientific and Technical Press, Moscow–Leningrad, 1932. Translated from *Manuale Logarithmico—trigonometricum*, 1797 (with numerous later editions in many languages).

22. F. GAUSS. *Five-figure Complete Logarithmic and Trigonometric Tables (Pyatiznachnyye polnyye logarifmicheskiye i trigonometricheskiye tablitsy)*. Gostekhizdat, Moscow–Leningrad, 1939. Translated from *Fünfstellige vollständige logarithmische und trigonometrische Tafeln*, Rauk, Berlin, 1870.

23. H. B. DWIGHT. *Tables of Integrals and Other Mathematical Formulae (Tablitsy integralov i drugiye matematicheskiye formuly)*. Foreign Literature Publishing House, Moscow, 1948. Translated from *Tables of Integrals and Other Mathematical Data* (3rd ed.). Macmillan, New York, 1957.

24. A. K. MITROPOL'SKII. *Brief Mathematical Tables (Kratkiye matematicheskiye tablitsy)*. Fizmatgiz, Moscow, 1959.

25. J. PETERS. *Six-figure Tables of Trigonometric Functions (Shestiznachnyye tablitsy trigonometricheskikh funktsii)* (3rd ed.). Gosgeodesizdat, Moscow, 1944. Translated from *Sechstellige Tafeln der trigonometrischen Funktionen, enthaltend die Werte der sechs trigonometrischen Funktionen von zehn zu den Bogensekunden*, Dümmler, Berlin—Bonn, 1929. English version published as *New Trigonometric Tables, Six Figures*, Government Printer, Pretoria, S.A., 1947.

26. YE. PRZHEVAL'SKII. *Five-figure Tables of Logarithms (Pyatiznachnyye tablitsy logarifmov)*. Uchpedgiz, Moscow, 1938.

27. B. I. SEGAL and K. A. SEMENDYAYEV. *Five-Figure Mathematical Tables (Pyatiznachnyye matematicheskiye tablitsy)* (2nd ed.). Fizmatgiz, Moscow, 1959.

28. L. J. COMRIE. *Barlow's Tables of Squares, Cubes, Square Roots, Cube Roots and Reciprocals of the Integers from 1 to 12,500 (Tablitsy Barlou kvadratov, kubov, kornei kvadratnykh, kornei kubicheskikh i obratnykh velichin tselykh chisel ot 1 do 12,500)*. Foreign Literature Publishing House, Moscow, 1950. Translated from *Barlow's Tables of Squares, Cubes etc.* (4th ed.). Spon, London, 1941.

29. L. S. KHRENOV. *Five-figure Tables of Trigonometric Functions (Pyatiznachnyye tablitsy trigonometricheskikh funktsii)* (4th ed.). Fizmatgiz, Moscow, 1962.

30. L. J. COMRIE. *Chambers' Six-figure Mathematical Tables*, vol. 2, Natural Values. Chambers, Edinburgh—London, 1949.

INDEX

245